The Great Japan Exhibition

Art of the Edo Period 1600–1868

EDITED BY PROFESSOR WILLIAM WATSON

ROYAL ACADEMY OF ARTS LONDON 1981–2
Catalogue published in association with
WEIDENFELD AND NICOLSON LONDON

House Editor Anne Dobell
Art Director Behram Kapadia
Designed by Trevor Vincent
for George Weidenfeld and Nicolson Ltd
91 Clapham High Street, London SW4

ISBN 0 297 78027 1 (casebound)
       0 297 78035 2 (paperback)

Set in Monophoto Photina and printed by
BAS Printers Limited, Over Wallop, Hampshire

Colour separations by Newsele Litho Ltd, Italy
Colour printed in Italy by Printers Srl for L.E.G.O. Vicenza

The Great Japan Exhibition

Cover illustration
no. 34 WATANABE SHIKŌ (1683–1755)
Flowering cherries at Yoshinoyama (detail)

The Great Japan Exhibition has been organized by the Royal Academy and
The Japan Foundation

It has been sponsored by:
Midland Bank International
in association with
The Observer
Overseas Containers Limited
Pringle of Scotland
Shell Sekiyu K.K.
John Swire

Air transport by British Airways.

Hotel accommodation provided by Grand Metropolitan Hotels.

We are grateful to the British Government for their help in agreeing to
indemnify this exhibition under the National Heritage Act 1980.

This catalogue has been produced by the Royal Academy with the assistance
of a grant from the Commemorative Association for the Japan World
Exposition.

A contribution towards the production costs of this catalogue has been made
by the Metropolitan Center for Far Eastern Art Studies.

Contents

Joint Patrons

His Imperial Highness The Crown Prince of Japan   His Royal Highness The Prince of Wales, K G, K T, G C B

Committees of Honour

JAPAN

His Excellency Zenko Suzuki
Prime Minister
His Excellency Sunao Sonoda
Minister for Foreign Affairs
His Excellency Naraichi Fujiyama
Japanese Ambassador in London
Bunichiro Sano
Commissioner, Agency for Cultural Affairs, Ministry of Education, Science and Culture
Kentaro Hayashi
President, The Japan Foundation

GREAT BRITAIN

The Rt. Hon. Margaret Thatcher, MP
Prime Minister and First Lord of the Treasury
The Lord Carrington, K C M G, M C
Secretary of State for Foreign and Commonwealth Affairs
His Excellency Sir Hugh Cortazzi, K C M G
British Ambassador in Tokyo
Sir Hugh Casson, K C V O
President of the Royal Academy
Sir David Barran
Chairman, Midland Bank Limited

Policy Committees

JAPAN

Tamio Amau
Director-General, Public Information and Cultural Affairs Bureau, Ministry of Foreign Affairs

Junpei Kato
Deputy Director-General, Public Information and Cultural Affairs Bureau, Ministry of Foreign Affairs

Yuzo Hatano
Minister, Japanese Embassy in London

Shigenobu Yoshida
Director, First Cultural Affairs Division, Ministry of Foreign Affairs

Masahiro Yamanaka
Deputy Commissioner, Agency for Cultural Affairs, Ministry of Education, Science and Culture

Sumiichi Furumura
Director-General, Cultural Properties Protection Department, Agency for Cultural Affairs, Ministry of Education, Science and Culture

Tetsuro Kitamura
Councillor on Cultural Properties, Agency for Cultural Affairs, Ministry of Education, Science and Culture

Kyotaro Nishikawa
Director, Fine Arts Division, Cultural Properties Protection Department, Agency for Cultural Affairs, Ministry of Education, Science and Culture

Kuniyoshi Date
Managing Director, The Japan Foundation

Tetsuo Tanaka
Executive Director, The Japan Foundation

Masaru Inoue
Head, Arts Department, The Japan Foundation

Masaaki Iseki
Head, Exhibition Division, The Japan Foundation

Kishō Kurokawa
President, Kishō Kurokawa Architect and Associates

Kiyoshi Awazu
Chief, Kiyoshi Awazu Design Room

GREAT BRITAIN

Sir Hugh Casson, K C V O, *Chairman*
President of the Royal Academy

Antony Butterwick
Director, Overseas Containers Limited

Roger de Grey, R A
Treasurer of the Royal Academy

The Earl of Drogheda, K G, K B E

Joe Earle
Assistant Keeper, Far Eastern Department, Victoria and Albert Museum

Sir John Figgess, K B E, C M G

Frederick Gore, R A
Chairman, Exhibitions Committee, Royal Academy

Sir Denis Hamilton, D S O

Sidney C. Hutchison, C V O
Secretary of the Royal Academy

Dr Oliver Impey
Assistant Keeper, Department of Eastern Art, Ashmolean Museum, Oxford

Sir John Keswick, K C M G

Roderick MacFarquhar

J.E.C. Macrae
Head of Cultural Relations Department, Foreign and Commonwealth Office

Graham McCallum, C B E
Director, John Swire & Sons Limited

Brian Nicholson
Joint Managing Director, The Observer

Sir John Pilcher, G C M G

Brian Quinn
Managing Director, Visnews Limited

Sir Julian Ridsdale, C B E, M P
Chairman, British Japanese Parliamentary Group

Tom Ross
Shell Group Public Affairs Co-ordinator

Lawrence Smith
Keeper, Department of Oriental Antiquities, British Museum

Geoffrey Taylor
Director and Deputy Group Chief Executive, Midland Bank Limited

John Waterton
Group Marketing Director, Dawson International Limited (Pringle of Scotland)

Professor William Watson
Head of the Percival David Foundation, University of London

Dr David Wilson
Director of the British Museum

Nicolas Wolfers
Assistant Director, Samuel Montagu & Company Limited
Exhibition Co-ordinator for the Sponsors

Sir Philip de Zulueta

Secretary
Norman Rosenthal
Exhibitions Secretary, Royal Academy

7

Executive Committees

Sub Committees

CATALOGUE
Professor William Watson *Chairman*
Natsuo Amemiya
Annette Bradshaw
Joe Earle
Robert Hickman
Dr Oliver Impey
Norman Rosenthal
Lawrence Smith
Nicolas Wolfers

CONSERVATION
Lawrence Smith *Chairman*
Alan Irvine
Annette Bradshaw
Dr Michael Pascoe
Norman Rosenthal
Denis Serjeant
Nicolas Wolfers

CONTENT AND DESIGN
Professor William Watson *Chairman*
Natsuo Amemiya
Annette Bradshaw
Roger de Grey
Joe Earle
Dr Oliver Impey
Alan Irvine
Norman Rosenthal
Denis Serjeant
Lawrence Smith
Nicolas Wolfers

FINANCE
Brian Quinn *Chairman*
Beth Borchardt *Secretary*
Trevor Clark
Roger de Grey
Christopher Hammond
Norman Rosenthal
Kenneth Tanner
Nicolas Wolfers

MERCHANDISE
Laurie Bray *Chairman*
Natsuo Amemiya
Elizabeth Balcon
Beth Borchardt
Annette Bradshaw
Lady Casson
Joe Earle
Hazel Elliot
Kevin Gavaghan
Griselda Hamilton-Baillie
Yuzo Hatano
Sue Henny
Norman Rosenthal
Christina Smith
Kenneth Tanner
Nicolas Wolfers

PUBLICITY
Griselda Hamilton-Baillie *Chairman*
Natsuo Amemiya
Elizabeth Balcon
Annette Bradshaw
Yuzo Hatano
Victoria Holmes
Colin Lewis
Alan Macdonald
Norman Rosenthal
Kenneth Tanner
Nicolas Wolfers

SPONSORS
The Japan Foundation
Natsuo Amemiya
Sue Henny

Midland Bank International
Christopher Hammond *Chairman*
Alan Macdonald
Nicolas Wolfers
Beth Borchardt *Secretary*

The Observer
Elizabeth Balcon
Barbara Binder

Overseas Containers Limited
Christopher Rankin
Terry Walsh

Pringle of Scotland
Gordon Farquharson
Jeannie Fraser-Allen

Royal Academy of Arts
Annette Bradshaw
Griselda Hamilton-Baillie

Shell Sekiyu K.K.
Malcolm Williams

John Swire
Graham McCallum
Christopher Ryder

私の手許に〝The British Press and The Japan - British Exhibition〟という、1910年にロンドンで開催された日本展に関する英国の新聞記事をまとめた報告書があります。この時は美術品ばかりでなく産業製品も紹介されたようですが、およそ70年前に英国の方々が日本を知ることに傾けられた情熱の一端を示すものとして今日これらを再読してみますと感慨深いものがあります。

　このたび足かけ5年にわたる日英両国間での慎重なる準備のもとに〝The Great Japan Exhibition〟が開催される運びとなりました。本展覧会では江戸時代の美術作品の各品が総合的に紹介されるわけですが、このような大規模な展覧会は日本国内においてのみならず世界のどの地域においてもこれまで開催されたことはありません。

　江戸時代の解釈および評価については様々な論がありますが、この時代が産業面、交化面において全てが「日本人の尺度」によって価値づけられた最後の時代であったとする意見や、又最近注目するものとして、日本の近代化の基礎がこの時代におかれたのであり、この基礎を理解することが20世紀の日本の経済技術の発展を知るうえで欠くべからざることであるという意見もございます。本展を通して英国の方々が、これらの点をどの様におうけとりになるか私共は楽しみにしております。

　文末になりましたが、本展実現のために多大な情熱を注がれた日英関係者の全ての方々にあつく御礼を申し上げますと共に、本展が日英相互理解の新たな契機となることを信じて疑いません。

国際交流基金理事長

林　健太郎

Preface

I have before me 'The British Press and The Japan-British Exhibition', a report summarising British newspaper articles on the Japan Exhibition held in London in 1910. This was an exhibition of industrial products, as well as art objects, of Japan, but I am deeply impressed as I read these articles, for they show an aspect of the great zeal with which the British people sought to understand things Japanese over seventy years ago.

We are happy to present to you now the Great Japan Exhibition, which has been in preparation for the past five years by the Royal Academy of Arts and The Japan Foundation. This exhibition is designed to introduce, in a comprehensive manner, some of the most important art objects of the Edo period. An exhibition of Japanese art on this scale has never been held anywhere in the world, not even in Japan.

There are many interpretations and assessments of the Edo period, a period of almost two and a half centuries when Japan was virtually closed off from the rest of the world. One view is that this was the last period when every phase of the industrial and cultural life of Japan was shaped by the values of the Japanese people themselves. On the other hand, one of the most noteworthy opinions in recent times is that this period formed the basis for Japan's modernisation and that it is essential to understand the foundations which were laid in the Edo period in order to understand Japan's economic and technological development in the twentieth century. We look forward to learning whether the British people will find such views appropriate as a result of seeing this exhibition.

Finally we wish to express our sincere appreciation to all those in England and Japan who have devoted their efforts to the realisation of this project and hope that the Great Japan Exhibition provides a new moment in the promotion of mutual understanding between our countries.

Kentaro Hayashi
President
The Japan Foundation

真にその名に値する日本美術展の開催はロイヤル・アカデミーの永年の念願でありました。この種の企画の実現には数多くの困難が伴うのが普通で、現に私達も勇気をくじかれることしばしばでしたし、時としてはそれは乗越え難く思われることもありました。1966年中国展を開催、これが大成功であったことに力づけられ、ようやく1977年に入り、日本美術展の開催という私達の永年の夢に本格的に取組むことになりました。中国展の影の立役者として栄配を振って来たW.ワトソン教授とも会合をもち、展覧会のコンセプトはどうあるべきか、またいかに最も良く達成され得るか、について討議を重ねました。展覧会の目的に関してはすぐに意見の一致を見ることが出来ました。それは普通の日本美術・宝物展に比し、一層壮観なもの、しかも質の高さ、規模の大きさ共に日本でさえもかって達成されたことがなかったものということでありました。多くの専門学者の意見を得て、私達は日本が世界にその扉を閉ざし非常にユニークな社会を発展させていた江戸時代、1600～1868年の美術品に焦点をしぼり、同時代の魅力的な文化的発展と社会的特徴を分かりやすく英国一般の人々に紹介しようと決意したのでありました。

ロンドンに於て駐英日本大使を通じ、まず公式の接触がもたれ、その後すぐにワトソン教授をはじめとする英国使節団が日本に送られました。日本側関係者はこの私達の企画を多大な関心を以って迎えてくれましたが、同時にこの余りにも野心的な計画が、実際に実現できるものかどうかについては疑いの念を抱いているようでもありました。事態ははじめから困難をきわめていました。日本人はその文化的遺産を実に驚くべき警戒心を持って注意深く守る傾向があり、実際特に有名な屏風絵やふすま絵のこわれやすくもろいことは、どんな西欧の絵画も比較にならないほどであります。が幸い、私達は互いに日本絵画の最高傑作が出品されないならば、この展覧会本来の意味は全く失われてしまうのではないかという点で意見の一致を見ることができました。つまりすでに西欧で知られている歌麿、北斎、広重といった版画家達に匹敵する偉大な日本の画家として、光琳、宗達、応挙、蘆雪などの名前を連ねることが私達の希望であったのです。

ロンドンあるいは東京において私達は日本の友人達、特に国際交流基金及び文化庁との間で数限りない会合を持ち、時間をかけていくつもの困難な障害を次第に乗越えてまいりました。その結果、欧米で見られる展覧会としては、前代末聞の規模と豪華さを誇りうる素晴らしい展覧会を開催できることになった訳であります。本展開催に際し解決すべき実際的、技術的ないくつもの課題がかってなく厖大なものであることは、とりも直さず、これがロイヤル・アカデミーが今までに主催した催しの中で最も経費のかかる事業であるということを意味しますが、この経費の主要な部分を引受けて下さった、ミッドランドバンク・インターナショナルをはじめとする英国スポンサー団体に対し心から感謝の意を表明する次第です。

この展覧会を実現させるに当って日英両国で、大変多くの方々が貢献して下さいました。ここでこの方々の御名前を一人一人挙げる事は困難ですが、6－9ページにこれ等の方々のお名前を記録し謝意を表させていただきました。すべての関係者の方々、特に美術品の所有者の方々が、ユニークでしかもその多くがこわれやすく、そのためにかって日本から持ち出されたことがなかった美術品を気前よくお貸しいただいた事に厚くお礼を申しあげたいと存じます。

最後に、本展は展示作品の質の高さのみならず、開国以降西欧世界を驚かせることになった江戸時代日本の創造性を、よりよく例証するためとられた作品の展示方法の点でも、文字通り注目に値する「江戸大美術展」であるということを改めて強調しておきたく存じます。

ロイヤル・アカデミー・オブ・アーツ館長

サー・ヒュー・カッソン
Sir　Hugh　Casson

Preface

It has long been the ambition of the Royal Academy to stage a truly worthy exhibition of Japanese art. The difficulties of realising such a project have always been daunting and at times seemed almost insurmountable. In 1977 however, encouraged by the enormous success of the Chinese Exhibition held three years before, we decided to have a serious try to realise our dream. A meeting was called to discuss with Professor William Watson – who had masterminded the Chinese Exhibition – what was to be the concept and how it could best be achieved. The aim was quickly agreed. It was to be something more spectacular than just an exhibition of Japanese Art Treasures – but something of a quality and scale that had never been attempted before, even in Japan. With the help of our advisory scholars we decided to concentrate upon the art of the Edo period between 1600 and 1868 when Japan was closed to the outside world and developed a highly individual society of its own – shown in such a way that the fascinating development and characteristics of that society could be easily understood by the visitor.

Formal and successful contacts were established with the Japanese Ambassador in London and shortly afterwards I visited Japan with Professor Watson. Our proposals were received by our Japanese colleagues with the greatest interest but also with some scepticism as to whether so ambitious a plan could ever be realised. The difficulties (not only financial) were immense. The Japanese guard their culture with an admirable jealousy and many of the greatest works of art, particularly the great paintings on screens and sliding doors, are of a fragility which makes any Western painting seem hardy in comparison. Yet all were agreed that unless major masterpieces of Japanese painting could be obtained the essential point of the exhibition would be invalidated. Our hope after all was to make the names of the great painters of Japan, Kōrin, Sōtatsu, Ōkyo, Rosetsu and others as famous in England as the great printmakers, Utamaro, Hokusai and Hiroshige.

Countless meetings in London and Tokyo between ourselves and our Japanese friends, particularly in The Japan Foundation and the Agency for Cultural Affairs, have gradually worked towards overcoming these difficulties so that we are now able to present an exhibition the size and splendour of which is unparalleled by any exhibition seen in Europe or America in living memory. The great logistical difficulties have meant also that this is certainly the most expensive exhibition the Royal Academy has ever staged, and we are immensely grateful to a consortium of British sponsors, headed by Midland Bank International, who have agreed to underwrite a major part of the costs. So many people both in Japan and this country have been involved in the creation of this exhibition that it would be impossible here to single out any names, though they are all recorded in the lists set out on pages 6–9.

Our gratitude to everyone involved is very great indeed but in particular to the owners who have generously parted with their unique and often extremely fragile works of art, many of which have never before left Japan.

In short this is a Great Japan Exhibition, remarkable not only for the quality of the works of art it presents but also for the manner in which they are displayed to illustrate and to explain the creative genius of Japan which in later years was to astonish the Western world.

SIR HUGH CASSON
President
Royal Academy of Arts

Editor's Note

The text of the catalogue is the combined work of the Academic Committee, with added historical essays by Professors W. G. Beasley and Masahide Bito and a foreword on the context of the exhibition by Mr Nicolas Wolfers. It has not seemed necessary to impose editorial consistency at every point. In some instances the contributors treat the same themes from different points of view which have an interest of their own.

Much thanks is due to the officers of the Agency for Cultural Affairs and The Japan Foundation in Tokyo, not only for assembling the exhibits, but also for their tireless response to our requests for information. We are particularly beholden to Mr Hayato Ogo and Miss Miyoko Inai in the Foundation's Tokyo headquarters. Mr Natsuo Amemiya, Director of The Japan Foundation in Great Britain, his deputy Mrs Sue Henny and their assistant Mrs Doreen Paylor, our constant and most agreeable collaborators, earn our great thanks and appreciation. We are no less indebted to Mrs Anne Dobell, Miss Antonia Demetriadi, Mr Behram Kapadia and their colleagues working on behalf of the publishers of this catalogue. In preparing the text we have greatly valued Mr Joe Earle's ever-ready help and scrupulous scholarship. To Miss Ho Chui-mei we are grateful for assistance in numerous editorial tasks.

We acknowledge with thanks the help we received from Mr J. Hillier (books and prints), Mr H. Tait (clocks), from Miss Sheila Nightingale for extended secretarial work, and in general from the staff of the British Museum's Department of Oriental Antiquities and photographic service.

Since the exhibition provides for the replacement of many important items by others of equal standing, the change being made for the second half, it has been necessary to indicate this in the descriptive entries by adding

F   for exhibits presented in the first half (24 October–20 December)

S   for exhibits presented in the second half (28 December – 21 February)

FS for exhibits presented throughout the duration of the exhibition.

The catalogue is arranged by categories of art, each division – painting, lacquer, ceramics, textiles etc – being preceded by an explanatory essay. A section following the historical chapters outlines the artistic development of the Edo period as a whole. Against the entries is indicated the gallery where the piece is exhibited:

G1   Gallery no. 1 etc.
CH   Central Hall
LR   Lecture Room
AR   Architecture Room

Inscriptions on the exhibits are transcribed in full, where possible, with their nature and placing indicated by the following abbreviations:

s.   signed
d.   dated
insc.   inscribed

The following abbreviations are used in giving the dimensions of an exhibit:

h height
w width
d depth
dm diameter

Where dimensions alone are given, they are in the order height, width, depth.

In the circumstances of obtaining loans from private collectors it was not possible in a few cases to ascertain dimensions in time for printing in the catalogue.

The authors of the introductory pieces to each section of the catalogue are indicated by the following initials:

WW   William Watson
LRHS   Lawrence Smith
JVE   Joe Earle
ORI   Oliver Impey

William Watson

The Great Japan Exhibition—A Foreword

Nicolas Wolfers, Exhibition Co-ordinator for the Sponsors

'The material progress of the world and the improvement of communications have effected a rapprochement between East and West which even a generation ago seemed far removed. Most of the people of this country are, however, still very ignorant of Japan, and much has to be done before they can pretend to have even an approximate idea of the life and methods of thought of one of the most remarkable people the world has seen. . . . A careful study of the art and thought of Japan may indeed make us pause to ask ourselves whether there is not something at least as good as, or better than, the utilitarian civilisation of the Twentieth Century.'

It was with these words that Queen Victoria's son, Prince Arthur of Connaught, as Honorary President, inaugurated the 1910 Japanese exhibition referred to by Professor Hayashi in his preface. Much of what he said then would still be valid today as an introduction to the Great Japan Exhibition. Prince Arthur had already played an important part in Anglo-Japanese relations, as a Patron of the Japan Society, which had been founded in 1891 with the help of the then President of the Royal Academy, and as leader of the Mission to present the Emperor Meiji with the Order of the Garter, an order of chivalry presented to both his successors to the Imperial Throne, which is why Japan's national flag now hangs in St. George's Chapel at Windsor. The 1910 exhibition had royal and imperial patronage, as does the Great Japan Exhibition through the joint patronage of His Royal Highness The Prince of Wales and His Imperial Highness The Crown Prince of Japan. This will be the first time in history that a Japanese Crown Prince has been patron of an event outside Japan.

The documents of that earlier exhibition are a reminder of the more than fifty-year period following the Meiji Restoration of 1868 when Japan was Great Britain's foremost friend in the Far East and Britain Japan's in the West. This relationship even led to the introduction of the first foreign popular song into the Japanese tradition, 'Auld Lang Syne', in 1881. Moreover, 1902 saw the start of the twenty-year Anglo-Japanese Alliance, when relations were at their closest.

Among the many special publications produced to celebrate the 1910 exhibition, one of the most comprehensive was *Japan Today* by Mr Kotaro Mochizuki, President of the Liberal News Agency, which gave a very detailed account of Japan's history, culture and economy. It is a striking coincidence that the painting chosen in the book 'to represent the artistic taste of the Japanese' is one of a pair of six-fold screens of 'Pines in Snow' by Ōkyo from which the logo of the Great Japan Exhibition was derived. Those magnificent screens did not actually come to London in 1910, but, through the generosity of their owner, Mr Hachiroemon Mitsui, we are privileged to be able to include them in the first part of our exhibition (no. 70). The 1910 exhibition is commemorated to this day by the almost full-sized Chokushi-Mon or gateway of the Imperial Messenger in Kew Gardens presented by the Kyoto Traders' Association.

Since 1945 Japan has tended to look primarily towards the United States of America and it is here that the closest political, economic and cultural ties have developed. However, the 1970s have seen greatly increased political, trading and, most recently, investment links between Japan and Europe. Cultural and educational exchanges have been slower to develop although some notable initiatives have taken place in both directions; for example, a number of leading Japanese companies have made large donations to the London School of Economics and Oxford University, and the Japanese government's English teaching recruitment programme, supported by the British Council, which arranges for British graduates to go to Japanese schools, colleges, universities and companies, is now in its fourth year. However, that mutual suspicions do remain is partly due to an ignorance of historical and cultural developments, and it is in this context that the Great Japan Exhibition at the Royal Academy is taking place. This has involved artistic co-operation between Great Britain and Japan on a scale not seen since the 1910 exhibition, and it is hoped that the exhibition will attract visitors in unprecedented numbers, not only from this country but from continental Europe and the rest of the world.

There were a number of reasons for the decision to concentrate the Great Japan Exhibition on the Edo period. Edo art achieved unique characteristics and high quality in its painting, prints, textiles, ceramics, lacquer and other media. The paintings and textiles in particular, which dominate this exhibition, are far less known in Europe than in the United States and it is hoped that this exhibition will go a long way towards redressing this imbalance. Furthermore, by restricting the exhibition to the Edo period it is hoped that it will be possible to show the development of Japanese art within a social and historical context to shed light on many aspects of pre-modern Japan which are still relevant today and still appear mysterious to Western eyes. The skill and originality of Edo artists and craftsmen and the cohesion and discipline of Edo society partly explain the phenomenal speed with which Japan's economy has grown since the nineteenth century.

It was especially this ambition to achieve a wider context which led Midland Bank International as prime sponsor to bring together an all-British and complementary sponsorship group, without whose support the Great Japan Exhibition would not have been possible. The Midland Bank Group includes the leading merchant bank, Samuel Montagu, the Thomas Cook travel and travellers' cheque service and the Forward Trust Group in leasing, factoring and instalment credit. Midland Bank's correspondent banking relationship with Japan dates back to the Meiji era, and Thomas Cook himself visited Japan in 1874. Midland's Tokyo representative office was given full branch status in 1978.

John Samuel Swire, founder of the Swire Group with its major trading interests, arrived in Yokohama from Liverpool in April 1867. Overseas Containers Limited are closely associated with John Swire, whom they have joined as a co-sponsor. They also have long historical links with Japan and are a foremost operator in the container trade between Japan and Europe. Of the other three co-sponsors, Shell have been established in Japan as investors since the turn of the century; Pringle of Scotland, founded in 1815, is a renowned member of the Dawson International Group, the world's largest purchaser and processor of cashmere, with a major stake in the Japanese market; and *The Observer*, founded in 1791, is Britain's oldest Sunday newspaper with many long-standing associations in Japan.

Midland Bank International and the Japan Information Centre, with the assistance of The Japan Foundation, have also compiled and helped co-ordinate and publicise a programme of Japanese related events in the fields of culture, education and sport, 'Japan in Britain 1981/2', which is taking place around the country until the end of the period of the Great Japan Exhibition. These events will include Kabuki at Sadler's Wells sponsored by The Japan Foundation and the investment bank Robert Fleming, the Stephen Sondheim musical about the end of the Edo period, 'Pacific Overtures', at the Mermaid Theatre, and the British première of the film 'Shōgun', based on the life of Will Adams.

In April 1600 Will Adams, who had been shipwrecked on the Japanese coast at Usuki in Kyushu, was the first Briton to set foot on Japanese soil. He took part that October in the decisive battle of Sekigahara, as a result of which three years later Tokugawa Ieyasu became shōgun. In 1611 Will Adams at last wrote a full account of his adventures to be taken back to Europe on a Dutch ship in the hope that it might eventually reach his English wife, friends and 'Unknown Countrymen'. In this letter he described the good treatment he and his men had received throughout from the Japanese (contrary to the perhaps more exciting versions portrayed in fiction) and the stages by which he had risen to the position of key adviser to the shōgun and a *hatamoto* or samurai with his own estate. By his Japanese name Miura Anjin, or as Will Adams, he is commemorated in four places in Japan: in the former Anjin-chō street in Tokyo, where he lived in Edo near Nihombashi; near the 'English House' at Hirado, where Britons of the London East India Company traded between 1613 and 1623; at Itō on the Izu Peninsula, where he built two ships for the shōgun and which has been marked by a poem by Edmund Blunden and a major festival each August; and at his estate at Hemmi near Yokosuka in the county of Miura, where his festival is also still celebrated each April at his cenotaph and where this epitaph is to be found:

> 'Ah! Sir Pilot, who wandered overseas to sojourn here,
> With merit you served the State and in requital were graciously entreated.
> Loyally mindful of favours, in death as in life you render loving homage;
> And from your tomb facing to the eastward
> For ever have in your guardian care the city of Yedo.'

Edo Japan: politics and foreign relations

Professor W.G. Beasley

Tokugawa political society

Japan in 1550 was a country suffering from the effects of nearly a century of civil war. In Kyoto the emperor was powerless to maintain his authority or defend the land rights on which revenue depended. Like his predecessors for many generations, he was compelled to leave the task of governing the country to his military deputy, the shōgun, whose office had been vested in members of the Ashikaga family since 1336. Nor did the Ashikaga perform that function with any notable success. Outside the capital city and the home provinces, which he controlled from his headquarters at Muromachi on Kyoto's outskirts, the shōgun's writ hardly ran. Remoter regions owed their allegiance to feudal lords, the daimyō, men who had won a position of local dominance by the sword and combined in their own persons the land rights formerly divided between the court, religious houses and lesser landholders of the area. The greatest of them – the Shimazu, the Mori, the Takeda, the Uesugi, the Maeda and their like – held what were in reality princedoms: consolidated territories administered from a central stronghold, which was garrisoned on a more or less permanent footing by their vassals, the samurai. The samurai themselves were in the process of being detached from their own smaller fiefs in the countryside to become soldiers and officials in regular attendance on their lords.

Given the weakness of the Ashikaga shōgun's position, it seemed likely that his rule would soon be replaced by that of someone better able to raise and command armies. Certainly there were already some daimyō who had self-confidence and military force enough to contemplate his overthrow. Yet in the struggle for national hegemony that went on for most of the next fifty years it was none of the great lords of the 1550s who were to succeed in that ambition. Instead, three new leaders emerged to give Japan once again a measure of political unity and strong government. First, Oda Nobunaga (1534–82), who, it is said, 'mixed the cake'; second, his one-time subordinate, Toyotomi Hideyoshi (1536–98), who 'baked it'; and third, their ally, Tokugawa Ieyasu (1542–1616), who 'ate it'. Their three castles – Azuchi, Fushimi (Momoyama) and Edo respectively – give the period its customary historical labels.

To summarise their achievements, Nobunaga brought the capital, Kyoto, and most of the central provinces under his control, deposing the Ashikaga and breaking the power of the principal Buddhist orders. Hideyoshi completed the military subjugation of the country, gaining an ascendancy which enabled him in the last few years of his life to launch a full-scale invasion of Korea, the first step, as he saw it, in a campaign to establish a Japanese emperor in Peking. Ieyasu was content with narrower horizons, at least geographically. After Hideyoshi's death he defeated an alliance of his rivals at the battle of Sekigahara in 1600; took the title shōgun in 1603, then devoted himself to creating a régime that would be proof against the failures and follies of his descendants for a long time to come. In this he succeeded: the last Tokugawa shōgun held office until January 1868.

Ieyasu's two immediate successors, his son Hidetada (1578–1631) and his grandson Iemitsu (1604–51), systematised the political structure which Ieyasu had devised. The key to it was a recognition that continuation of the shōgun's power depended on perpetuating a land settlement which victory had made possible. Landholdings were recorded – as a result of extensive cadastral surveys – in terms of assessed crop yields, measured in *koku* of rice (one *koku* equals approximately 180 litres or five bushels). In 1651, out of a national total of about twenty-eight million *koku*, the shōgun held four million. Members of his family and his direct vassals, including those who ranked as daimyō in their own right, held another thirteen million. Lords not in direct vassalage to the Tokugawa, known as *tozama daimyō*, altogether held ten million, leaving only about one million *koku* to be shared by the imperial court and a number of the more important shrines and temples. Tokugawa preponderance was reinforced by the geographical distribution of these lands. The main holdings of the shōgun and his followers formed a 'central stronghold' round the Tokugawa castle town of Edo (modern Tokyo) and in the provinces linking that city with Kyoto and Osaka. Some of the shōgun's vassal lords (*fudai daimyō*) were also given strategic territories elsewhere, controlling important communication routes or commanding areas whose loyalty was doubtful. The wealthiest of the *tozama* were relegated to the periphery: the north-east and south-west provinces; the Japan Sea coast; Shikoku.

The shōgun's government, known as the bakufu and located in Edo, had two main functions. One was to administer his lands. These were divided into estates, each roughly equivalent in size to the domain of a feudal lord of middle rank, and put under the supervision of samurai officials, whose principal tasks were to collect tax and maintain order. Tax was assessed on villages, not individual cultivators. It was left to the village headman and the village elders to apportion the burden within the

community. They were also held responsible for settling such civil disputes as might arise within the village and for ensuring compliance with bakufu regulations for the control of land and population. The penalties exacted for failure in these duties were made deliberately frightening.

A similar system of administration was applied to the towns which came under the bakufu's immediate control: Edo itself, Kyoto, Osaka, Nagasaki, and one or two more. However, no attempt was made to intervene in the territories and castle towns assigned to daimyō, not even to tax them. They remained under the exclusive jurisdiction of their lords, who usually adopted methods modelled on those of Edo. Most of Japan, in fact, was governed by these 'little bakufus'. Some were very small indeed, for the minimum landholding that would qualify a vassal-in-chief for the status of daimyō was 10,000 koku, comprising perhaps twenty or thirty villages. At the other extreme, the Maeda (with over a million koku) controlled two provinces or more. Out of a total of about 250 daimyō – there were a few less in the seventeenth century, rather more in the nineteenth – under one-fifth were territorial lords of real substance, holding lands in excess of 100,000 koku.

The second function of Edo's officialdom was to provide Japan with a central government, principally designed to supervise the feudal lords and other members of the ruling class. In constitutional importance the first of its concerns was the imperial court, since the emperor was the source of the shōgun's legitimacy, conferring office, bestowing honours. Controlling the court did not in practice pose many problems. A senior Tokugawa vassal was always appointed governor of Kyoto. One of his duties was to convey the shōgun's wishes to the emperor's ministers, usually in the politest terms, and to ensure that they were observed. Another was to insulate the court from politics. The emperor and his courtiers were expected to remain within the palace quarter. Marriage links with feudal lords required bakufu permission, as did conferment on them of court rank and title. Moreover, under regulations issued by Ieyasu in 1615 the members of the court were enjoined to devote themselves to scholarship and the arts, not to affairs of state. In return, the bakufu guaranteed a modest provision for their incomes. Thus Kyoto under the Tokugawa remained a city of great social prestige, famous as a centre of classical culture and religion, but not possessed of vast wealth or political influence.

Stability depended still more on control of the daimyō, whether tozama or fudai. In part this was ensured by another set of regulations issued by Ieyasu in 1615, requiring them to take action against rebels and malefactors (including other lords, if need be), imposing restrictions on castle-building and marriage alliances, banning luxury and licentiousness. Such rules gave ample excuse for penalties to be imposed on suspect lords, even to confiscation of fief. To ensure that they could be enforced, daimyō were required to spend much of their time in the shōgun's capital. As formulated under Iemitsu in 1635 and 1642, the provisions concerning sankin-kōtai, or 'alternate attendance', stipulated that each lord must spend half the year in Edo. During the months he spent in his own territories, wives and children had to be left as hostages in the Edo residence (yashiki). One consequence was to bring about a rapid increase in Edo's population, which because of this system was bound to include at any given time a substantial proportion of Japan's ruling class. Another was to impose heavy financial burdens on the domains, since the cost of going to and staying in the capital for the daimyō and his considerable retinue – costs mostly payable in cash – took up a large percentage of disposable revenue.

There are some features of this political structure which it might be useful at this point to emphasize for the benefit of readers whose understanding of feudal society rests on a knowledge of medieval Europe. By the middle of the seventeenth century most samurai were no longer fief-holding. Only a few higher-ranking ones still held land, from which they derived feudal dues. Most lived in their lord's castle town, serving in civil or military offices appropriate to their inherited status and receiving stipends from his treasury. As a result they had become more urban than rural: more able to impose their will on the merchants of the towns than were their European counterparts, less directly involved in the affairs of the countryside, which they supervised as officials rather than residents, often from offices in the towns. Thus a discussion of Tokugawa Japan must take account of the fact that up to fifty per cent of town-dwellers lived in samurai households. Nevertheless, this should not be taken to imply that the village was escaping from feudal control. Only samurai were allowed to bear arms. Collectively, a lord's vassals could impose their will on commoners in his territory at least as effectively as any European knights or lords of the manor.

The character of political society has a bearing on the development of Japanese culture in this period. The preservation of Kyoto as an enclave dominated socially by the court nobility; the existence of Osaka, a city primarily devoted to commercial and financial activities, having few samurai residents; the fact that daimyō had a large measure of independence, which enabled them to support in their own castle towns, if they wished, schools of art or scholarship which were not necessarily fashionable – all these things contributed to diversity. Yet there were even stronger factors making for cohesion. One can cite the uniformity of feudal administrative institutions, status divisions and social attitudes (codified as bushidō), the pride of place accorded to Edo, socially and economically as well as politically; the ties binding it to a network of provincial castle towns through sankin-kōtai, and the existence of a shared literary tradition, expressed in a common written language. The common thread is that this was above all else a samurai society, one in which the habits, beliefs and predilections of members of the feudal ruling class were the principal determinants of taste. Only gradually did the growth of a wealthy merchant class modify this situation, by bringing into being another kind of patron for art, literature and the theatre. Even at the end of the period samurai values still had a central role, if only as objects of satire or debate.

The Christian Century and seclusion

The 'shared tradition' of seventeenth-century Japan was by no means exclusively Japanese in origin. In fact, to men of any education – most court nobles and Buddhist priests, many daimyō and samurai, a small percentage of commoners – it was in large part Chinese. Chinese influences had first become significant a thousand years before, but since about 1400 there had been a fresh influx of Chinese culture into Japan, associated with the growth of Sino-Japanese trade and the spread of Zen Buddhism. Feudal lords of the sixteenth and seventeenth centuries followed its new fashions. To own paintings in the style of the Song, to collect Chinese porcelain, to build ceremonial tea-houses and landscape gardens, all were evidence that they had put campaigning behind them in the search for a more 'civilised' respectability. In the same period, Confucianism, which gave ethical sanction to social inequalities, emerged as the preferred ideology of the feudal class. Samurai saw themselves as 'ministers', bearing responsibility for 'good' government and the welfare of the people (though without admitting that failure to provide them would warrant the loss of inherited privilege). Some became Confucian scholars, well versed in the Classics and the commentaries. Thus Japanese feudalism acquired a Confucian vocabulary.

The arrival of Europeans at first did little to dilute this prevailing Chineseness. The Portuguese reached Japan in the 1540s, the Spanish some fifty years later. In 1600 a Dutch ship arrived off the Japanese coast, piloted by an Englishman, Will Adams. In 1613 came the first expedition of the English themselves. All these were voyages in search of profit, preferably profit in some easily portable and exchangeable form. Japan had just the cargo the foreigners sought: silver from her newly-exploited mines. To secure it, however, they had to supply, as the English factor, Richard Cocks, put it, 'commodities to their liking . . . which is raw silk and silk stuffs, with Siam sapon and skins'. In short, they had to conform to the needs of a Japanese market already developed by trade with China. This meant that access to China was a condition of success. The Portuguese were able to obtain it through Macao, the rest by dealing with the Chinese junks which came to Manila and the other ports of South East Asia. In this way Europeans became carriers of a commerce conducted directly or indirectly between China and Japan. One result was that the trade did not become substantially

a vehicle for the introduction of European products or a knowledge of Western civilisation into Japan. Its most important contribution in this respect was firearms, brought in by the Portuguese in their early ventures and soon manufactured by the Japanese. They brought fundamental changes in the nature of warfare; they gave the country's feudal rulers a more-than-economic interest in the management of the trade, thereby providing a foretaste of what was to happen on a much larger scale in the nineteenth century; but they did not direct Japanese attention away from China culturally.

Christianity was potentially more far-reaching in its impact. From the time when Francis Xavier arrived at Kagoshima in 1549, the first of many Jesuits to work in Japan under Portuguese patronage, the European priests and traders had close ties. Royal ships provided the Jesuit order with transport and the opportunity to acquire funds through profitable investments. The Jesuits for their part served as negotiators and interpreters, skilled in making agreements with Japanese feudal lords. Indeed, it was on members of the feudal class that the Jesuits concentrated their religious efforts, too, aided by a belief among daimyō that where the priests were made welcome the 'great ships' would follow, bringing gold and guns. As a consequence, by the end of the century the order was able to claim several hundred thousand converts, mostly concentrated in Kyushu and the area round Kyoto. Their numbers included two or three influential daimyō.

This success was threatened by the appearance of religious rivals: first the Franciscans under the protection of Spain, seeking to spread Christianity by an appeal to 'the people'; then the Dutch and the English, bringing with them the animosities of the Reformation (though without evangelical purpose). The accusations and counter-accusations they all made about each other in the hope of influencing the Japanese, partly out of religious conviction, partly in the pursuit of commercial advantage, undermined the position of the Europeans as a whole. It has to be remembered that these developments took place in a period when Hideyoshi and Ieyasu were concerned to give Japan unity and stability. Buddhism, long viewed with suspicion in this context because of its institutional (and military) strength, had been reduced to order by Nobunaga. His successors were able to view it as potentially an instrument of government. Confucianism was emerging as an ideological reinforcement of feudal rule. In these circumstances there was little chance that Japanese military hegemons would acquiesce in the spread of an alien faith that not only preached allegiance to a distant Pope but also denied the Confucian principles on which, as Hideyoshi wrote in a letter to the Viceroy of the Indies at Goa in 1591, 'the foundations of our relationships between sovereign and minister, parent and child and husband and wife are established'.

Both Hideyoshi and Ieyasu were confident of their ability to control the foreign religion without losing the trade. In 1587 Hideyoshi issued orders banning Christianity and expelling European priests, though he made no serious attempt to implement them. If, as seems likely, they were meant as a warning, it was sharply underlined ten years later in response to the overt missionary activities of the Spanish friars. In 1597 seven of them were executed, together with nineteen Japanese converts. After Hideyoshi's death in the following year and Ieyasu's rise to power, no further action was taken against the Christians for a decade or more, because the new shōgun was anxious to avoid foreign entanglements; but in the last few years of his life Ieyasu, too, became concerned about security, being anxious to transmit an orderly Japan to his successor, Hidetada. Between 1612 and 1615 military operations were undertaken against Osaka, the stronghold of Hideyoshi's surviving son; regulations were issued to define the rights and duties of court nobles and daimyō; and Christianity was again proscribed, a number of high-ranking converts, as well as priests, being arrested.

This was the prelude to a generation of persecution carried out under Hidetada and Iemitsu. Thousands of priests and converts were ordered to recant under threat of death and torture. Some did. Many were martyred. Survivors fled from Japan or went into hiding. A few small communities managed to preserve the vestiges of their religion in secrecy, despite the fact that those who were suspected of membership of 'the evil sect' were ordered to prove their religious loyalties by 'trampling' on Christian symbols (fumi-e); but for the most part Christianity was eliminated as an influence on Japanese life.

One corollary of persecution was a deterioration in the conditions for foreign trade, not only for Catholics. Ships coming from abroad were no longer free to visit any part of Japan at will, while imports were handled by monopoly guilds of merchants under Tokugawa licence. The English factory, finding no profit on these terms, was withdrawn in 1623. A year later Spanish trading rights were cancelled by the bakufu on the grounds that Spain had territorial designs upon Japan. Dutch and Portuguese trade was allowed to continue, though under restrictions, the former at Hirado, the latter at Nagasaki. From this time on the fury of religious persecution began to die down, mostly for lack of victims, but it soon became apparent that Edo officials were no longer willing to accept it as axiomatic that the profits from trade were worth its political risks. In 1633 a new decree, revised and strengthened in 1635, forbade Japanese to live or trade overseas on penalty of death. This put an end to the voyages made for many years by Japanese junks, sailing to the ports of South East Asia under the authority of government Red Seal (shu-in) permits. Japanese who had taken up residence in the Philippines, Siam, Malaysia and elsewhere had to choose between return and permanent exile. Replacing them, Chinese junks began to come to Nagasaki in increasing numbers.

In the closing months of 1637 a peasant revolt broke out in the Kyushu domain of Shimabara, not far from Nagasaki. Many Christians took part in it and it proved unusually difficult to suppress, a circumstance which persuaded the authorities that the rebels must have had foreign help. With this as pretext the Portuguese were ordered to leave in 1639, never to return. When Macao sent a mission to appeal against the decision, its leaders were executed. As a final step, the Dutch were moved from Hirado in 1641 and housed in the artificial island of Deshima in Nagasaki harbour, where for the next two hundred years they were to be the only Europeans allowed to live in Japan. The Chinese, too, were segregated, in their case in a special compound within the city.

The decision to 'close the country' (sakoku) was consistent with Tokugawa Iemitsu's other policies: a sharper definition of official duties and bureaucratic practices; spelling out rules for 'alternate attendance'; support for Neo-Confucian orthodoxy. The emphasis throughout was on inhibiting change, such as might pose a threat to Tokugawa dominance. It was inevitable, if coincidental, that knowledge of the West should have been sacrificed to the same end. During the 'Christian century' Japan had acquired much practical information, not least from the Jesuits, concerning, for example, mathematics and astronomy, gunnery, cartography, movable-type printing and techniques of mining. After 1640 the main source of information was cut off. The end of the export of silver soon reduced foreign trade to minor importance. In other respects Japanese contact with the Dutch was restricted because of suspicions of Christianity, suspicions which by 1700 must have seemed Europe's only enduring gift. Of European languages, Dutch alone was studied, and that by a handful of Nagasaki interpreters, using it for simple commercial purposes, which was all their vocabulary compassed. Accordingly, Europe's seventeenth-century scientific revolution passed Japan by. China, resuming its traditional role as the chief external stimulus to Japanese art, philosophy and religion, offered nothing comparable.

From Tokugawa to Meiji

The stability guaranteed by Tokugawa government created conditions favourable to economic growth, which in turn weakened samurai power. During the seventeenth century agricultural production increased substantially. Domestic commerce grew, as samurai consumers, concentrated in castle towns, acquired a taste for better living – an expensive taste, straining the resources of all but the highest ranks. Simultaneously, the costs of urban life and of the travels made necessary by 'alternate attendance' put the finances of domains in jeopardy. By the Genroku period (1688–1704) many lords were in debt, like their vassals. In fact, the label Genroku is used to describe a new phase in the development of Japanese society, one in which rich merchants moved to the centre of the stage. As members of powerful guilds they were simultaneously the creditors of daimyō and their partners in the management of feudal revenue. As townsmen (*chōnin*) they were patrons of the artists, actors and geisha who belonged to the non-samurai sub-culture, emerging especially in Edo and Osaka, known as *ukiyo*, the 'floating world'.

Samurai officials reacted in two ways to the problems which these developments posed. One was to attempt to restore the conditions obtaining in the early Edo period: first, by 'good' government, that is, by ensuring the efficient collection of tax from a carefully regulated peasantry, while exercising economy in expenditure; second, by sumptuary laws, imposed on the ruling class (and others) in the name of Confucianism, in order to reduce samurai debt by stifling costly appetites. The earliest and most successful application of these methods was by the eighth Tokugawa shōgun, Yoshimune (1684–1751), who restored for a time at least the bakufu's solvency. Later in the century his grandson, Matsudaira Sadanobu (1758–1829), acting as regent, tried again with rather less effect. Between the two, Tanuma Okitsugu (1719–88) exemplified the alternative strategy. Exercising power as the favourite palace attendant of Yoshimune's grandson, Ieharu, Tanuma set out to exploit the commercial economy for the benefit of feudal government. His measures included, for example, establishing state monopolies, the profits of which depended on an alliance between political authority and merchant expertise. The treasury certainly benefited. Tanuma, however, was condemned by conservatives at the time, and has been by many historians since, for contributing to the growth of corruption and luxury.

More significant is the fact that both economic strategies failed. As a result, by 1800 it was clear that wealth in Japan no longer accorded necessarily with power. The bakufu, the domains and individual samurai continued to get deeper into debt to merchants, many of whom were able to secure samurai rank by marriage or purchase. The penetration of a money economy into the villages brought a transformation of rural society which was reflected in a rising tide of peasant revolt. Thus Japan of the early nineteenth century took on some of the appearance of Europe in the late Middle Ages: a world in which the seeds of capitalism were already sown, in which feudal lords and their vassals looked like soon becoming anachronisms. There were even signs of what might be called a renaissance, involving attacks on Neo-Confucianism on the part of more 'classical' schools; criticism of Chineseness by spokesmen for a reviving Shintō; a renewed interest in Western civilisation in the form of 'Dutch studies' (*rangaku*), especially in things that could be studied visually, like anatomy or oil-painting or surveying. The rise of new art forms depicting the contemporary

scene (*Ukiyo-e*) might be taken as part of the same process.

The difficulty about using these developments as an explanation for the fall of the Tokugawa bakufu is the time scale. From the end of Genroku to the resignation of the last Tokugawa shōgun, Yoshinobu (also known as Keiki; 1827–1913), is over a century and a half. During that period, or at least until nearly the end of it, the power of shōgun, daimyō and samurai was nowhere successfully challenged. In other words, however greatly the régime was undermined by social and economic change, the resulting discontents did not quickly find a focus, such as might have served to bring about the bakufu's overthrow. Indeed, when eventually they did, it was in the context of relations with the West, not of domestic grievances.

'The compulsory seclusion of the Japanese', stated the *Edinburgh Review* in 1852, 'is a wrong not only to themselves but to the civilised world.' What it meant was that to exponents of laissez-faire and economic rationality Japan's refusal to open her ports to trade, other than to the Dutch and Chinese, was an affront. Edo did not agree. Yet during the previous sixty years bakufu officials had gradually been made aware that their country was becoming an object of attention to foreigners who were far more powerful and ambitious than those Iemitsu had expelled. Starting in 1792, Russia had begun to show an interest in securing access to Japan, largely for the sake of supplying her settlements round the Sea of Okhotsk. Rebuffs led to conflict between Japanese and Russians in the Kuriles. At about the same time British ships appeared off the Japanese coast again: a private trading venture in 1791; a frigate demanding supplies in 1808 (and seizing hostages until they were forthcoming); an attempt by Raffles to divert the Dutch trade into British hands in 1813–14, when he was temporarily lieutenant-governor of Java. None of this did much more than produce symptoms of nervousness in Edo, but news of a British war with China in 1839–42, ostensibly about opium, turned nervousness into alarm. 'How can we know', a Confucian scholar wrote in 1847, 'whether the mist gathering over China will not come down as frost on Japan?'

In the event it was not the British or the Russians but the Americans who came demanding entry. To the United States, rapidly developing its territorial hold on the Pacific seaboard, Japan had a potential value, not so much for its trade, which seemed likely to be small, but for its ability to provide food, water and fuel (including coal) to ships on the route to China. China was vast, its commerce, men believed, a source of almost limitless wealth. By comparison Japan was insignificant. It was for this reason that Commodore Matthew Perry, when he brought his squadron to Uraga and Kanagawa in 1853–4, demanded the opening of ports rather than rights of trade. The bakufu, facing superior military technology, was forced to give him what he asked. When others followed him – Stirling for Britain, Putiatin for Russia – they were offered the same. However, once the admirals had pushed the door ajar they were quickly replaced by consuls and diplomats, men for whom the expansion of commerce was an article of faith. In 1858 the American consul, Townsend Harris, combining lectures on economics with dire warnings about the risks Japan would incur by thwarting Britain, secured a commercial treaty based closely on those which governed the relations of the powers with China. Within weeks, Britain, France, Holland and Russia had done the same. Accordingly, in the summer of 1859 Nagasaki, Yokohama and Hakodate were opened to foreign trade, to be supplemented within a year or two, the agreements promised, by Edo, Osaka and Hyōgo (Kobe).

The significance of these events for Japanese politics is that in signing the treaties the bakufu, reluctantly, but, as officials saw it, necessarily, had run far ahead of feudal opinion. There were daimyō and samurai, it is true, who were well informed enough to recognise the inevitability of coming to terms with the West, though not all of them were willing to say so publicly. Most were simply aware of the disgrace. Japan had abandoned seclusion at the point of a gun, taking the first steps along a road which in China had led to disaster. What is more, in taking the decision about the American treaty Edo had knowingly flouted the Emperor's wishes. Thus to its earlier failure to solve the problems associated with commercial growth – its policies had by this time produced rapid inflation, of which samurai were the most vociferous critics – the bakufu had now added dereliction in its primary duty, national defence, coupled with an arrogance towards the court that left it open to the charge of disloyalty. It is not surprising that during the winter of 1858–9 it became the target of bitter hostility, which brought together many of the latent discontents of a changing society.

One characteristic of samurai as political activists was that they bore arms and were willing to use them. During the next few years there were attacks on bakufu leaders – for example, the regent, Ii Naosuke, who had signed the treaties, was assassinated in 1860 – and on many of their subordinates, as well as on foreigners in the treaty ports. There were plots to seize power in some of the great domains, attempts to form a daimyō alliance against the shōgun, even a plan for the Emperor to lead a crusade to expel the foreigners. Adding to the turbulence, the representatives of the powers intervened on two occasions to demand compensation for injury to their citizens: in 1863, when a British squadron bombarded Kagoshima; and in 1864, when a joint British, French, Dutch and American expedition destroyed batteries that had fired on foreign ships in the Straits of Shimonoseki. By this date it was already becoming apparent that the shōgun was not much better able to govern Japan than he was to defend it. In 1866 he fought, and failed to win, a war against the daimyō of Chōshū. From then on, it seemed, the issue was what remnants of Tokugawa power could be saved from the wreck. It turned out to be not very much. In November

1867 Yoshinobu offered to resign. Within weeks a *coup d'état*, beginning with seizure of the imperial palace, stripped him of his lands and office, opening the way for a decree (3 January 1868) which 'restored' imperial rule in the name of the young Meiji Emperor. A brief civil war confirmed the victory.

The Meiji Restoration, as it is called, marked the beginning of an era in which new leaders pursued the goal of Japanese equality with the countries of the West through a far-reaching programme of political, economic and military reforms on Western lines. 'Using the barbarian to control the barbarian' was one way of describing what they set out to do. 'Enrich the country, strengthen the army' was another. In just over three years the domains had been abolished and their lords relegated to a position of social prestige but political impotence. A centralised bureaucracy was created to serve the imperial régime. Land tax, payable in cash, was substituted for feudal dues in 1873. In the same year a conscript army replaced samurai units as the centrepiece of national defence. A start had by then been made on building a railway network and establishing an education system (both in 1872). Finally, a high-ranking mission to America and Europe in 1871–3, led by Iwakura Tomomi (1825–83), came back persuaded that economic development was a necessary condition of power. Thereafter Japan moved steadily into the age of industry.

Thus one legacy from the Edo period was a search for security and esteem that eventually led Japan to challenge the West in a competition for empire. Another was a fashion for things Western which reflected a long-established curiosity about the outside world. A Confucian scholar, Aizawa Seishisai (1782–1863), writing in 1825, had commented on 'the weakness of some for novel gadgets and rare medicines', which led many of his countrymen to 'admire foreign ways'. In the Meiji period, when information about such matters became readily available, the 'weakness' produced popular enthusiasms for Western art, music, literature, clothes, entertainment and much else, all encouraged in some degree by the government on the grounds that Japan must, for the sake of her international standing, be seen to be 'civilised'. As a result, by 1890 the Edo period seemed more remote, culturally and politically, than could have been conceivable a generation earlier. Yet it was not on that account wholly lost to view. Rather, it became, both for Japanese and foreigners, what it has remained ever since: the most familiar embodiment of the Japanese tradition.

Society and economy in the Edo period

Professor Masahide Bito

The Special Character of the Period

The Edo period of Japanese history is that in which the effective government of the country was located at the centre of what is now the city of Tokyo. After the battle of Sekigahara in 1600, Tokugawa Ieyasu made his base there and imposed his authority countrywide over the daimyō, the feudal lords. In 1600 or 1602 Ieyasu was appointed shōgun by the imperial court at Kyoto, his universal rule being thus legalised. It lasted from 1603 until 1868, the year of the Meiji Restoration, the *Ishin*, when the Tokugawa house restored power to the emperor. These dates define a political phase of Japanese history and a period of particular social organisation; but in sociological, economic and cultural terms, the Edo period forms one with the Azuchi-Momoyama (1568–1603) period, and is frequently termed *Kinsei*, the Early Modern Age. The town of Azuchi (now in Shiga prefecture) arose at the end of the civil war which engulfed the whole country for about a century after 1467, during the Sengoku period. Oda Nobunaga, the warrior who undertook the political unification of Japan, chose it as the site of the castle which he made his chief base of operations. In 1591 Toyotomi Hideyoshi inherited the supreme rule in pursuance of Nobunaga's will and made his headquarters at the two castles of Osaka and Fushimi, the latter, situated to the south of Kyoto and called later Momoyama, giving this name to the period in which Hideyoshi represented the central power. In 1598 Hideyoshi died of illness and two years later the rule passed to Tokugawa Ieyasu. Thereafter political stability was maintained for some 270 years. The Azuchi-Momoyama period may be seen as the time in which this stable social organization and political order finally took shape. Already in the Sengoku period the tide of history was carrying the country towards this goal: the feudal lords, each entrenched in his domain and wielding autocratic power in maintaining peace within his own boundaries, contributed towards the final settlement.

The shōgun's government was termed the bakufu – 'tent government'. In the seventh century the ancient Japanese state had been set up on the Chinese model. From the end of the eighth century, when Kyoto became the capital, until the Meiji *Ishin* of 1868 this form of state was maintained without a break, but in the tenth century warriors of the military clans, the samurai, increasingly took control of their own territories as the venality of state offices undermined the strength of central government. The warriors, *bushi*, were the descendants of local officials or members of powerful provincial families, or belonged to one section of the top class of farmers. They were organised as bands consisting of masters with their retainers. At their head stood Minamoto Yoritomo, who in 1192 was appointed shōgun by the imperial court. As Controller of Warriors he was invested by general consent with military command, and with administrative powers *vis-à-vis* the feudal territories. He established his military government at Kamakura in east Japan, in the modern Kanagawa prefecture. The title of shōgun under which he ruled formally designated an officer commissioned to subdue 'barbarians', in his case the population of east Japan, which had remained outside the imperial pale. Thus arose the Kamakura bakufu which, with the imperial court, constituted a double-based authority. In 1333 the bakufu fell and for a moment exclusive power reverted to the court. But support for the imperial power had come from *bushi* who had withdrawn their allegiance from the bakufu, and many of these soldiers presently rallied to Ashikaga Takauji. In 1338 this daimyō became shōgun in his town and inaugurated the second bakufu, that of Muromachi, with headquarters in Kyoto. This régime erected by the military was more powerful than its predecessor in its dealings with the imperial court. In every region a feudal head was appointed as local potentate ruling on behalf of the bakufu, and a hierarchy of master and retainers was established in every locality. But at once, in defiance of the bakufu's orders, disputes broke out between the clans, and the weakness of the bakufu as an organ of central government was made manifest. With the development of agriculture and the spread of trade at the beginning of the fifteenth century, the upper farming and commercial classes were militarised, peasant rebellion became frequent and in many parts of the country armed self-governing townships sprang up. The doctrine of power-based meritocracy spread even to the ruling class, and the more powerful subordinates increasingly usurped the position of daimyō. Meanwhile the nobles and great priests on whom the imperial structure had always built were sinking beneath the pressure of a vital popular movement. Their political status and their economic control alike were lost and in their stead was being established a regional control of the population based on the naked power of the daimyō. In the Edo period the transformation was completed: the single government authority was now the military, in a system built of territorial units ruled by feudal chiefs.

In contrast to the remarkable change in Japanese society wrought by the introduction of European culture from the time of the imperial restoration of 1868 – remarkable in the eyes of visiting Europeans as much as in the eyes of the contemporary Japanese – the earlier period has commonly been designated *feudal*. A sharp line seemed to divide modern society from the old. But recent opinion has questioned this distinction more and more. In the usual periodisation the Kamakura and Muromachi periods are designated *Chūsei*, Mediaeval period, in contrast to *Kinsei*, the Early Modern age, but the boundary between the Ancient and Mediaeval periods is less easily drawn than that between the Mediaeval period and *Kinsei*; while the transition from *Kinsei* to the Modern age beginning in 1868 is comparatively smooth. In short, Japanese history is best divided into two parts, the main break falling between the Mediaeval and the Early Modern periods.

The so-called Christian century embraces the formative stage of the society of the Early Modern Age and the new religion rapidly gained momentum in its opposition to Buddhism. It found its converts in all classes of society, from daimyō to commoners, but in 1587 Toyotomi Hideyoshi issued for the first time a decree of expulsion against the missionaries. Under his Tokugawa successor the exclusion policy was gradually intensified, and finally in 1639 the Edo bakufu completely forbade the Spanish and Portuguese from coming to Japan and Japanese citizens from taking passage abroad. The only exception to this was the permission granted to Dutch and Chinese ships to trade under strict government regulation at the single port of Nagasaki. Through this policy of closure, *sakoku*, the Christian religion was practically banished from Japan. The reason for the closure lay in the suspicion harboured in official quarters that the Spanish and Portuguese were using their religious mission as a cloak for the preparation of an armed invasion. So complete was the prohibition that all trace of Christian influence vanished in Edo culture.

This turn of events was not, however, solely a matter of Christianity. In the Middle Ages both Buddhism and Shintō had a great following and both produced men distinguished by their piety and learning whose meditation and experience issued in original religious thought of every kind. The Buddhist faith, anciently the special preserve of the nobility, spread among commoners, while Shintō, the popular religion of tradition, joined with it so that its various gods came to be regarded as separate manifestations of the Buddha. The temples and shrines scattered to every corner of the land became centres around which provincial society gathered. This tendency was encouraged by the efforts made by certain temples, especially those of the Shin sect, to organise themselves locally into self-governing entities independent of the bakufu, in the political movement called *ikkōikki* (*ikkō* – a term for the Shin sect). In this context took place the rapid diffusion of Christianity, which to some extent came to occupy the traditional place of the Buddhist religion.

The Early Modern period was, however, an age of secularisation and scant religious feeling. In the arts and in other branches of Edo culture masterpieces with religious significance are rare, an aspect of the period in striking contrast with the religious art and thought of the Middle Ages and yet one predictable from the changes which had occurred in the social order. The prohibition of Christianity was in the first place a political measure, but the conditions which ensured the success of the policy were created by changes in the social structure. Buddhism took advantage of the exclusion of Christianity and in the Edo period spread to all classes of the population. This expansion was, however, one of formal organization. The regular annual observances of Buddhism lost their character as expression of religious faith and there was a pronounced tendency to turn them into mere customary ceremony. The deficiency of religious sense encountered today among the Japanese is to be ascribed to the circumstances of Edo times. While secularisation may not equate with modernisation, consideration of the religion in its purely social rôle suffices to throw into relief the radical change which sunders the Mediaeval from the Early Modern period.

Social rank determined by the separation of warrior and farmer

'Separation of warrior and farmer' is the term now used to designate the revolutionary social change which took place between the Mediaeval and the Early Modern periods. The military class, indifferently called *bushi* or samurai, represents broadly the rulers in a feudal society in which farmers were the ruled. The distinction is not one merely of social rank. When the samurai who had hitherto lived in the farming villages were collected together in the settlements around the castles of shōgun or daimyō, their relation to the farming population altered: whereas they had previously been in close touch with their commoner-neighbours, they were now segregated as a distinct superior class and contact with the rest of the population became indirect, the new location of their residence making the social change manifest. Although the separation of warrior and farmer had been part of the policy of daimyō in their territories already in the Sengoku period, it had not been made a regular system. It was constituted by Toyotomi Hideyoshi's administration in about 1590 and after a survey the principle was applied to the entire country. The survey was undertaken as the basis of a tax to be imposed on the productive capacity of land calculated uniformly in terms of *kokudaka*, the standard of productivity expressed as an equivalent in rice (one *koku* being about 180 litres). The estates or salaries given by feudatories to their samurai were assessed as so many thousand or hundred *koku*, giving a fixed rating, the *kokudaka*. Land and the peasants who farmed it were allotted to the samurai on a *kokudaka* scale, and the samurai collected a tax on produce usually of about 40 per cent. Once this tribute had been exacted, the exercise of arbitrary authority was not permitted. Most of the samurai below the middle rank did not, however, have land or peasants assigned to them at all and received their *kokudaka* rating in actual rice, or perhaps a part of it in cash equivalent. After the separation of warriors and farmers had been put into effect, the samurai no longer held their ancestral estates. Land was interchangeable with other land or salary, and their holdings were awarded arbitrarily at the whim of the feudal lord. Even the assigned territories of daimyō were often changed on the orders of the central administration. On these occasions the daimyō had to move quickly and took with them the samurai under their command, but left behind the farmers, merchants and craftsmen who had been under their supervision. Arriving in Japan at the end of the sixteenth century, the missionary Luís Fróis and his companions noted how different the Japanese social order was from the European feudalism which it superficially resembled. The samurai had a duty of military service to daimyō or shōgun, as the daimyō themselves must serve the shōgun. The number of men who were to do service in war, and the kind of arms they bore, were fixed in proportion to the *kokudaka*. The latter also determined the standard of taxes due from farmers to their landlord, as a quantity of rice calculated on the cultivated area, and again usually about 40 per cent, part of which might be rendered as money. The chief duty of the farmer was to see that this tax was duly paid to the samurai landholder, or to a daimyō or the shōgunal administration. In 1588 a 'sword hunt' was mounted against farmers and all their weapons confiscated, so that they could no longer make samurai of themselves or raise rebellion. They were to confine themselves to agriculture.

Thus the samurai assumed military obligations and the farmers accepted taxation to the limit set by their *kokudaka* rating, and the principle of separating warrior and farmer was fully realised. The system was so uniformly and rationally followed throughout the country that each man's duty seemed to be that of an official of the state. In these terms the policy of the time appears as the restructuring of the state and the creation of a new social order in its population. The policy of separation reduced social fluidity, defined social functions and created conditions of stability for a political disciplining of society.

Together with the separation of warrior and farmer went the separation of farmer and merchant. Commodity economy had penetrated to the villages in the Muromachi period, and persons who had accumulated wealth from trade or metallurgy appear frequently. Craftsmen and merchants moved continually from one district to another for their business. When the social separation had created the settlements beneath the castle walls, they took up residence there for the most part, or in the feudal towns. According to their trades these men were ordered to supply the goods and the labour necessary to the economic life of the vassal communities, receiving in compensation the privilege of freedom in business or the monopoly of their trade. As inhabitants of the towns they were known as *chōnin* – a word meaning 'townsmen', but implying 'merchants'. In town administration and military defence they had no right of self-government, being placed under the control of *machi-bugyō*, the executive officers of the samurai, and to the extent of this subjection their position resembled that of the peasants. Since this trade and industry was settled in the towns, the shōgun and the feudal lords affirmed their right to control economic activity within their territories.

Thus Edo society came to be composed of the three classes: military, peasants and *chōnin*. Separate social functions led to separate social responsibilities and contributed to the stability of the whole. A certain logic underlay the system and its fruit was 270 years of peace. From the start of the Edo period the trend towards realistic thinking grew stronger, as the religious sense declined. On the other hand the worship of human persons as deities was a new religious phenomenon and something characteristic of the age. A beginning of this is seen in 1599, the year after Toyotomi Hideyoshi's death, when the foundation of his shrine, the Hōkoku Daimyō-jin, was celebrated at a site in the hills east of Kyoto. Mythical heroes had previously been identified with deities, but never before had a historical ruler been worshipped directly as a god. Authority was thus apotheosized and Hideyoshi was still powerful in his grave. Hideyoshi's successor, Tokugawa Ieyasu, was also given divine status as Tōshō Daigongen and worshipped in Sumpu (Shizuoka) and Nikkō. These men were not deified in recognition of personal qualities but as protectors of the political order which they had established. In this sense an ancient religious tradition was revived. The powerful rule of the régime represented by Hideyoshi and Ieyasu was in part supported by an idea of rebuilding the state as it had existed from ancient times. Although as head of the traditional state, with his court and nobles, the emperor did not possess real authority in government, the appointment of the shōgun and the creation of such divine titles as Tōshōgu Daigongen were put into effect by imperial command. Contrary to the mistaken explanation often given by Europeans arriving in Japan during the Edo period, the emperor was not a mere symbol invested with religious dignity. The Edo reconstruction of the state fitted with the current of realism characteristic of the time, just as it was a primary factor in the revival of the culture of the royal court.

The expansion of industry and culture

The sixteenth century, when the new social order took shape, and the following century were times of remarkable progress in every branch of industry. There was in the first place an increase in metal products centred on gold and silver. It is well known how the merchants of Portugal and Holland brought raw silk which they had acquired by exchange in China and made the export of silver from Japan their main objective. The rise in exports of precious metal was facilitated by the development of engineering works and by an improvement of ore-refining techniques. Gold and silver used in decorating the rooms of the castles which symbolized the authority of the new rulers created the extravagantly magnificent atmosphere which the times demanded.

From the middle of the seventeenth century the production of gold and silver declined and that of copper increased, becoming now the main article of the Dutch trade. All three of these metals were coined by the bakufu. While there was a tendency for the quantity of this money in circulation to increase rapidly through the seventeenth century, in response to the commercial expansion, the production of gold and silver fell, so that from the end of the century their export was restricted, or a policy adopted whereby the growth of circulation was maintained by debasing the metals.

With the advent of peace and the improvement of public works great advances were made in embanking rivers, to the advantage of agriculture, now an important industry. Long irrigation canals were opened, increasing the area under cultivation. At the end of the sixteenth century the usable land amounted to about 1,630,000 hectares and in the eighteenth century to about 3,000,000 hectares. Agricultural tools also were improved and the level of produce per unit raised. The independence of the two- or three-man farm increased and agriculture was increasingly established on the basis of small-scale enterprise. Irrigated rice was the chief crop, and the improvement of the strains was taken in hand. The cultivation of cotton, tobacco and tea as cash crops became general. Cotton became the material for the clothing of the population at large, instead of the traditional hemp, and indigo was grown widely for dyeing it. To supply the silk worn by the upper classes, sericulture spread to many parts of the country, and the quality of the product was gradually improved. The Chinese raw silk which was an important item in the import trade at Nagasaki could now be replaced by the home article. Fishing, salt-making, forestry, paper-making, textiles, pottery and lacquer goods were all departments of craft which now made conspicuous progress.

Along with the advance of industry in all its branches, the system of communications and transport was put in full order for the advancement of commerce. Land routes had been put under bakufu supervision and operated with the interests of the central administrative authority and of military requirements as prime objectives. There was hence little vehicular traffic and the transport of goods was greatly hindered. This difficulty was solved by the development of river and inshore transport and

particularly by the inauguration, about the middle of the seventeenth century, of the sea route from the north-east to Osaka passing through the Inland Sea, and along the Pacific coast to Edo. The latter became the great artery of trade between Osaka and the capital.

By the recognition of the status of the *chōnin* and through the concentration of commercial operations, the towns gained extraordinarily in size and prosperity. All this meant that both government and the feudatories with their retainers needed to turn the rice of their *kokudaka* income into money to meet the needs of urban life, an exchange which further spurred on the growth of trade. Not only rice was involved in this process. The feudatories were obliged to plan the exploitation of their lands on a financial basis and endeavoured to secure specie by shifting the produce of their territories to the centrally placed towns. The latter were Edo itself and Osaka, both under the direct administration of the bakufu. By the ordinance called *sankin kōtai* the daimyō with their following were obliged to spend alternate years residing in Edo, so that in any year one half of their number was present in the capital. This influx, added to the *chōnin*, raised the population to an estimated million by the beginning of the eighteenth century, a figure which puts Edo among the largest cities of the world at this time. Osaka and Kyoto had each about 350,000 inhabitants. Besides its traditional repute as a centre of artistic culture, Kyoto flourished as the home of the refined artistic craft of silk-weaving and dyeing. Osaka gathered in and expedited the goods produced in western Japan and along the Japan sea coast, in its particular rôle as starting point for transport to Edo. It became the commercial heart of all Japan.

In the seventeenth century the most advanced economic life of the country was centred on Kyoto and Osaka while Edo and its hinterland, the Kantō plain, were undeveloped. This contrast is to be seen also in the cultural field. During the Genroku period, which includes the end of the seventeenth and the beginning of the eighteenth century, a flowering of the arts to which the epoch gives its name – the Genroku culture – was at its finest in the *kamigata*, 'top region', as the Kyoto-Osaka sphere was called. Since the social divisions arising from the warrior/farmer separation gave commoners no opportunities for rising in the social scale, it was natural that they should turn their energies into economic and cultural channels. Popular culture, the 'culture of *chōnin*', flourished where commercial prosperity was at its height. But though the wealth of merchants was undoubtedly its main support, not all aspects of Genroku culture are to be explained in this way.

The essential characteristic of the culture is the principle of actuality which guides its pursuit of truth, the spirit of realism in which it is conceived. In the literature of the period the novel is represented by Ihara Saikaku, *haiku* poetry by Matsuo Bashō, the drama by Chikamatsu Monzaemon. Their works are the peaks of Edo literature, and they all share the realism of the times. In the interpretation of the classics it is insistence on genuine proof and on objectivity that marks out the scholars of the Edo period, to a degree unparalleled in earlier history. Motoori Norinaga brought to a successful conclusion the publication of the national literature in the latter half of the eighteenth century. The Confucian scholars Itō Jinsai and Ogyū Sorai disregarded the latter-day commentaries and looked for the original meaning of the Chinese text, bringing the new objectivity into their branch of learning. Arai Hakuseki devoted himself to the study of Japanese history and tried to give rational explanations of the causes of social change. In science Seki Takakazu earned great repute for his pioneering work in the realm of higher mathematics.

What were the causes giving rise to this realistic philosophy? Apart from Ihara Saikaku and Itō Jinsai, the men whose names have been mentioned were all samurai by origin; but they had nearly all experienced adversity in their early years, which may in part explain their attitude. Having won their release from the confines of social rank, they rose beyond them to a human compassion which embraced the lowest strata of society. They devoted their energies to understanding the minds of men who bore every kind of lot in life. While the Edo system has behind it a certain logic as stabilising the social order, it involved many inconsistencies in the constraints it placed on individual freedom. An awareness of these inconsistencies, an effort to see beyond them to the social realities, is an undercurrent in the activity of all these men.

In 1702 forty-seven retainers of the former lord of Akō, Asano Naganori, invaded the mansion of the high bakufu official Kira Yoshinaka and murdered him in an act of revenge for an insult he had offered their master, an event which aroused the greatest interest in the population at large, for it brought out sharply a contradictory aspect of the samurai's social ethos. The samurai carried his swords as symbol of his ruling-class status, and saw the defence of his honour as his highest duty. On the other hand bakufu law strictly forbade duelling and vendetta. Death was the punishment for duelling regardless of the right and wrong of the parties, for it was essential to demonstrate the authorities' determination to punish the action as a crime. There was recognition of the samurai's right to cut down a commoner who insulted him, saying as he did so 'kirisute gomen' – 'I shall exercise my right to cut you down.' But if no proof could be shown that the insult had been offered the murderer risked punishment himself. The only officially approved 'private fight' was in the case of the murder of a parent or elder brother, and then it was necessary to submit a report beforehand and obtain the formal permission of one's master before proceeding. The circumstances were still worse in the Akō case, for an entire band of men had gone forth on an armed action

planned to retrieve the honour of their dead lord. As a matter of public order the bakufu could not tolerate such a deed and commanded the perpetrators to commit *seppuku*. But people felt great sympathy for the act of revenge, and saw it performed in many a play. Called *Chūshin-gura*, 'A Treasury of loyal retainers', and other titles, the story of the Akō event has remained the best loved plot of drama and novel in Japan until the present day. The secret of its popularity lies in the nature of the deed itself: that those men should break the law and venture their lives in order to defend the reputation of their lord and their own appealed not only to the samurai themselves, but to the whole population who lived under the restraint of the Edo class system.

Tr. WW

Art in Momoyama and Edo

Professor William Watson

The Momoyama period (1568–1600) which saw the establishment of the new feudal order in Japan also saw changes in Japanese art, affecting its patronage, its relation to tradition and its receptivity to innovations of all kinds. In all these respects it ushered in the singular creation of Edo artists. An alliance of architecture and painting promoted by the building and decorating of castles of unprecedented design and structure reinforced a movement for the reassessment, by rejection or free adaptation, of the China-derived subjects and methods favoured formerly by imperial court and Ashikaga shōguns alike. When the restraints of sinicising style were relaxed, the emphatic and wholly un-Chinese decorative taste of native tradition came irresistibly into its own. The process had begun already in painting in the early sixteenth century, at the hands of Kanō Motonobu. His grandson Eitoku (1543–1590), decorator of Hideyoshi's castles and palaces and the most distinguished member of the Kanō school in his generation, perfected the schemes of landscape glimpsed behind a gorgeous foreground of tree, plant and fowl, so well suited to enliven the walls and screens of the vast castle rooms, in the straightforward terms demanded by robust daimyō taste. The new style combines the broad manner of the Chinese Zhe School, already communicated to Japan by Sesshū in the fifteenth century, with the strong-coloured realism of the early Yamato painters. It transforms these traditional elements by imposing on them a characteristic pattern of curving masses and sweeping perspective alternating with passages of exquisite detail. This manner proves to be fundamental to the art of the new age in nearly all its forms, whether quintessential and expressive or craftsmanlike and repetitive.

The great castles built between 1580 and 1610 conceived as regional fortresses dominating areas of populated flat land are designed as tower-like piles of retreating storeys, remotely influenced by western architecture. The earliest of them, Matsumoto castle in Nagano prefecture, is framed in wood, but all the later ones (Nagoya, Osaka, Himeji, Inuyama) have thick stone walls (nurigome-zukuri) intended to resist cannonade. In plan several fortified areas centre on the main keep. High inner and outer walls of ashlar masonry, inclined at a considerable angle, present a forbidding aspect, contrasting with the spacious interior ease of the keep, where the upper storeys are designed as vast rooms surrounded by uniform panelled walls or divided by similar sliding screens. Neither the shape of the rooms nor their surround of flowered landscape, much gilded and silvered, assumed a special orientation of host and guest, lord and subject. Nowhere appears the hierarchic intent of the imperial audience hall and of the Chinese palace and temple styles which had previously dominated in official architecture. The rejection of the pillar-and-beam wooden architecture of the older tradition, with all that this implied in artistic adornment, could hardly have been more categorically stated. But the awe-inspiring castles are still town architecture. In their outer precincts lived the military and the servitors, around their gates gathered the community of merchants and craftsmen essential to them, and the streets of growing towns passed beneath their walls. Defence and residence were reconciled.

For the building of his Azuchi castle Nobunaga set a precedent by summoning craftsmen from Kyoto, Nara and Osaka. Extended patronage by the castle builders multiplied the numbers and product of the artisan class whose influence was to prevail so strongly in the Edo period and fostered the growth of a new urban architecture. The exteriors of town houses, subject to the shōgunate's strict sumptuary edicts, already followed a comparatively austere tradition. This was the style of domestic architecture founded in the fourteenth century by the cultivated nobility who wished to escape from palace grandeur and to harmonise their residences with surrounding gardens and with the natural scene. The nobles' sukiya style evokes, even if remotely, the simplicities of the farmer's cottage and the wood-gatherer's hut, and from its inception the restraining spirit of the tea ceremony, cha no yu, hovered over plan and decor.

In the Momoyama age however this concept was inevitably subjoined to decorative splendour, at its peak in Ieyasu's Kyoto palace, the Nijōjō, with walls and doors treated by leading artists, everywhere displaying lacquer and dark-gleaming wood. The plan of the Nijōjō provides a series of rectangular, nearly square, blocks linked in stepped fashion, the spacing and extent of retreat of each block arising only from the sense of fit and varied proportion, without regard to the pomp of symmetry and of the hierarchic ordering of the buildings. Here the scale is immense, but at the Katsura palace on the south-west outskirts of Kyoto means have been found of reducing the façades to more acceptably human proportions, and to endow even the largest units with an air of comfort and intimacy. In these buildings proportioning by rectangular module is maintained throughout the larger and the smaller rooms of the interior. The delicacy observed in

Himeji Castle. The main keep.

assigning areas to wall, window, entrance, cupboards, shelves and the recesses called *toko no ma* in which paintings and ornaments are placed arises from an essential concern of all Edo design: to afford satisfaction by the division of the field before ever significant motifs, colours, or textures are applied. Inside the rooms only the changeable positions of pairs of folding screens depart from the prevailing rectangularity. The Katsura palace was built in the opening decades of the seventeenth century by Kobori Enshū, tea ceremony master and architect extraordinary, who undertook here to embody his ideals of cultivated candour and embowered rusticity in a larger edifice and garden than had been contemplated for this purpose ever before.

In Edo domestic building incorporating some of the Katsura qualities appears to have been led by the guild of carpenters headed by the Heinouchi family. The sides of houses were divided by barred windows, folding shutters, door panels (*renji-mado, shitomi-dō, tobira*) in dimensions echoing the modules of the interior design. For great houses a surrounding garden with ponds, contrived landscape vistas, well groomed trees and seasonal shrubs was indispensable, designed by the strict canons of an art which had never enjoyed so much attention or given so much pleasure as in Edo times; and at the Katsura palace one may see how closely garden, pavilions, verandahs and wide-doored rooms blend into an ordered and soothing whole. In a small town house the garden may be reduced to a miniature landscape in a moist and shady patio, but it is seldom absent. After the fire of 1654 which destroyed the greater part of Edo, the houses of the commonalty and of the daimyō alike, the government issued orders against luxury in the rebuilding. An edict of 1668 forbad doors of cedar or *keyaki* wood, decorated eaves brackets, elaborate windows projecting from reception rooms (*tsuke-shoin*), carved ornament of all kinds or the use of decorated paper on sliding doors. The lively sculpture of animals and plants which might otherwise have adorned the Edo mansions may be seen today at Nikkō on the funerary shrines of the shōguns. Only the *ajouré* designs on wooden transoms seem to have escaped penal attention and are frequently the most noticeable decorative features of Edo houses.

The tradition of *cha no yu* portends more than restraint in domestic architecture. During the Yoshino period (1334–92) tea-tasting parties attended by elegant society were held in a two-storeyed pavilion affording a wide view of garden and wood. A Buddhist painting or statue set the tone and commemorated the priestly channel along which the tea-drinking habit had reached Japan; for the beverage had been introduced from Tang China by the sainted Saichō and Kūkai (Kōbō Daishi) at the turn of the eighth and ninth centuries. Soon the custom arose of giving fine

29

Interior of the folding teahouse (see exhibit no. 274).

tea to guests, and at the end of the fifteenth century the shōgun Yoshimasa is said to have served it in his library. The intense cult of tea is however something different, a social observance launched formally by the priest Shukō, who was entrusted by the shōgun with the making of rules both for the preparation of the tea and for the behaviour of the participants in the ceremony. The method he adopted of grinding the green tea of Uji to a powder (*matcha*) has been followed to the present day. Later, Sen Rikyū elaborated the procedure which is still observed and prescribed the proper design of a tea-hut. From the time of Shukō, through his disciple Jōō and the latter's follower Rikyū, the tradition was brought down to the time of Hideyoshi. In the meantime it had become the province of priests of the Zen sect and by that token the ceremony recommended itself to the military class.

From the start *cha no yu* had been associated with the idea of the rustic and natural. This concept was rescued from the threat of over-sophistication by Shukō with his principle of *sosō*, the beauty of rough unworked materials and of unaffected behaviour. Towards the end of the

Muromachi period, in the first half of the sixteenth century, the qualities of *sabi* (rust, patina, the antique look) and *wabi* (the quiet taste of the solitary) were sought in all the literary arts and were naturally posed also as ideals of the tea ceremony. Whereas *wabi* had referred previously to the unpretentiousness of the equipment, Rikyū extended the idea to the whole environment of the ceremony, equating *wabi* with the quietude and conciliation into which the whole performance should resolve.

Close to the earth and its growth, the simplicities of the tea-hut are contrived to give the greatest sense of relief from the dusty path of the phenomenal world. The floor need be no larger than ten square metres. The windows are mere openings stopped with bamboo lattice and fine white paper. The same paper covers the walls, or these are left as untreated plaster. The pillars of the structure are natural tree stems, unsquared; all fittings are of untreated pine and cedar bark, and unpainted wood; the roof is pyramidal and unframed, or supported by a central pillar. The interior provides a *tokonoma* and a hearth for the kettle. After washing his hands at a stone basin or a fortuitous-looking pebbly pool, the visitor follows the stepping stones of the silvan approach to pass, crouching, through the low 'sidling door' (*nijiri-guchi*) into the hut. Apart from the tea-drinking rite, *cha no yu* was an occasion for aesthetic sensibility. Tea-bowls and others works of art and craft, suitably endowed with *sabi*, notable for their association with illustrious owners or makers, or curiously exotic, were to be admired and appreciated. This side of the occasion was cultivated above all in the Edo period, the unsophisticated, 'unwrought' (*takumazaru*) quality of tea bowls and all manner of small craft objects being subjected to *saininshiki*, 're-cognition'. No longer the privilege of the rich, *cha no yu* was now a pleasurably elegant moment for all. To admirers of art it gave opportunity to pass judgment and to exercise the faculty – never more prized than in the Edo period – which appraises the materials of craft. In earlier times patronage by nobles and by the military ruling class had concentrated the crafts around the centres of government, Kyoto, Nara and Kamakura, especially at the first, the ancient imperial city where courtly standards persisted from an early period. An immediate effect of the changes wrought by Nobunaga and Ieyasu was the scattering of craft-work to the provinces, with consequent complication of styles and multiplication of the product. Weaving spread from the ateliers at Kyoto also to Hakata, Yamaguchi and Kiryū; Edo rivalled Kyoto with its manufacture of arms and their ornament. Under the Tokugawa shōguns the dispersal was accelerated. Lacquer-craft took root in the Aizu district of Mutsu province, in the Noto and Echizen provinces, on the Tsugaru peninsula; textiles prospered almost everywhere; iron sword guards (*tsuba*) with curiously imagined ornament were made in Chōshū, Higo and Owari. All of this enterprise represented a diminution of demand at Kyoto while ensuring a wide imitation of the traditional Kyoto designs. Merchants travelled widely and craftsmen moved readily to other centres, the growing predominance of Edo making the shōgunal capital a nodal point of commerce and other communication.

For the first time in Japanese history the mercantile middle class (*chōnin*) became the most numerous and best-paying customers, pressing their taste for richly ornamented goods at the keenest prices, with a penchant towards lacquer with pictorial decoration, fancy sword furniture (although *chōnin* were mostly forbidden the port of arms), *inrō* (the little 'seal boxes' worn at the belt, now holding medicines or any small objects), and dyed and embroidered textiles of every kind. As the confusion attendant on the adoption of the money economy grew, nobles and samurai were impoverished and increasingly indebted to city merchants, but their custom hardly flagged and their sophistication is still to be detected in the refined and traditional designs used in craft-goods. In contrast with the sober styles favoured by adherents of *cha no yu* and by persons of education generally, the gorgeous new ceramic of Kyoto and other centres catered for the growing class of *nariagari-mono*, the newly rich, whose origins might be urban or rural, and whose demand for the highly ornate was no less than that of the more solidly established merchant class. But the distinction of class taste is not easily drawn, except at the extremes of reticence and vulgarity. The different branches of the new art do not tally exactly with the social divisions, and as a group stand in contrast only to the taste of determined traditionalists and to the work of scholar painters. The arts of the theatre, its costumes and actor prints, and the allied arts of the pleasure quarters, served a clientèle spread broadly through society. Yet the rise of a wholly new devotion to genre subjects in painting (and indeed in minor ornament also) must be attributed to the change in class allegiance, and to the desire of a population newly conscious of its security and economic pull to see its extravagant pastimes and fashions blazoned forth. That class certainly knew what it liked and we have ever since enjoyed the verve and wit of the art it sustained. For invention and technical mastery, beguiling narrative and blithe humour, let alone unshakeable artistic integrity, there is little anywhere with which it can be compared. A constant vigour runs through all the branches of Edo art. When ornament is profuse it still features in compositions retaining the haunting felicities of pattern which we gave above as the hallmark of the age. Animation, freshness and originality were required of artist and craftsman and their product was examined in the most competitive spirit.

Among the decorative arts we may look to textiles for the fullest characterization of the essential Edo style, both in its traditional aspects and in those aspects which mark the change of patrons and market. The outer garment had ever been taken as a field for the explicit display of

View of the interior of the Tenkyū-in, Kyoto, showing the sliding doors painted with plum-tree and birds, and tigers and bamboo (exhibit no. 13)

Hasegawa Tōhaku (1539–1610). Details of the left-hand screen of a pair of screens decorated with pines in black ink on a light ground (see p. 38, introduction to Painting Section).

ornament more directly than has been the custom in the West. It is composed almost exclusively of lengths of cloth uncut along the warps and so extending to both selvedges, tending therefore to angularity in the outline of the garment and presenting flat areas where the detail of ornament may appear to advantage. The make-up did not cut across units of ornament, so that whenever these units appear only in part, this is deliberate design. The more formal the purpose, the stiffer the garment and its angularity more pronounced. Reluctance at cutting the elaborately figured weaves imported from China from Tang times onwards may have influenced the design. All the varieties of gowns and coats, now distinguished by a score of names referring to social and professional usage as much as to design, are said to derive historically from the *kosode*, or 'small-sleeve', a very plain under-garment of the people which eventually became the normal and much decorated outer garment of nobles and officials. The garments differ by length in the body, by the length, width, attachment and opening of the sleeves, and by the disposition of the rectangular pieces of weave of which they are composed. The fabric of the sleeves may be placed with warps horizontal, or vertical in keeping with the main lengths. Back and front of the garment, made each of two pieces, may allow the fabrics to fall the full length undivided, possibly with contrasting pattern (*katami-gawari*), or may be divided horizontally into several segments exchanged in alternation with each other (*dangawari*). Again, the whole area provided by several adjacent lengths may be treated as a single field for

ornament and filled with a single large unrepeating design. The last method was favoured specially in the Edo period, for it allowed full scope to the taste for bold pictorial motifs.

During the Momoyama and Edo periods figured and flowered fabrics, woven with skills to which Chinese weavers had repeatedly contributed, were in universal demand. In the mid-sixteenth century weaving shops established at Hakata in Chikuzen, well away from the strife of the central provinces, produced a great variety of silks. Sakai, near modern Osaka, was noted for gold brocade woven in the manner introduced from China in the Ming period. In Kyoto the weaving shops of Nishijin were supported by the Tokugawa government, which decreed that all silk fabrics required by the imperial court and by the nobles should be made there. From the Kamakura period onwards Kyoto weavers had produced fabrics with raised ornament in Chinese style and in the Edo period they still furnished the richest cloths of all. It was not however with woven stuffs, but with dyed cloths that the most inventive future lay. Various methods of dyeing had been practised in Japan as early as the eighth century, when styles current in China (there the result of influence from central Asia) were widely imitated. But simple tie-dyeing and stencilling were soon abandoned in sophisticated use as brocade weaving was developed in response to further influence reaching Japan from the mainland. From Muromachi to Momoyama another dyeing method prevailed, *tsujigahana* ('flowers of the cross-roads'), which proved more effective than either the block-printing or simple tie-dyeing of earlier times. By detailed sewing of the areas to be dyed a variety of colours was introduced into a more or less precise pattern of flowers and leaves, and these finished by the brush with ink and coloured pigment. But since the ground was merely the reserved area of the cloth, the outlines were apt to be unclear and the ornament appeared on one side of the cloth only. Even when three or four colours of dye were used the result was far from competing with woven design.

From 1650 great efforts were made to improve dyeing technique, in the hope of establishing its independence from other methods, but until this goal was reached by the painter Miyazaki Yūzen in the early eighteenth century, dyeing had generally to be supplemented by embroidery or stencilling. In the Momoyama period *nuihaku*, embroidery combined with the application of gold and silver foil, or embroidery eked out with stencilling, secured the dense rich effects now in demand, the embroidery being often of a fineness which makes it difficult to distinguish from weave. Extraneous influences which bore on textile design came from the Ryukyu islands and specially from the painted chintzes (*sarasa*) introduced by the Portuguese traders. Both encouraged abundant animal and vegetable ornament. The habit of banded and blended colour (*ungen*) was gradually abandoned for organic design with more natural graded tones. These influences and the pre-Momoyama tradition still do not account for the new departure in textile design which, more than anything, characterizes Edo taste: large-scale pattern of open structure and realistic detail, making of the entire field of ornament a glimpse of garden or landscape, or a telling arrangement of familiar elegant objects. The ornament may be introduced obliquely and may leave large parts of the field blank. In *kata-suso* (shoulder and skirt) design only the upper and lower quarters of the *kosode* receive ornament, the two parts corresponding like an interrupted view of the same passage of nature. Colours are strong and unambiguous, match of tone rather than of spectrum range being the main concern. If some practical factor contributed to the change in decorative sense it must lie in the constraints of expanded dyeing techniques and of the methods followed in adapting them to the portrayal of real subjects both animate and inanimate.

The Edo fires of 1657 and 1658 could only increase the demand for textiles. A pattern book of 1666 (*Shinsen o-hiinagata*) already shows the prominence of the large oblique designs, and a generation later the invention of a method of paste-resist dyeing (*nori-oki*) by no less than the Kanō artist Morikage, pupil of Tan'yū, is a sure sign of the concern of leading screen painters with fashionable design. Dyeing by various methods of resist and stencil seems to have become a hobby of the well-to-do, as it has continued to be in Kyoto to the present day, and their experiments herald the perfection of technique achieved by Yūzen shortly after 1700. Meanwhile sumptuary laws in 1682 and 1683, in which extravagance in dress was specially reproved, did little if anything to stem the demand or to inhibit the technical advance of the trade. With *Yūzen-zome* established at Edo, Kyoto (here known as *Kamogawa-zome*) and in Kaga province the modern scene was set: thenceforward nothing could be added to method. In the mixture of dyeing and embroidery the former predominated, especially in Edo in the eighteenth and early nineteenth centuries. The costumes of *Nō* resisted the temptation to lapse into technical virtuosity, but in other spheres the germs of decadence were present already in the eighteenth century, when multiplied linear intersections and meanders began to tell against the unity and drama of *ōgara*, the 'large build'. In Kaga scarlet, green and purple were much used, many varied colours were combined in single units of design, graded colour (*bokashi*) was subtly contrived, and the patterns of pintados and Ryukyu cloths sometimes faithfully copied. This provincialism suggests the direction of decline. The *kosode* was becoming the *kimono* of recent times, on which the *obi* sash acquired an increasingly prominent rôle.

In the painting of the Edo period may be seen a tolerably complete reflexion of the political and intellectual allegiances of the day, besides the divisions of taste which we have recounted. The establishment is represented particularly by the interior decorators of the Kanō line. The work of Eitoku and his studio associates in the castles of Azuchi and Osaka, and in the Juraku palace, was long ago destroyed by fire, but paintings preserved in Kyoto temples and some other buildings, and the practice of their immediate successors, testify satisfactorily to the castle style. Kanō artists enjoyed the patronage of the shōgunate until its fall, their later style descending inevitably into stereotype and banality. Even at its official level the Kanō 'daimyō style' was central between two traditions with which it could be allied: that of the Tosa school whose colourful pictures descended from very ancient native art; and a black-ink style which represented a surviving taste for the closely sinicising painting favoured by the Ashikaga shōguns. When Kanō Tan'yū and his two brothers moved from Kyoto to Edo early in the seventeenth century, the school divided into two branches, one in each city, and more subdivision was to follow. The Kaihō school and the work of such Kanō painters as Tan'yū incorporate a larger proportion of the pre-Momoyama taste, while artists of the Hasegawa line aimed at reinstating all the rich effects of the black-ink (*sumi-e*) which traced its ancestry to the great Sesshū. Painting of this kind reflects a persisting upper-class taste. It is logical that this manner should be chosen by Uragami Gyokudō (1745–1820), the samurai turned painter and the greatest exponent of ink-style in East Asia in his time, who brought an aristocratic ardour to the cultivation of Chinese poetry, calligraphy and philosophy.

Painting in the poetic and realistic idiom of Tosa was fostered at the imperial court. Mitsuoki (1617–1691) added to the conservative vocabulary some elements reminiscent of Kanō work, producing thus a blend not dissimilar from that adopted by Kanō Naonobu in the Momoyama period, before daimyō taste was imposed so fully on the school. But the latter-day Tosa were back-looking. Their importance lies less in their own invention than in their rôle as contributors, by the revival of traditional methods, to the artistic atmosphere in which the popular school presently set itself to mirror the fashion and leisure of Edo middle-class society in its colourful 'pictures of the floating world' (ukiyo-e). In the wood-cut prints and illustrated books of this school is distilled an essential part, though by no means the whole, of the Edo vision. These works have also familiarised occidentals with conventions of figure-drawing, composition and perspective whose origins are to be sought a thousand years earlier.

Yamato-e, the native tradition preserved officially in the Tosa school, was divided from sumi-e by a gulf no less than that which to-day separates Japanese Western-style painting (yōga) from traditional styles as a whole. Its method is in no way calligraphic, its perspective and psychological slant distinct; it uses intense opaque colour and is preoccupied with the literature, saints, courtiers and commonalty of Japan. The arresting use it makes of mass in the composition is far removed in feeling from the reticent spatial felicities sought by black-ink painters. But even in relation to the legacy of Yamato-e the Tosa attitude was now timidly antiquarian. The truer embodiment of the Yamato spirit lay elsewhere, and not in the established schools. The patronage of discerning Kyoto nobles went chiefly to a group of artists led by Hon'ami Kōetsu (1558–1637) at the art-craft village of Takagamine on the northern outskirts of the city. A commoner by birth, Kōetsu unaccountably succeeded in epitomising the virtuoso amateur ideal of the aristocrat, expressing it in painting, calligraphy, lacquerwork and pottery. With his contemporary associate Sōtatsu and with Ogata Kōrin (1658–1716), who inherited the leadership of the movement, Kōetsu founded the bond of sound design and thoroughgoing craft technique which was applauded throughout the Edo period and is acclaimed in Japan today as the quintessential aspect of her art.

Sōtatsu remains a shadowy figure, a humble painter of fans at the start, and his work was probably executed on co-operative studio lines; but the reality of the style which tradition attributes to him and to his pupil Sōsetsu is not to be doubted. The great screens combine large elements and detail, expanses of uniform gold and passages of brilliant colour, in a manner which is at once a powerful reinterpretation of the purposes of Yamato-e and a clear manifestation of the basic trend in Edo composition. Kōrin is now virtually apotheosed as the exponent of this art; his major works: the screens Kakitsubata (Irises) and Kōhakubai (Red and white plum blossom) are probably the best-known paintings today in Japan. In lacquer he is more likely to have been designer than executant, the celebrated Suminoe river (no. 162) and Deer and bush clover (no. 165) (both ink-stone boxes, suzuribako) showing well his individuality. Among Sōtatsu's memorable works is the (pair) six-fold screen depicting a scene from the fourteenth chapter of the Genji monogatari (The Tale of Genji), Miozukushi (The Navigating Post), with broad divisions of wood, shore, sea, river and bridge.

Varying degrees of remove from the main accredited styles are found in the work of painters who in the Edo context must be classed as individualists. All of them show response to influence now reaching Japan from abroad. The members of the Nanga (Southern painting) school differ much among themselves but have in common their adherence to a near-Chinese style of conservative stamp, in landscape and in pictures of legendary and literary personages, trees, rocks and flowers. Here belong Ikeno Taiga (1723–76) and Yosa Buson (1716–83), the most original of the group, the former giving a fairly close version of the style of certain Chinese literati painters of the fifteenth century and the latter adapting that manner more completely to the lush Japanese scene. Both have been impressed also by examples of contemporary Chinese painting which filtered into Japan through Nagasaki. More significant however for the future course of Japanese art are the individualists who experimented in western realism. Their work owes nothing to the Europeanising art of the late sixteenth century, the so-called southern barbarian (namban) paintings depicting visiting Portuguese with their ships, and Japanese imitating their clothes and manners, for art of that class had ceased utterly with the suppression of Christianity. The new western influence came largely in the form of the illustration in Dutch scientific books, especially those on anatomy. The playwright and yōga artist Hiraga Gennai (1726–79) did much to disseminate the principles of the new perspective. This activity was part of the Dutch learning (Rangaku) so keenly followed by the intelligentsia, the Dutch books obtained through the Hollanders' merchant settlement on the island of Deshima off Nagasaki being the only channel by which knowledge of Europe might reach Japan during the period of closure. Pre-eminent among the Rangaku enthusiasts was Shiba Kōkan, an exceptionally gifted draughtsman and technician, whose curiosity embraced all the western science and art coming within his reach. He was specially attracted to landscape executed according to vanishing-point perspective and to copper-plate engraving as a means of rendering the Japanese scene drawn on this principle. In Kōkan's work, drily intellectual but to his contemporaries compelling, appears a new dimension of Edo art, destined to affect even the popular style. The rational adoption of the western mode witnesses to the energy and receptivity of artists and to their promise for the post-Edo world.

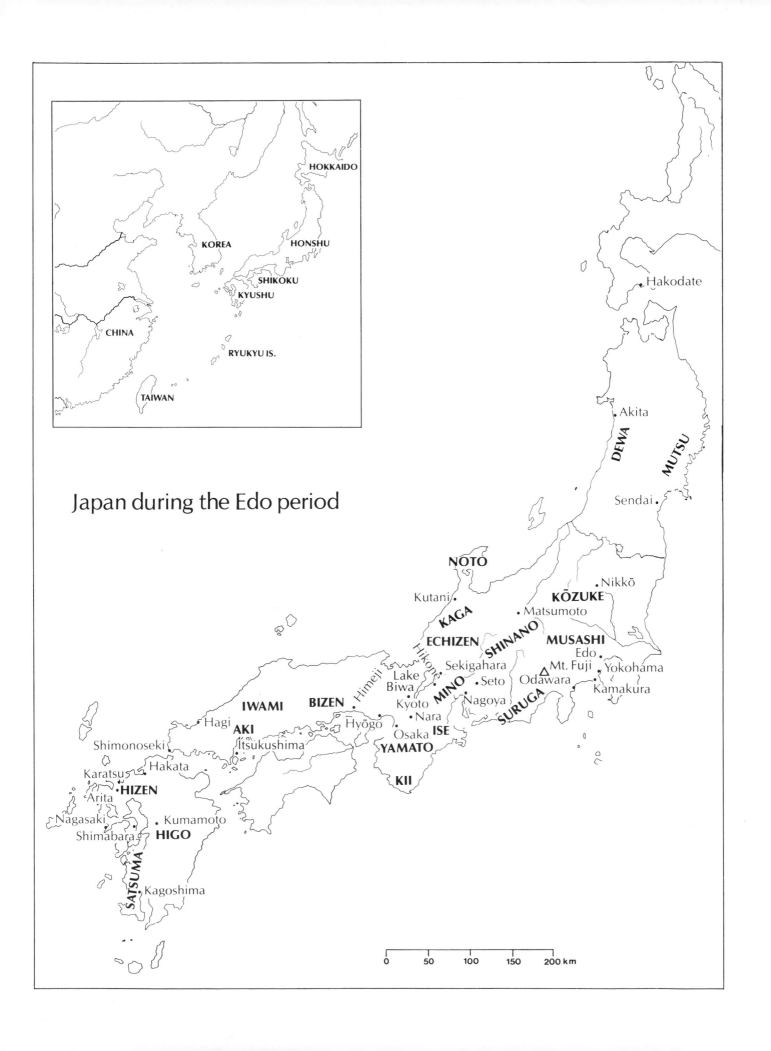

Japan during the Edo period

HOKKAIDO

KOREA

HONSHU

SHIKOKU
KYUSHU

CHINA

RYUKYU IS.

TAIWAN

Hakodate

DEWA MUTSU

Akita

Sendai

NOTO

Nikkō

Kutani

KŌZUKE

KAGA

Matsumoto

ECHIZEN SHINANO MUSASHI

Hikone Sekigahara Edo

Lake Mt. Fuji Yokohama
Biwa MINO Seto Odawara

IWAMI BIZEN Kyoto Nagoya Kamakura

Hagi Himeji Nara SURUGA

AKI Hyōgo ISE

Shimonoseki Itsukushima Osaka

Hakata YAMATO

Karatsu KII

HIZEN

Arita

Nagasaki Kumamoto

Shimabara HIGO

SATSUMA

Kagoshima

0   50   100   150   200 km

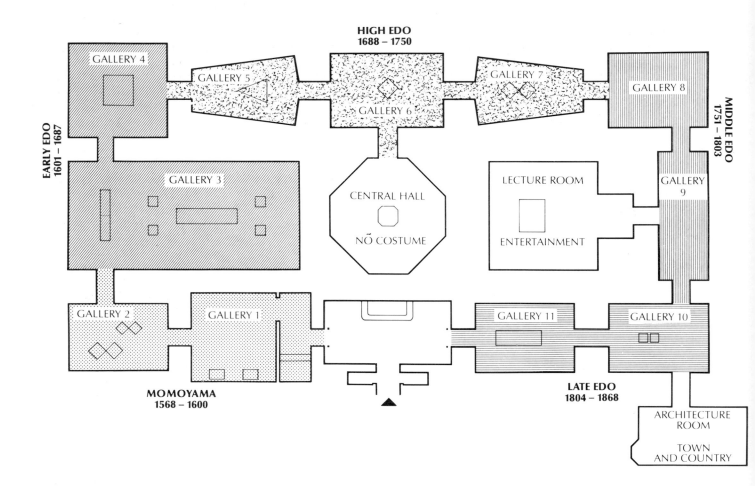

HIGH EDO
1688 – 1750

GALLERY 4

GALLERY 5

GALLERY 6

GALLERY 7

GALLERY 8

EARLY EDO
1601 – 1687

MIDDLE EDO
1751 – 1803

GALLERY 3

CENTRAL HALL

NŌ COSTUME

LECTURE ROOM

ENTERTAINMENT

GALLERY 9

GALLERY 2

GALLERY 1

GALLERY 11

GALLERY 10

MOMOYAMA
1568 – 1600

LATE EDO
1804 – 1868

ARCHITECTURE
ROOM

TOWN
AND COUNTRY

Painting

By the beginning of the Momoyama period, that is, by the middle of the sixteenth century, Japanese secular painting was running in two parallel courses. Though both these lines depended ultimately on Chinese sources, one, since its origin in the twelfth century, had come to be thought of as native Japanese painting, *Yamato-e*. The other was a more recent import – the ink painting style derived from the Zhe school. This latter style, in spite of its more or less secular content, was at first the prerogative of Buddhist monks in Kyoto.

In these two styles, we see the origins of almost all the styles to be used by the painters of the Edo period. Just as the styles depend, however remotely, on Chinese sources, so do most of the conventions of Japanese painting. By conventions we mean background knowledge that the Japanese viewer would take for granted: these include subjects of paintings, the shapes on which they appear, the medium in which they are done and the methods of depiction; most particularly this latter includes the characteristic vertical perspective.

As these conventions are often markedly different from those taken for granted by a western viewer, they must be discussed here. The main subject matter for secular painting, the most serious, the 'classical' subject, is landscape. Here one must consider that landscape painting derived from Buddhist painting and so has Buddhistic overtones; in the Muromachi, the ink landscapes of the monk painters can be seen as a direct expression of Zen, but by the Momoyama this has changed into a more avowedly decorative purpose. Landscape has become a subject in its own right and no longer needs any Buddhistic interpretation. Landscape painting was the necessary accomplishment of most artists and many amateurs; Kanō artists became the teachers of painting everywhere. Their use of ink and brush became the standard first of excellence, and, later in the Edo period, of a decadence which inspired revolt and reaction.

Figure painting is quite different. No interest centres on the human figure as such in any form of Japanese painting, even erotica. Instead, the figure is used either to tell a story, or as a pointer in a painting to suggest scale or mood. The Kanō artists painted pictures in their own variation of Chinese styles; naturally enough they used Chinese-style figures. Tosa artists liked the simplified, conventional figures of *Yamato-e*: these were echoed by the Rimpa artists and continue into the figures in *Ukiyo-e* paintings and prints. Here, however, they hark back not to the courtly mode of twelfth-century *Yamato-e*, but to the hand scrolls of the same period that told simple Buddhist stories with humorously drawn scenes of the common people.

In *Ukiyo-e* figures achieve a new prominence, but even here the interest is on the scene and on the depicted person's reaction to the scene, not upon the figure. The great portraits of statuesque *oiran* by Kaigetsudō artists (no. 99) are really fashion plates as much as portraits, and much of the genre painting of the Edo period is more about what people wear than what they are.

Natural history subjects are also often depicted in all schools of Japanese painting. This partly arises from the bird and flower pictures of China, but it more expresses the closeness to nature that is felt by the Japanese. In the middle Edo, a few artists such as Shikō (nos 33, 39) and Kōrin (nos 36, 40–43), actually drew from specimens in the hand. This is quite out of keeping with the standard, Chinese-derived aim of the artist to capture the essence of a subject rather than to depict it accurately. At the end of the Edo period, even *Ukiyo-e* artists returned to landscape (nos 104, 107, 117–126) and to natural history (as in Utamaro's *Insect Book*) for prime subject matter, while individualists such as Jakuchū (no. 44), Rosetsu (nos 49, 54) and Sosen (no. 50) devoted most of their energies to animal painting.

The traditional formats of Chinese paintings are the scrolls, either hanging vertical scrolls or horizontal hand scrolls, and the album leaf, which can be of different shapes and sizes. These are also used by the Japanese, and adapted to Japanese custom with ease. For larger effects, wall painting is very rarely used, but instead, the sliding doors and folding screens provide large decorative surfaces on which to paint. The hand scroll derives from the reading scroll and is unrolled from right to left. With the reader or viewer seated on the floor and the scroll in front of him on a low table, just so much of the scroll is unrolled at any one time as can comfortably be held with the arms apart and on the table: this is usually a stretch of 40–50 cm. Because of this, hand-scroll painting is usually broken up into scenes by the artist either by a gap between individual pictures or by some sort of visual break between scenes. The hand scroll format can therefore be used as an album of individual pictures, or as a landscape, which is in effect a travelogue, or to depict a story in which the protagonist may appear many times. Many horizontal *ōban*-size prints of the later *Ukiyo-e* painters suggest a hand scroll (nos 119, 123).

The hanging scroll is the normal decorative painting of the *tokonoma*, the display alcove, which was first widely in use towards the end of the sixteenth century. In the Edo period the hanging scroll (*kakemono*) becomes the most usual shape of painting. Normally such paintings are hung individually, but sometimes a set of two to four is appropriate (nos 46, 75). The hand scroll (*makimono*) is less common. Both types of scroll have to be rolled up to be stored. This means that they take up little room, and so collections can be kept even in small houses, providing appropriate pictures for particular occasions. Rolling up implies considerable sophistication in the method of making the mount of the picture so that the paper or silk does not crack or pleat. It also means that the ink and paints used must soak into the paper or silk; there can be no *impasto*, or it would flake off.

This is not the case for the album leaf, which is not rolled, nor for the larger decorative surfaces of sliding doors (*fusuma*) and folding screens (*byōbu*). For large effects of decoration, pairs, fours, or even eights of sliding doors could be decorated (nos 13, 14). Sliding doors are the divisions between 'rooms' of the highly modular Japanese house; always in straight lines, and at right angles to other straight lines, these could be removed bodily to allow two or more rooms to become one, divided only by the plain wooden pillars at the angles. The artist painting on sliding doors had to remember that the doors could be slid open and shut, and so his scene had to look good both individually and in pairs. With pairs of doors, one slides behind the other; with four or more doors, the two central doors would be opened symmetrically.

It is the folding screen that cuts across the rectilinear arrangement of the rooms. As a free-standing pair (screens were always in pairs) it could be placed anywhere in the room that was appropriate to an occasion, perhaps as a background to an important person or as a division between groups of persons. Both these formats allowed the artist room to paint large-scale subjects and to use, if he wished, chalk-powder (*gofun*) to raise part of the painting out of the flat surface. In some cases he could even cut through the screen and insert real bamboo-grille windows.

Gold leaf was often used as a background on which to paint and powdered mica sometimes provided a glossy background. This latter is more common on the folding fan, which in its method of folding is comparable to the screen, on a small scale. The folding fan, itself a Japanese invention, provides, because of its shape, one of the most interesting of the formats available to the Japanese artist. For broad effect, painting would be done on paper, either sized or unsized, while for more detailed painting silk was more appropriate. The vertically-held brush was capable of producing strokes of varying thickness even in one movement. Variation in the intensity of ink, implying intensity of colour, was produced by differential dilution of the ink, and while a heavily loaded brush produced a fluid and continuous line, a lightly loaded brush could make a scratchy, uneven line where required. In the Shijō school (nos 51, 52) above all, where fluency of line was the paramount consideration of the painter, virtuoso performances of brushwork were made in either ink or colour.

But it was the Kanō school which produced the outstanding decorative device for large-scale works in particular. To Kanō Eitoku (1543–1590) is attributed the first use of gold leaf as a background on which to paint. Blank areas of gold leaf, unpainted, can be used to depict land (no. 7), cloud or mist (no. 16), sky (no. 18) or even an indeterminate area in which the subject exists (no. 12). Whether Eitoku invented this idea, or took it from newly-imported Spanish and Portuguese religious painting, is uncertain, but the idea was brilliantly effective and perfectly suited the grandiose daimyō taste of the time. The use of more or less horizontal bands of blank areas, often of gold leaf, to break up a picture into different areas becomes a commonplace after Eitoku; whereas before empty areas had suggested distance, now distance was not necessarily depicted by these 'cloud bands'. They became a mere visual device.

Areas of empty space are essential in landscape painting that uses the conventions of vertical perspective. Neither Chinese nor Japanese painters used geometric perspective until the experiments of Shiba Kōkan (1747–1818, see no. 48) and his fellow *Rangakusha*. Instead the perspective is vertical – that is, the higher up the picture, the further away is the object depicted. But with this is correlated not only the absence of a fixed vanishing point, but also of a fixed view point. When looking at any scroll, the viewer can begin at the bottom of the picture and work his way up. But he is always looking downward, as if he were half-way up a mountain on his side of the picture. As his eye travels up the picture, so he himself travels up his own mountain, still looking down on his subject, until he gets two-thirds of the way up the picture; here he stops while his eye travels on up the picture until it is on his own level, and then continues on upwards to the distance, so that when looking at the top of the picture, the viewer is looking upward. This can be

seen particularly well in some of the Chinese-style landscapes of the Nanga school, such as those by Mokubei (nos 86, 87) and Hankō (no. 81), but it is equally visible in earlier paintings, such as those of Naonobu (no. 15) or Morikage (no. 26).

In the same way, with a hand scroll, the viewer looks down on the scene, but the scene is always at right-angles to the viewer – he travels along with the scene, rather than casting his eye across it. Because of this moving view point, the painter cannot use light and shade, *chiaroscuro*; masses such as rocks and mountains and subtle shapes such as folds of cloth or flower petals can be built up by a mass of strokes, or suggested by a few simple strokes, or by variations in intensity of ink or colour. It is noticeable that Japanese painters very rarely depict the sunlight, throwing shadows it would be impossible to ignore; the moon by daylight, with its automatic reference to autumn, is, however, a favourite subject. It creates no shadows.

Within all these conventions, there are differences that distinguish the various schools of Japanese painting. These various schools themselves descend from the earlier styles, the Tosa and the Kanō. Only briefly in the late sixteenth century were these conventions upset by outside influence other than Chinese; the arrival of westerners in Japan provided new models to imitate, to lampoon and ultimately to reject. The conventions of western art, though tentatively exploited by Shiba Kōkan (no. 48) and others in the Edo period, only become important in Japan in the second quarter of the nineteenth century. The Chinese-based heritage, as received by the Tosa and Kanō schools, remained the source of Japanese styles. The Tosa school depends for the effect of its painting on areas of flat opaque colour enclosed by simple outlines, where drawing is precise and conventional. The Kanō school on the other hand makes the greatest use of linear effect, even when this is combined with rich colour. Much Kanō work is pure ink-painting, without colour, in which the character of line and touch is of exclusive importance. Markedly dissimilar in the early Momoyama period, Tosa and Kanō later in the sixteenth century and through the Edo period draw closer together. Distinction between the two schools blurs at the edges and the practice of schools may overlap to such a degree that attribution of the works exclusively to one or the other tradition is sometimes misleading.

Attribution to Eitoku is beset with doubt (no. 7), but one is on surer ground with Sanraku (nos 8, 13), who worked with Eitoku for Hideyoshi at Jūrakudai. On Hideyoshi's death, Sanraku remained in Kyoto, while his nephews Tan'yū (1602–1674, nos 14, 18, 25) and Naonobu (1607–1650, no. 15) moved to Edo to found the Kajibashi school.

The success of Kanō Eitoku in the sixteenth century had not gone unnoticed by other painters, and two schools arose in competition with the Kanō. The first was that of Hasegawa Tōhaku (1539–1610), who may well have studied under Eitoku's father Shōei (1519–1592). A particularly brilliant painter, Tōhaku was equally at home in ink or in colour. His most famous ink paintings are of a specially Japanese scene, cryptomeria trees in the mist, in shades of ink only, and with very little reference to Chinese painting in their brushwork (see p. 32).

A seventeenth-century offspring of the Kanō school, off the true line, as it were, is the genre school that, by a fusion with yet another of Tosa influences, becomes the popular style that is formative to *Ukiyo-e*. This style uses small figures drawn with some humour and an element of caricature that is rarely wholly lacking in Japanese painting, and depicts scenes from

PAINTING

contemporary life in and around Kyoto, such as the dog-chasing game (nos 65, 66). This combination of styles was possible because of the declining state of the Tosa school.

The Tosa painters took their style from the *Yamato-e* hand scrolls of the Heian period, best exemplified by the twelfth-century paintings of the tenth-century novel *Genji monogatari*. Areas of flat colour form the decorative impression of the finished work, but the underpainting of ink shows how the work was built up on a more or less rigid framework, which left no room for virtuoso performances of brushwork. Under-statement was less in evidence in the earlier stage, when great attention was paid to details, especially of dress and of architecture. This style was brilliantly recreated by Tosa Mitsuyoshi in his Genji albums (no. 9). Mitsuoki simplified his pictures by including less detail or fewer figures, enlarged the scale of his figures and softened the brushwork in accordance with Kanō teaching. He also used the gold-leaf background with great skill and often depicted natural history subjects, especially quails (no. 16). This style has much in common with the Sumiyoshi substyle (no. 69), whose exponents were connoisseurs and valuers of early Tosa paintings, as well as fine painters.

Much the most important relation of the Tosa school is the Rimpa. This is the 'decorative' school, and is associated particularly with the names of Kōetsu (1558–1637), Sōtatsu (died c. 1643) and Kōrin (1658–1716). The relation of Tosa and Rimpa is complex, being more that of the two having a common ancestor in the *Yamato-e*. Kōetsu was a professional sword-appraiser who was a connoisseur of the arts, a calligrapher (no. 24), and a brilliant amateur craftsman (nos 150, 158). Around him were gathered, at Takagamine, a group of painters and craftsmen which included Sōtatsu (nos 19, 24) who probably worked in a fan-shop and who is known to have repaired and copied *Yamato-e* paintings, and Ogata Sōken (1621–1687), a wealthy Kyoto cloth-merchant, best known as the father of Kōrin (nos 36, 40–43).

The style known as Rimpa was formed at Takagamine, probably under the influence of Kōetsu, and first defined by Sōtatsu. In his Genji paintings Sōtatsu often used figures exactly copied from *Yamato-e* originals which are rearranged and adapted to form a brilliantly decorative effect: simplified and gorgeous at the same time. Although Kōrin was his outstanding follower, even copying some of his paintings, Sōtatsu's stylistic successor was Fukae Roshū (1699–1757). In Roshū's painting (no. 35) Sōtatsu's brilliance in composition is softened and perhaps weakened, just as Kōrin's successor Hōitsu (1761–1828, nos 37, 38) was to soften the work of Kōrin. Kōrin's reliance on Sōtatsu, apart from the actual copies, was more remote. He extended the range of work in the Rimpa style into many areas, utilising many of the same techniques as did Sōtatsu, for instance the mixing of colour on, say, a tree trunk (no. 43) by the dripping of colour pigment on to an area of wet colour (*tarashikomi*). A hundred years after Kōrin, Sakai Hōitsu revived his style: Hōitsu almost inevitably made the style prettier, and hence slightly less effective to the modern viewer, in accordance with the taste of his time. He in turn was followed by Suzuki Kiitsu (1796–1858), a more imaginative painter who adhered less closely to the style of Kōrin.

Another, but earlier, painter influenced in part by Rimpa was Watanabe Shikō (1683–1755, nos 33, 34, 39), a more eclectic painter than Kōrin or Hōitsu. Unusually for his time, he made a sketch book of natural history, drawing from specimens in the hand. Such work was a formative influence on Maruyama Ōkyo (1733–1795), whose 'return to nature' started the Maruyama school. Although Ōkyo actually copied Shikō's sketch book and had also studied western techniques of painting – he once painted scenes for a peep-show in western style (no. 56) – his 'return to nature' was in reality more a substitution of one type of convention for another. He was capable of the most brilliant passages of brushwork and of producing the most splendid decorative effects (nos 45, 53, 70, 71).

One school that ran counter to this tendency was the Nanga school, a loose affiliation of painters who, reacting to the decline of the Kanō school, looked to China for new inspiration. Whereas the Kanō had looked to the Chinese 'northern school', the Nanga, 'southern painters', emulated the latter-day exponents of the 'southern school', the scholar painters of the sixteenth and seventeenth centuries. Such paintings as they saw were not always of high quality: several Chinese painters visited Nagasaki, notably Shen Nanpin, who spent two years there from 1731; but none of these painters was good enough to warrant the great effect they had on the *bunjin* painters. Among the men who studied with Chinese masters was Gion Nankai (1677–1751, no. 73), but the style did not really emerge as something distinct until the time of Ikeno Taiga (1723–1776, nos 74–77) and Yosa Buson (1716–1783, nos 58, 59). An eccentric, almost wild element of the painting of Taiga was taken up by Uragami Gyokudō (1745–1820, nos 78, 79) and, to a lesser extent, by the potter Aoki Mokubei (1767–1833, nos 86, 87); while a much softer and more academic approach was that of Tanomura Chikuden (1777–1835, no. 80). Buson in his later years was influenced by one of his own pupils, Matsumura Goshun (1752–1811, nos 51, 52).

Goshun had been a pupil of Ōkyo, but moved to the studio of Buson, where he was treated as an equal. His consequent fusion of the styles of Ōkyo and the Nanga is now known as the Shijō, after the street in Kyoto where he lived. This is a style that favours a modified realism, but that seeks perfection of the fluid line. Variations of the Shijō school were those of Kishi Ganku (1749–1838) and Mori Sosen (1747–1821). Ganku was famous for his paintings of tigers, for he owned a tiger skin. Sosen on the other hand was famous for his paintings of monkeys (nos. 50a, b, c, d).

If some artists fit into all moulds, some fit into none. Among the two individualist painters who stand out at this period are Itō Jakuchū (1716–1800, no. 44) and Nagasawa Rosetsu (1754–1799, nos 46, 49, 54, 57). Jakuchū specialised in two completely opposing styles, the one a very wild and unconventional ink-painting style, the other an extraordinarily detailed, brilliantly coloured style, in which he painted animals (especially exotic varieties of chickens) with even more realism than that of Ōkyo, but with the placing and decorative effect of the Rimpa.

Rosetsu, after being expelled from the studio of Ōkyo, developed his own style of ink-painting. His paintings of animals in particular have a vivid quality not common in Japanese painting, while his sense of the placing of his picture on the surface area is the equal of that of Kōrin. He even dares, in a set of four *fusuma*, to leave one almost completely blank (no. 57).

It is in the *Ukiyo-e* school of the artists who designed the well-known wood-block prints that we see the fusion of all the styles of Japanese painting. The customers for *Ukiyo-e* paintings were the newly rich townsmen (*chōnin*) and the idle peacetime samurai who inhabited the *demi-monde* of the Yoshiwara pleasure quarter

39

of Edo and the similar quarters in Osaka and other big towns. The subjects depicted on these prints and in their paintings were the inhabitants of this world, the courtesans and the 'green' houses, the tea-house girls, bath girls, actors, wrestlers and other heroes of the day. The styles were truly popular, sometimes showy, sometimes of surprising elegance.

The style first coalesces, mostly from the fusion of the genre Kanō style and late Tosa that we have described earlier, in the mid-seventeenth century in the hands of book illustrators such as the painter Hishikawa Moronobu (d. 1694, no. 67). Black-and-white single- and double-sheet book illustrations were followed by broadsheets sold separately, which were often either memento pictures of famous places or theatre prints relating to a particular performance. Sometimes these were hand coloured. As printed work began to sell in large quantities, so it became more commercialised and specialised. Publishers commissioned designs from artists, supervised the block cutters and printers, both of whom had to be very considerable craftsmen, and finally sold the finished prints to the public. Undeterred by frequent sumptuary edicts, publishers continued to issue series of prints, and subschools of artists continued to create or reflect the latest fashionable style and to depict the newest figure, the prettiest girls and the most gorgeous *kimono*.

In the early eighteenth century the Kaigetsudō artists (no. 99) depicted large-scale paintings and prints of actors and courtesans. These statuesque figures contrast strongly with the contemporary work of the Torii school which, under Torii Kiyomasu (fl. c. 1696–mid-1720s, no. 109) specialised in bombastic theatrical posters. In the second quarter of the century, Okamura Masanobu (1686–1764, no. 110), among others, was experimenting with three-colour printing in a softer and more subtle style that was to lead into the work of Suzuki Harunobu (1724–1770, nos 102, 103, 137). To Harunobu is credited the sudden popularisation, in 1764, of colour printing from as many as ten blocks, by reference to a black-and-white key block, which transformed the print into the full colour print. Great technical advances in printing skill, such as the wiping off of the colour from parts of a block, gave the print a new subtlety, and innovations such as blind print embossing (*gauffrage*) and the use of metallic pigments enabled the print-makers to cater for a new market, the private societies which ordered particularly fine prints (usually *surimono*). Harunobu started a new fashion for prints of delicate and fragile girls – his favourite was Osen, a tea-house waitress (no. 102).

The Katsukawa school of Shunshō (1726–1792, nos 64, 64b, 111, 138, 139) and his followers, as specialists in theatre prints, started a new style whereby an actor was depicted at the culminating moment of a theatrical episode: this became a central theme in *Ukiyo-e*. Actor portraits were made more dramatic by the use of the portrait bust – the so-called large head (*Ōkubi-e*) – supposedly invented by Shun'ei (1762–1819, nos 115, 116). Wildest of all were the startling caricature portraits by Sharaku (fl. 1794–1795, nos 112, 113). A new grandeur was given to full-length figures by Torii Kiyonaga (1752–1815, no. 104) and also by Utamaro (1754–1806, nos 108, 140) and his contemporaries, and by the prolific Utagawa Toyokuni (1769–1825).

Landscape appears as a print in its own right in the 1820s, a curious reversal of the direction of print-making back into 'classical' subject-matter, when Hokusai (1760–1849, nos 64c, 117, 118, 125, 126) produced the first of his great series the *Thirty-six Views of Fuji* (nos 117, 118, 125, 126). The success of this series embarked the young Hiroshige (1797–1858, nos 121, 122, 124, 127, 128) on his course as a landscape print-maker. One of the most famous series of prints is his *Fifty-three Stations of the Tōkaidō Road* (no. 124).

In the closing years of the Edo period, foreigners other than Dutch or Chinese appeared more often in Japan, particularly in Yokohama. As in the seventeenth century, the *namban* screens had depicted curiously dressed and ill-mannered 'southern barbarians', so in Yokohama in the nineteenth century prints were made to depict the new arrivals and their black ships. A school of print-makers arose to make these prints. Yoshitora (fl. c. 1850–1880) and Sadahide (1807–1873) worked in this line. Their best product, like the best of Kunisada (1786–1864) and Kuniyoshi (1797–1861) belies the view that a long period of decline occurred in the print masters' style before 1868.

The Edo period can be seen as one of the great ages of Japanese painting. The slow decline of the traditional schools of Kanō and Tosa is offset by the rise of the inventive Rimpa and the vigorous and brash *Ukiyo-e*. Renewed interest in China brought about the Nanga school, and new ideas on brushwork and colour created first the Maruyama and then the Shijō schools. Foreign studies provoked the experiments of Kōkan and Denzen (1748–1822, no. 47), and allowed some of the later *Ukiyo-e* artists to use geometric perspective. It was an age of sustained innovation and achievement.

ORI

Anonymous

1 *Portrait of Toyotomi Hideyoshi*

F/G1 絹本著色豊臣秀吉像

Ink and colours on silk
insc. in praise of Hideyoshi by Nanka Genkō, a prominent
priest
Hanging scroll,
110 × 62 cm
d. 1598

KŌDAIJI, Kyoto
Important Cultural Property

This portrait must have been painted very soon after Hideyoshi's
death. It was not the custom in Japan at this period to portray
political figures during their lifetime, so images had to be made
posthumously. The great military ruler's connections with the
Kōdaiji temple in Kyoto had been strong, and hence the
preservation of this portrait there.

Anonymous

2 *Portrait of Toyotomi Hideyoshi*

S/G1 絹本著色豊臣秀吉像

Ink and colours on silk
insc. in praise of Hideyoshi by Nanka Genkō, a prominent
priest
Hanging scroll, 110 × 59 cm
d. 1600

MYŌKŌJI, Kyoto

Hideyoshi is shown in this and the previous painting seated
behind a curtain of state and dressed as Kampaku, or Regent, the
highest official position he was able to reach. No Japanese, even
an Emperor, was ever portrayed sitting on a chair or throne,
except for the chief priests of certain Chinese sects of Buddhism,
but he is shown on a raised dais. This portrait, done two years
after his death, shows the unexpectedly thin, wizened face which,
unflattering as it is, was clearly a close likeness.

1

2

Anonymous

3 *Portrait of Tokugawa Ieyasu*

F/G1 紙本著色徳川家康像

[repr. in colour on p. 145]
Ink and colours on paper
Hanging scroll,
114 × 56.3 cm
1642
MUSEUM OF HISTORY AND FOLK CULTURE, Chiba

Portraits of Ieyasu, founder of the Tokugawa regime, abounded in the seventeenth century, when his prestige was extremely high, especially after the removal of his remains to the Nikkō mausoleum in 1617. In the Rinnōji Temple in Tochigi there are eight different portraits of him dating between 1638 and 1647, all quite distinct. This portrait is based on the most formal of them, with Ieyasu in court dress; it is dated 1642. In all the portraits he is shown as an unassuming, rather mild-looking round-faced man, an aspect which belies the extraordinary forcefulness of his character and achievements.

Anonymous

4 *Portrait of Tokugawa Ieyasu*

S/G1 紙本著色徳川家康像

Ink and colours on paper
Hanging scroll, 81.5 × 37 cm
TŌSHŌGŪ, Shizuoka

Like the preceding painting, this was done after Ieyasu's death, since portraits of living political figures were never done at this period. Ieyasu came from the Shizuoka district and he was commemorated by a special shrine there.

Anonymous

5 *Water-wheel and bridge with willow-trees in the moonlight*

F/G2 紙本金地著色柳橋水車図

[repr. in colour on pp. 146–7]
Ink and colours over gold leaf on paper,
with some silver leaf
Pair of six-fold screens,
each 149 × 360 cm
Late 16th/early 17th century
TOKYO NATIONAL MUSEUM
Important Art Object

The strong composition, with its sweep of a bridge across two whole six-fold screens, was a favourite one for the screen format and a number of versions exist; but none equal this example and the almost identical one in the Kyoto National Museum (no. 6) in the refinement of their execution. Both use gold leaf over specially built-up designs in gesso (*moriage*) on the water-wheel, and special patterns are similarly built into the rounded shapes in the water which represent the baskets of stones used as breakwaters on Japanese river-banks at that period. The compositions rely on the contrast between the gold-leaf areas and the darker expanses of patterned waves, and on the play of green willow-fronds over the gold. These paintings may be regarded almost as supremely elegant pieces of decorative but portable furniture. This design was formerly attributed to Kanō Eitoku, but there is no good reason to associate it with him. Rather it forms part of the general decorative repertoire of the Momoyama period. There is a tradition that the bridge is the one at Uji, near Kyoto, and the fast-flowing waves, formally but excitingly depicted in silver leaf now darkened by age, certainly suggest the fast-running Uji River with its tree-lined banks.

Anonymous

6 *Water-wheel, bridge and willow-tree in the moonlight*

S/G2 紙本金地著色柳橋水車図

Ink and colours over gold leaf on paper, with some silver leaf
Pair of six-fold screens, each 149 × 324 cm
Early 17th century
KYOTO NATIONAL MUSEUM

For discussion of this composition, see the preceding. This version is in rather fresher condition and the more flowing willow-fronds are clearly from a different hand. It may be from the very end of the Momoyama period, when a looser, more relaxed atmosphere was beginning to be seen in screen-painting.

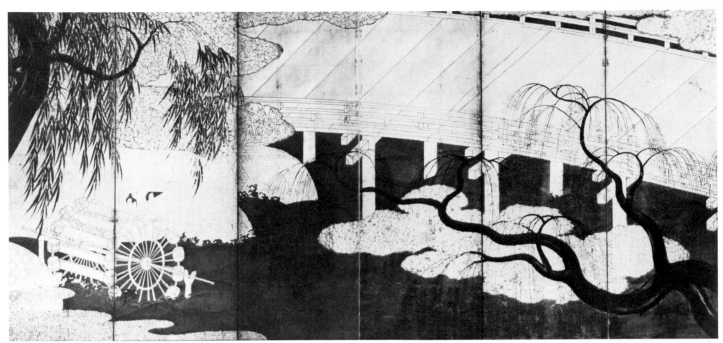

left-hand screen

6

right-hand screen

Attributed to KANŌ EITOKU (1543–1590)

7 *Hawks, pines and rocks*

F/G2 紙本金地著色松鷹図

[details repr. in colour on p. 148]
Ink and colours over gold leaf on paper
Pair of six-fold screens, each 161 × 360 cm
Late 16th century
TOKYO NATIONAL UNIVERSITY OF FINE ARTS

These works are attributed to Eitoku on the paintings themselves by the Kanō artist and art historian Einō (1631–1697), who was a pupil of Kanō Sanraku, Eitoku's son-in-law. Einō's attribution, therefore, seems based on a fairly direct tradition, although there is no conclusive proof. In any case, the powerful, horizontal composition and the reduction of the interest of the picture to the foreground elements are very much in the style of Eitoku and his immediate pupils.

Hawking was the prestige sport of the samurai class, and the two hawks are painted with all the pride and ferocity of the great military families who had won in the great power-struggle which had begun in the mid-fifteenth century. The unbending pine boughs and simple rocks also symbolize the patrons for whom they are painted. The screens are both representative of the uncomplicated taste of the military. The artist has, however, made a complex pattern out of these simple elements, composed of the contrasts of gold, blue, green, the pale brown of the tree-trunks and boughs, and the white of the lingering snow of the left-hand screen and the hawk on the right.

left-hand screen

7

right-hand screen

KANŌ SANRAKU (1559–1635)

8 *Dragon of the storm, tiger with bamboo*

S/G2 紙本金地著色竜虎図

[repr. in colour on pp. 150–1]
Ink and colours on paper
Pair of six-fold screens, each 178 × 357 cm
MYŌSHINJI, Kyoto
Important Cultural Property

These powerful works have the violence and tension which Sanraku sometimes put into his earlier works, while he was still dominated by the forceful example of his master Eitoku and before he became an established figure as head of the Kyoto branch of the Kanō school. The emphasis is all on the foreground, as with Eitoku. But the sense of the movement is

Sanraku's own, and so is the tension between the directions of the design elements. Thus the tigers are facing and opposing the wind, which comes from the storm dragon.

The dragon and the tiger, both originally beasts of the four compass points in Chinese art, were adopted in Japanese temples as symbols of the power of Buddhist doctrine. They frequently appear in Kyoto temples in the Edo period both on folding screens and on sets of *fusuma*, but they lack the original energy of these Momoyama examples. Sanraku has created tension between the two screens themselves by depicting the dragon, with its whirling and flaming jewel of everlasting faith, mostly in ink, while the tigers are done in bright colours. The male tiger is shown with stripes and the female with spots, in the manner traditional in Ming China, from where Sanraku drew his models. The combination of the dragon with a plum-bough is rather rare and arresting.

44

TOSA MITSUYOSHI (1539–1613)

9 Scenes from the Tale of Genji

FS/G2 紙本金地著色源氏物語図　土佐光吉筆

Ink and colours over gold leaf on paper
Album leaves, each 26 × 23 cm
Sealed *Tosa Kyūyoku*
c. 1610–13
KYOTO NATIONAL MUSEUM

The great prose novel *Genji monogatari*, written about AD 1000 by the court lady Murasaki, remained a major subject for Japanese art from as early as the twelfth century onwards. The fifty-four chapters were illustrated in hand scrolls of all or part of the text, on fans, in albums with digests of the chapters and even on screens. The style for depicting this courtly romance was always detailed and conservative, in the native manner known as *Yamato-e*. From the fifteenth century onwards, and perhaps earlier, the official court painters in this style were the Tosa school. They fell on hard times with the decline of the court during the power struggles of the late sixteenth century, but Mitsuyoshi carried on and then revived their fortunes. This was due to the new market for Japan's classical past provided by the ever richer and more numerous merchant class, who had the money and leisure to become new patrons of art. Mitsuyoshi moved to Sakai, the mercantile port south of Osaka, later in his life and seems to have prospered there.

Under Mitsuyoshi and his successors, and the Rimpa School artists, Genji pictures enjoyed a new vogue among the middle-class public until the late seventeenth century. Mitsuyoshi's great series of album leaves, however, remain the most perfect done over the whole period. Their attention to detail is minute, their colour brilliant, their line sensitive and their designs strong and coherent, though static in their tradition. The *Yamato-e* conventions are powerfully retained – the point of view is high above the foreground, gold clouds link the parts of each composition and provide a foil for the pigments, buildings are looked into from above as if roofless and there is almost no recession.

F a] Chapter 7 (The Festival of Maples). Prince Genji, in chequered trousers, with the sceptre of his rank, is seen visiting the young Murasaki, whom he intends to be his mistress and whom he is looking after in his house. She is seen with her nurse and another lady with her splendid doll's house which Genji has had made for her. The nurse is a little worried by this sign of immaturity. (See p. 46.)

S b] [repr. in colour on p. 149]
Chapter 3 (Utsusemi). The young Prince Genji secretly watches his beloved Utsusemi, wife of the Governor of Iyo, playing *go* with a companion. He peers through a crack in a painted sliding door. Beyond the ladies are sets of books in their wrappers, stacked on their sides. By the lady on the left can be seen the back of a folding screen.

F c] Chapter 5 (The young Murasaki). On a visit to the country outside Kyoto to seek a cure for his illness, Prince Genji gets his first glimpse of the child Murasaki who is to become his greatest love. Genji is seen peering through a brushwood fence into the house where she lives; he is accompanied by his retainer Koremitsu. It is cherry blossom time and Murasaki with a group of older women views it from the verandah of the comparatively rustic house.

S d] Chapter 24 (Butterflies). The scene is a boating party on the

9c

9d

artificial lake at the residence of Murasaki, Prince Genji's principal mistress. The boats have dragons or phoenixes at the stern in Chinese style. One bears ladies visiting from the Empress Akikonomu and the other Murasaki's own ladies. To the left *Bugaku* dancers entertain on an artificial island. The title 'Butterflies' refers to boy dancers in a later part of the chapter.

Anonymous

10 *Arrival of a Portuguese ship at Nagasaki, with a Jesuit chapel*

F/G3 紙本金地著色南蛮人渡来図

Ink and colours over gold leaf on paper
Pair of six-fold screens, each 155.8 × 335 cm
Late 16th/early 17th century
HIS MAJESTY THE EMPEROR OF JAPAN

Most *namban* screens follow a clear pattern of composition. One screen is dominated by a Portuguese ship or ships coming to harbour, with scenes of unloading exotic goods, some of them Chinese. The other shows the foreigners ashore, sometimes with a Christian chapel newly set up. This example is no exception, but it is unusual in the largeness of the figures. They are even bigger than the so-called 'large figure' screens of the *Genji monogatari* in the Imperial Collection, which are attributed to Kanō Eitoku. The emphasis placed on the foreigners themselves is

even allowed to distort the ship and make it seem smaller in proportion. These screens are dominated by their foreground, and the conventionalised golden clouds are used to eliminate rather than to suggest a wider perspective. This too recalls the method of Eitoku and his pupils.

Certain aspects of the Portuguese are emphasised – those which differentiated them from the more familiar Chinese traders: their long noses, beards and moustaches; their tall hats and baggy breeches; their high ships; their fondness for pet animals; and, of course, their strange Christian religion, with its missionary zeal which was always such a surprising element to the Japanese. Here priests are shown grouped round a portrait of a saint, probably Francis Xavier, the missionary to Japan. The Japanese women shown observing the foreigners and in implied proximity to them indicate the extreme social freedom of the Momoyama period, which was later to be repressed somewhat under the Tokugawa regime.

left-hand screen

right-hand screen

11 ·   left-hand screen

Anonymous

11   *Arrival of Portuguese ships at Nagasaki with a visit ashore*

S/G3   紙本金地著色南蛮人渡来図

Ink and colours over gold leaf on paper
Pair of six-fold screens, each 151 × 322 cm
AGENCY FOR CULTURAL AFFAIRS
Important Art Object

These screens are more typical of the *namban* style than the preceding painting, with more than one ship, a less intense foreground and small human figures which can be seen in detail only when viewed from close to. The composition over the pair is linked together by the long gold cloud running upwards from the ships. This joins the quayside buildings leading to the roadway which slants back down the right-hand screen. As in all *namban* screens, there is an effect of cheerful brilliance, achieved by the simple contrasts of gold leaf, blue water, green trees, and the bright, varied colour of the foreigners' dress. In this example, there is less emphasis on the Christian aspect, although crosses can be seen on the ships' masts and on the eaves of the building converted for use as a chapel. The right-hand screen is dominated by the procession of Portuguese, led by the newly arrived Captain-General who is accompanied by the even more exotic black servants or slaves acquired elsewhere in their mercantile empire.

    12a

11   right-hand screen

ANONYMOUS, KANŌ SCHOOL

12   a] *Cherry-blossoms and pheasants*
      b] *Pine-tree, red maples and birds*

a] F/G3 紙本金地著色桜花雉子図
b] S/G3 紙本金地著色松楓禽鳥図

Ink and colours over gold leaf on paper
Two sets of four sliding doors, each 196 × 163 cm
c. 1614
NAGOYA CITY, Aichi
Important Cultural Property

These grand doors represent the official Kanō style at its most
confident. Nagoya castle was built between 1610 and 1613 to
house the most powerful branch of the Tokugawa family after
the shōgun himself and to guard the road between Kyoto and
Edo. It dominated central Japan. The Kanō school were
commissioned to decorate the sliding doors (which amount to
complete wall-paintings), wooden doors, panels and ceilings, and
the vast scale of the work placed a strain on their artistic
invention which is certainly less daring and more repetitive than
in the Momoyama period. But there is no denying the richness
and skill of these works, which were done for the first room of the
omote shoin. The pine and maple composition is on the reverse
side of the doors, and faced into the adjoining room. They have
been attributed to Kanō Sadanobu (1597–1623) who however
was very young at the time. In their formality, the Nagoya

12b

paintings contrast with the livelier and more inventive decorated rooms in the Tenkyūin (no. 13) which were the work of Sanraku and Sansetsu. Significantly, the latter were a less 'official' branch of the Kanō group and less associated with the Edo government.

Although Nagoya castle was completely destroyed in the Second World War, the paintings were mostly preserved and are now exhibited permanently in the rebuilt castle.

13a

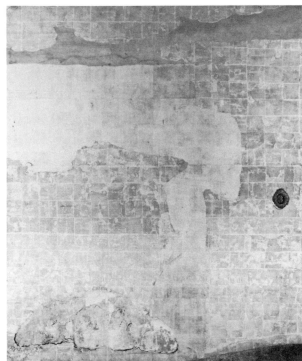

KANŌ SANRAKU (1559–1635) and KANŌ SANSETSU
(1589–1651)

3   *a] Flowering plum with pheasants*
    b] Tigers in a bamboo-grove

S/G3
F/G3   紙本金地著色 梅遊禽図　狩野山樂・山雪筆
             虎竹林図

Ink and colours over gold leaf on paper
Two pairs of four sliding doors, each 191 × 143 cm
1631 or soon after

TENKYŪIN, Kyoto
Important Cultural Property

The Tenkyūin is a sub-temple of Myōshinji temple complex in the
north-west of Kyoto. It was built in 1631 by the sister, whose
name is unknown, of Ikeda Terumasa. She is always known by
her religious name of Tenkyūin-dono. The *hōjō* (abbot's quarters)
are decorated with sliding doors (both on paper and wood) and
various wall-panels painted by Sanraku and his pupil Sansetsu.
They are considered the finest of all the early Edo period painted

13b

rooms, combining the strength of the Momoyama style with Sanraku's greater elegance and more refined sense of colour, and the contrast of different planes of movement which may have been Sansetsu's particular contribution.

The copper-pheasant on a plum-bough is from the *ninoma* (second room) of the *jōkan*, or upper part of the building, which has spring and winter scenes. It is distinguished for its elegant overall design, restrained colours and for the extreme tensions

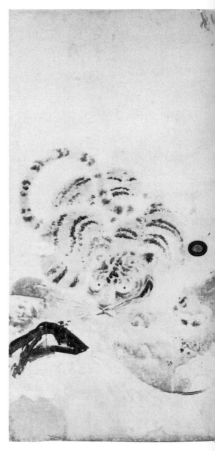

14

between the almost straight lines with which the rocks are hatched in opposing directions. The *shitchū*, or central part of the building, is more grandly decorated with tigers among forest bamboos. Again the jaggedly thrusting directions of the trunks convey a strong sense of movement. The tigers themselves are a gentler version of the type painted by Sanraku in no. 8.

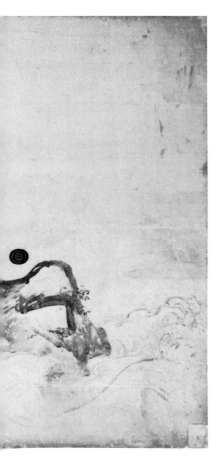

KANŌ TAN'YŪ (1602–1674)

14 Tigers and rocks by the water

F/G3 紙本墨画岩上猛虎図　狩野探幽筆

Ink on paper
Set of four sliding doors, each 190.5 × 142.5 cm
c. 1650
TOKUZENJI, Kyoto

These doors represent Tan'yū's skill as a *suiboku* artist, which
was at least equal to his skill as a colourist. Indeed, his advances
in the impressionistic, suggestive use of ink, especially for
landscape, were perhaps his most important contribution
(compare no. 15 by his younger brother Naonobu). The tigers
and rocks are from the *nakanoma* (central room) of the *hōjō*
(abbot's quarters) of the Zen sect Tokuzenji Temple, which also
includes doors of dragons and clouds. The latter have Tan'yū's
signature with the Buddhist title *Hōgen* ('Eye of the Law') which
he used between 1638 and 1665. All the *hōjō* paintings are in
ink only, and are perhaps the artist's finest exercises in that
medium. The sense of both movement and space was lost in the
Kanō school after Tan'yū's death, and could only be recaptured
by later artists looking towards European and Chinese models.

KANŌ NAONOBU (1607–1650)

15 The Eight Scenes of the Xiao-xiang rivers

S/G3 紙本墨画瀟湘八景図　狩野尚信筆

Ink on paper. *Naonobu hitsu* ('by the brush of Naonobu')
Pair of six-fold screens, each 155 × 347 cm
c. 1640–1650
TOKYO NATIONAL MUSEUM

This is Naonobu's remaining masterpiece and shows him to have
been the equal of his older brother Tan'yū in brush and ink. This
work may claim to be the finest work in the Kanō ink landscape
style perfected by Tan'yū. The 'Eight Scenes of the Xiao-xiang
rivers' is a traditional Chinese subject. It was based on the
scenery around the confluence of the two rivers in Hubei
province, and was much painted from the late Song period
onwards. It became known in Japan since it was often done in
the easily portable album format. The titles of the scenes were:
1] Autumn moon over the lake
2] Lingering snow with river and sky
3] Evening glow at the fishing village
4] Evening bell of the distant temple
5] Returning sailboats on a distant shore
6] Sunset sky over a hill town
7] Night rain over the two rivers
8] Wild geese landing on flat sands
Naonobu has skilfully combined four each of these into each
screen. Although the subject matter is in theory Chinese, there is
a distinctly Japanese cast to the landscape. Indeed, there are
references to Lake Biwa to the east of Kyoto, which was one of
the few areas of Japan with scenery open enough to be compared
with the Xiao-xiang views. Naonobu has however retained the
Chinese convention of catching glimpses of the eight subjects
through a general misty haze.

15

left-hand screen

right-hand screen

TOSA MITSUOKI (1617–1691)

16 *Quail, millet and foxtail, with autumn flowers*

F/G3 紙本金地著色粟穂鶉図　土佐光起筆

[repr. in colour on pp. 152–3]
Ink and colours on gold over paper
s. *Tosa shōgen Mitsuoki hitsu* ('by the brush of Tosa Mitsuoki Officer of the Bodyguard')
Pair of eight-fold screens, each 100 × 354 cm
FUKUOKA COLLECTION, Kanagawa

Mitsuoki profited from the Tosa school revival, begun by Mitsuyoshi (no. 9), to become a successful commercial artist, with many commissions from patrons of the townsman class; although from 1654 to 1681 he was also official painter to the Kyoto Court. The theme of quail and millet, derived from Chinese Song album and hanging paintings, was a favourite Tosa theme in miniature, but Mitsuoki expanded it in these screens to its largest scale. Beyond a detailed, moving foreground of autumn plants with birds he has interposed a middle ground of golden mist, and beyond that distant, rounded hills. The whole composition combines broadness and detail in a way typical of Edo period art. The coherence of the composition, the two very long screens meeting each other at the low point of two slanting foregrounds, is unprecedented in the Tosa school and shows Mitsuoki as a true son of the seventeenth century. Moonlight is implied, though not stated, by the golden glow of the mist and the dark silhouettes of the hills. The scene in fact probably represents the moor of Musashino near Edo, famous for its moonlight views and the scene of a number of romantic nocturnal stories.

TOSA MITSUOKI (1617–1691)

17 *Events of the year at the imperial court*

S/G3 紙本著色年中行事図　土佐光起筆

Ink and colours on paper
Pair of six-fold screens, each 140 × 350 cm
s. *Tosa shōgen Mitsuoki hitsu* ('by the brush of Tosa Mitsuoki Officer of the Bodyguard')
SEN SŌSHITSU, Kyoto

Under the Tokugawa government the Emperor and his Court were reduced to almost complete powerlessness, confined to the palace at Kyoto far from the centre of politics. They were kept occupied much of the time by the numerous annual ceremonies which were considered essential. Many of these were connected with the Shintō religion in which among living men the Emperor held the most exalted place. Other observances were more a matter of political ritual and often simply entertainment or amusement. Mitsuoki became official court painter in 1654 and one of his tasks, as with his predecessors, was to record these events. Pictures of this sort, whether on hand scrolls, in albums, or on screens, were known as *Nenjū gyōji*, and examples exist from before the Momoyama period. Traditional though the subjects are, the startling and even stark composition of these screens is typical of the mid seventeenth century and of Mitsuoki himself, who added much that was new to the Tosa repertoire. The scene recorded here is the 'small obeisance' which took place at the New Year, when all the nobles of high rank paid their respects to the Emperor. In this painting he is half hidden at the top right. The nobles are in their most formal Chinese-based attire.

17

left-hand screen

right-hand screen

KANŌ TAN'YŪ (1602–1674)

18 *Pine-trees in the four seasons*

F/G3 　紙本金地著色四季松図　狩野探幽筆

[repr. in colour on pp. 154–5]
Ink and colours over gold leaf on paper
s. *Kanō Hōgen Tanyū Morinobu hitsu* ('by the brush of Tan'yū
Morinobu, Eye of the Law, of the Kanō School') on the left-
hand screen
Pair of six-fold screens, each 157 × 367 cm
c. 1640–1650
DAITOKUJI, Kyoto
Important Art Object

In these large screens Tan'yū combines power and delicacy in a
manner which is typical of the Edo period. The four massive
pines, representing the four seasons, are placed with assurance
on an almost empty gold-leaf background. A hint of a stream, left
in reserve in the paper, links the two screens. The details are
sensitive and the red and yellow ivy creeping round the autumn
tree can compare in lightness of touch with Sōtatsu's almost
contemporary green ivy-leaves over gold in *The narrow ivy road*
(no. 19). Tan'yū has used the *Yamato-e* tradition of a very high
point of view to take a dramatic glance at the pine-tops, except in
the summer subject, where he boldly reverses the process and
cuts off the top of the full-blown tree by an implied mist.

Attributed to TAWARAYA SŌTATSU (?d. 1643)
Calligraphy by KARASUMARU MITSUHIRO (1579–1638)

19 *The narrow ivy road, with waka poems*

S/G3 　紙本金地著色蔦の細道図　伝俵屋宗達筆

Green pigment over gold leaf on paper, with ink calligraphy
Sealed *Inen*
Pair of six-fold screens, each 158 × 358 cm
c. 1615–1620.

PRIVATE COLLECTION, Japan
Important Cultural Property

The startling swaths of green represent the banks of a lane
overhung with ivy. The lane itself is shown by a slightly darker
tone of gold leaf. Every Japanese would recognise this as a
reference to an incident in the *Ise monogatari* (Tales of Ise). This is
a fictional poetic biography of the ninth-century poet and lover
Ariwara no Narihira, each episode of which explains how one of
his poems came to be written. At Mount Utsu in Suruga province
Narihira and his companion came to a gloomy, narrow pass
overgrown with ivy and other creepers. They met a wild man
who recognised Narihira as a courtier he had once known. He
asked the poet to remember him to his lost lady and recited the
following *waka* poem:

*By the side
of Mount Utsu in Suruga
I can meet you
neither in reality
nor in my dreams.*

On the gold leaf at the top of the screen seven of his own poems
have been written by Karasumaru Mitsuhiro, a prominent
courtier well known for his poetry and calligraphy. The poems
are a sort of commentary on and expansion of Narihira's, which
was too well known to need to be included. They are written in a
consciously antique style which fits well with Sōtatsu's
preoccupation with early *Yamato-e* painting. They read as
follows:

1] As I go along the mountain way, I see, rather than the
road under the rank ivy, the remains of yesterday's
flowers.

2] In the dew on the summer mountains I see yet again the
green mist of the road covered with ivy.

3] As the green ivy leaves drip on Mount Utsu, once more
the shadow of old flowers falls on my dreams.

4] Though we write we do not meet, and my love-letters
sent to the capital can only hint. . . .

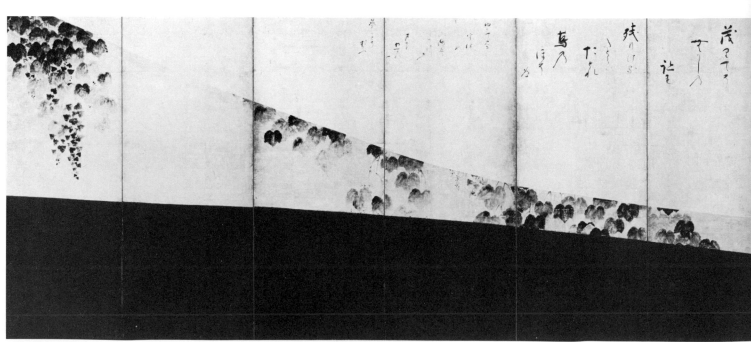

19   left-hand scre

5] For a thousand long years after, how many men will descend like this the unchanging ivy road?

6] The past too is overgrown, but it has left far behind the searchings on the narrow road of ivy.

7] My thoughts are dreamlike as, seated to view the scenery of Mount Utsu, I forget the reality in front of me.

These superbly designed paintings have been attributed to Sōtatsu's studio, which used the seal *Inen*, but they are so much more powerful than any other studio works that the design at least must be given to Sōtatsu. For brilliant simplicity of effect they are unequalled in Japanese art.

MIYAMOTO MUSASHI (1584–1645)

20 *Shrike on a tree-stump*

F/G3 紙本墨画枯木鳴鵙図　宮本武蔵筆

Ink on paper
Sealed *Musashi*
Hanging scroll, 126 × 55 cm
IZUMI CITY, Osaka
Important Cultural Property

Musashi (sometimes known as Niten) was Japan's greatest swordsman and the author of a classic work on swordsmanship. He was deeply versed in ink painting and the spirit of Zen Buddhism, both of which allied control and spontaneity as in swordfighting. His few remaining paintings are remarkable for their sharp power; this shrike is the best known, with an edge then quite lacking in the Kanō and Kaihō Schools in which he trained.

20

right-hand screen

22

MIYAMOTO MUSASHI (1584–1645)

21 *Bodhidharma*

S/G3 紙本墨画達磨図　宮本武蔵筆

Ink on paper
Hanging scroll, 91 × 39 cm
EISEI BUNKO, Tokyo

For Musashi see no. 20. Bodhidharma, founder of the Zen sect of Buddhism, was always a favourite subject for ink painters. Musashi's sharp, controlled line differs markedly from the Bodhidharma portraits by the priest Hakuin which affect roughness. This painting has come down in the Hosokawa family, for whom Musashi worked late in his life.

School of SŌTATSU

22 *Flowering plants*

F/G3 紙本金地著色草花図　伊年印

[one door repr. in colour on p. 156]
Ink and colours over gold leaf on paper
Sealed *Inen*
Set of four sliding doors, each 169 × 72.8 cm
c. 1630–1640
KYOTO NATIONAL MUSEUM

The seal *Inen* is thought to be a mark of Sōtatsu's studio. The works which bear it are close to his style and methods, but lack his power of design. There seems to have been a demand for screens and doors in his fresh, colourful manner among the townsmen of Kyoto, and his studio met that demand. The style is in marked contrast to the official Kanō manner which was used

21

in temples and castles. It is cheerful and domestic. These typical examples reduce the plants to simple, decorative elements without ink outline. The background gold leaf is used to shine through the colour, or to divide petals, as in the poppy heads and hollyhocks here. The flowers are dotted around in clumps; they grow straight out of the gold, with no attempt to represent either the soil or the background. There is a wide use of *tarashikomi* (puddling one pigment into another) and uneven application of colour to give life and variety.

23

left-hand screen

TAWARAYA SŌSETSU (*fl. c.* 1640–1650)

23 *Flowering plants of autumn*

S/G3 紙本金地著色秋草図　俵屋宗雪筆

[right-hand screen repr. in colour on p. 157]
Ink and colours partly over gold leaf on paper
s. *Sōsetsu ga* ('painted by Sōsetsu') and sealed *Inen*
Pair of six-fold screens, each 159 × 364 cm
c. 1640–1650
TOKYO NATIONAL MUSEUM
Important Cultural Property

The Sōtatsu studio seal of *Inen* was used sometimes alone (*cf.* no. 22) or sometimes with an artist's signature. Sōsetsu was Sōtatsu's immediate successor, and these works are the finest produced by the studio. Banks of grass are suggested by different tones of gold leaf, and their shapes are similar to those in Sōtatsu's *Narrow ivy road* (no. 19). From them clumps of sumptuously coloured autumn flowers grow with a hint of naturalness, and there is a suggestion of misty sky in the very pale gold above. The white chrysanthemums stand up in white *moriage* (gesso) and give an effect of great brilliance.

TAWARAYA SŌTATSU (d. 1643)
HON'AMI KŌETSU (1558–1637)

24 *Scroll of waka poems*

FS/G3 紙本金銀泥絵四季草花図下絵和歌巻　絵　俵屋　宗達筆
　　　　　　　　　　　　　　　　　　　書　本阿弥光悦筆

[section repr. in colour on p. 157]
Ink calligraphy over designs painted in gold and silver
Sealed *Inen*
Hand scroll, 34 × 922 cm
c. 1610
HINOHARA COLLECTION, Tokyo

The scrolls of poetry produced by Sōtatsu and Kōetsu jointly are a uniquely Japanese artistic phenomenon. They combine the poetry of Japan's mediaeval past with the work of a great artist and a great calligrapher in a format which is both traditional and new. Kōetsu was one of the 'three great calligraphers' of the early seventeenth century. The others were Nobutada and Shōkadō.

He developed a new version of the courtly cursive writing style of Kyoto which is distinguished for its grace and liquid sense of flow. As a background for his calligraphy Kōetsu commissioned his friend and associate Sōtatsu to produce papers with light designs in gold and silver wash. This too was a mediaeval tradition which Sōtatsu had studied. Although this scroll bears the *Inen* seal which is associated with Sōtatsu's studio, the painting is so accomplished and the designs so perfectly placed that they must be attributed to the master himself.

KANŌ TAN'YŪ (1602–1674)

25 *The founding of the Tōshōgū shrine (Tōshōgū Engi)*

FS/G3 紙本著色東照宮縁起絵巻　·狩野探幽筆

Ink and colours with gold wash on paper, the text in ink over gold-leaf designs
The last s. *Kanō Morikuni*
From a set of five hand scrolls, each h 47–49 cm
1640
TŌSHŌGŪ, Tochigi
Important Cultural Property

In these narrative hand scrolls in a very traditional format Tan'yū illustrated the life of Tokugawa Ieyasu from his birth until his burial in the great mausoleum of the Tōshōgū at Nikkō. The text was written over elaborate gold-leaf designs by two prominent priests of the time. In these elaborately organised works, in which long sections of illustration alternated with text, Tan'yū consciously showed himself capable of the hand-scroll style, once the preserve of the courtly Tosa painters. He uses the convention of the very high point of view and of long bands of cloud in pale colours and areas of gold wash linking parts of the composition. But there is a 'scenic', decorative element in the scrolls which is Tan'yū's own and of his age. This is noticeable in the peaceful scenes leading up to Ieyasu's birth, with noble houses set in an intimate, green landscape (first scroll). In the second scroll, Tan'yū shows he could handle depictions of crowds of people in his scenes of Ieyasu's great victory at Sekigahara in 1600.

25 (second scroll)

left-hand screen

26   right-hand screen

KUSUMI MORIKAGE (*c.* 1620–1690)

26 *Agriculture in the four seasons*

F/G5   紙本著色四季耕作図　守景筆

Ink and light colours on paper
s. *Mugesai* and sealed
Pair of six-fold screens, each 151 × 347 cm

AGENCY FOR CULTURAL AFFAIRS
Important Cultural Property

Morikage came from Kaga province, centre of the Maeda lands.
The Maeda were the greatest of the *Tozama*, the lords who had
opposed the Tokugawa family and were not inclined to pay more
than surface respect to them. Similarly, Morikage fell foul of his
teacher Kanō Tan'yū for his unorthodoxy, and it was perhaps
not an accident that he was recalled to be official painter to the
Maeda. His sympathy for the agricultural classes was in itself
unusual when their sufferings were officially condoned since the
whole Edo social system depended on their unrewarded labour.
In several pairs of screens like this one, Morikage depicts both the
hardness and humanity of their lives, as well as its perpetual
labour. Here the stages of planting, growing, reaping and
threshing rice are shown from left to right. The ploughing of the
dry paddies is done by oxen, but the planting out in the freezing,
spring-flooded paddies, the reaping, and the threshing are all
back-breaking work done by hand. Morikage links these events
separated by time by a coherent single river landscape, with
distant rounded hills, and by stressing the practical difficulties of
travelling across it. His handling of ink washes to express
distance, mountains and mist is uniquely soft and his figures are
lovingly outlined and delicately coloured.

27

Attributed to KUSUMI MORIKAGE (*c.* 1620–1690)

27 *Agriculture and silk production*

S/G5　紙本著色耕織図

Ink and light colours on paper
Unsigned
Pair of low eight-fold screens, each 90.4 × 344 cm
NARIAIJI, Kyoto

Although these delightful low screens are unsigned, the
attribution to Morikage on grounds of style and subject is almost
certain. The setting of farmers' thatched houses in a soft, misty,
hilly landscape with a river, the affectionate and detailed
depiction of everyday life in the country and the clear, light
colour on the figures all point to the master from Kaga. One
screen is devoted to the processes of rice agriculture, while the
other shows stages in keeping silkworms, boiling the cocoons
and winding the thread. There is a strong suggestion from the
dress of the peasants that these scenes are set in China, to which

left-hand screen

right-hand screen

Morikage can never have been, but which was officially admired for its supposedly admirable Confucian system. Silk was produced in Edo period Japan, but demand was so great that much was imported from China through the Chinese merchants at Nagasaki.

KUSUMI MORIKAGE (*c.* 1620–1690)

28 *Staying cool under an arbour of 'evening glory'*

F/G5 　紙本淡彩納涼図　守景筆

[detail repr. in colour on p. 160]
Ink and light colours on paper
s. *Morikage hitsu* ('by the brush of Morikage') and sealed *Kusumi*
Two-fold screen, 151 × 168 cm
TOKYO NATIONAL MUSEUM, National Treasure

28

A peasant family are enjoying the cool on a summer evening
under an arbour of 'evening glory' gourds outside their small
house. They sit on a woven mat which is a portable version of the
tatami which form the flooring unit of a Japanese house.
Morikage was almost unique among Kanō school painters for his
genuine sympathy with the peasant class. Other Kanō artists,
such as his master Tan'yū, did depict peasants in political
paintings showing the four classes of society in their proper
places, but Morikage alone sees them as human beings with
worth of their own. His view of this family is affectionate and
sympathetic, without the burlesque element so often used to
depict people from the lower end of society. Morikage has used
ink, grey wash and slight touches of pink and blue to suggest the
subdued colours of a moonlit evening. The moon itself is
expressed by the off-white paper left in reserve from the ink-wash
which covers the rest of the background. The screen is probably
adapted from sliding doors.

HANABUSA ITCHŌ (1652–1724)

29 *The Four Accomplishments*

S/G5   紙本著色琴棋書画図　英一蝶筆

[detail repr. in colour on p. 161]
Ink and colours on paper with gold leaf
s. *Hanabusa Itchō zu* ('picture by Hanabusa Itchō') and sealed
Pair of six-fold screens, each 158 × 367 cm
c. 1720
SEN SŌSHITSU, Kyoto
Important Art Object

Itchō travesties the four traditional accomplishments of the
Chinese gentlemen in a Japanese version set in a temple and
shrine. The four are playing the *koto*, playing chess, and
practising painting and calligraphy. The groups of people are put
in a thoroughly traditional setting derived from the *Yamato-e*
style, with clouds of gold leaf linking them and glossing over any
awkwardnesses where the subject does not quite fit the overall
composition. From right to left, the groups are:
1] Court nobles playing the *koto* and the *biwa* (lute) in a *shinden*
(sleeping-quarters) looking out on to flowering cherries.
2] Nobles and priests playing *shōgi* (Japanese chess) and *go* on a

29

left-hand screen

right-hand screen

verandah overlooking an iris pond.

3] Young nobles learning calligraphy in a temple schoolroom overlooking red maples.

4] Shintō priests and a priestess in the *emadō* (hall for votive paintings) of a shrine, with snow lingering on the roof.

The screens thus describe the four seasons. Itchō, originally a rebel from the Kanō School, became known for his pictures of ordinary people. Late in life he returned to his more formal roots, both artistically and politically, but the group of jolly children around the *emadō* perhaps show that in his late years he could put people of different classes easily together in the same picture.

Anonymous

30 *Craftsmen at their work*

FS/G5   紙本著色職人尽図

Ink and colours on paper
Eight from a set of twelve sheets, probably wall panels, each
60 × 50 cm
Second half of 17th century
AGENCY FOR CULTURAL AFFAIRS

There was in Japan a deep respect for craftsmanship. In a populous society with in general enough food to maintain it, special skills were encouraged and admired. The Tokugawa government endorsed this attitude to craftsmen by making them third of the four official classes of society, above the merchants whom, however, they mainly served, especially as the wealth and numbers of the merchant class increased and with it the demand for new luxury goods such as *netsuke* or fine dolls. Makers of swords and mirrors, and carpenters, had always had high prestige. To these were now added the inventors of new textile techniques, the printers of decorative papers, the makers of fine pottery, porcelain and lacquer, and many others.

The intense interest taken in craftsmen by the townsman class was reflected in paintings and prints of their activities, known as *shokunin zukushi* or 'conspectuses of craftsmen'. These often took the form of hand scrolls or albums, but some sets exist which seem to have been originally panels in merchants' houses, perhaps filling the areas of wall above built-in alcoves or cupboards. The present set is by an unknown artist probably trained in the Kanō school. Kanō artists often increased their income by carrying out less exalted commissions for popular scenes on walls or screens or hand scrolls. The affection shown for the humble craftsmen is rather similar to that of Morikage for the farmers (nos 26, 27).

a] *Making fans.* Among the processes for making folding fans (*ōgi*) are sizing the back, sprinkling gold leaf, pasting on designs, folding, and fitting the sticks. Some round *uchiwa* fans are lying completed on the *engawa* next to the cut-out paper bases for the folding fans.

b] *Making stationery.* This is not a paper-maker's, but a shop where paper is made up into blank albums and hand scrolls for amateur painting and calligraphy. Professionals would normally work on separate sections of paper, to be mounted properly later by a *hyōgushi* (master-mounter). One man is cutting, another pasting. A small Buddhist altar is to the left.

c] *Making bows.* This was a prestigious craft, being concerned with the needs of the samurai class. Some samurai retainers, clearly customers, stand outside the shop and sit on the *engawa*.

d] *Dyeing materials.* The long lengths, probably of cotton which was not made very wide, are being prepared by two men for

a

30e

dyeing, apparently by the paste-resist method through a stencil. They are then put through the vats by a woman and hung up to dry by a boy on the lattice above the shop built for that purpose. At the front, a woman is putting a finished length on to a roller. The other end is held by an unseen person using strings.

e] *Weaving.* At the front thread is being fed onto bobbins on a wheel. Behind there are two foot-looms. A child above is setting up the warps. In the back of the shop threads are being put onto reels.

f] *Building carpentry.* This was also a prestigious craft, the Japanese for carpenter, *daiku*, meaning 'great craft'. This seems to

c

d

g

h

have been because it was in fact allied to architecture (as mediaeval European master-masons were also architects). An elevation of a temple building can be seen at the back of the shop; next to it is a sleeping boy. Carpenters are marking timbers with an ink-line, and another is removing excess wood with the long-handled plane. A woman brings refreshments on a tray. The carpenters' own premises are delightfully dilapidated.

g] *Making tubs and buckets.* The cooper is knocking the last slat into a tub, while his assistant prepares the binding material. The cooper's wife, suckling a child, sits and watches.

h] *Making a shovel.* This is apparently a smith of agricultural implements, and the workshop seems to be in the country. A new shovel is being hammered by the man on the left; the one on the left holds it, hot from the fire, on the anvil with tongs.

The Priest HAKUIN (1685–1768)

31 *Bodhidharma, with calligraphic inscription*

F/G5　紙本墨画達磨図　白隠慧鶴筆

Ink on paper
s. 'the old man Hakuin in his eighty-third year' and sealed
Hanging scroll, 131 × 58 cm
1767
EISEI BUNKO, Tokyo

Hakuin did paintings as exercises in the pursuit of Zen Buddhist
enlightenment. Subjects were fairly limited since the repetition of
significant motifs was thought to help uncover ever deeper layers
of meaning. One of these subjects was the Bodhidharma, founder
of the Zen sect. He was of Indian origin and is shown with a
distinctly 'foreign' appearance with sunken eyes, large nose and
beard. Hakuin was the best of the artists who painted in this
abbreviated style. His works have force derived from his own
profound personality and the extreme strength of his ink line.
The latter was a result of his mastery of calligraphy (nos 97, 98).

The Priest HAKUIN (1685–1768)

32 *Bodhidharma in meditation*

S/G5　紙本墨画達磨図　白隠慧鶴筆

Ink on paper
Sealed
Hanging scroll, 126 × 55 cm
EISEI BUNKO, Tokyo

The founder of the Zen sect is shown seated in meditation, a
process which he carried on for nine years so that he lost the use
of his legs. The mixture of humour and a deeper meaning are
very typical of Zen painting. The line is intensely calligraphic and
the work seems more closely related to written characters than to
pictorial art. The inscription above is in an unusually gentle and
cursive style for this usually rather stark calligrapher.

WATANABE SHIKŌ (1683–1755)

33 *Flowers and trees of the four seasons*

F/G6　紙本著色四季草花図　渡辺始興筆

[repr. in colour on pp. 158–9]
Ink and colours on paper
s. *Shikō ga* ('painted by Shikō') and sealed
Pair of six-fold screens, each 124 × 266 cm
HATAKEYAMA MEMORIAL MUSEUM, Tokyo
Important Art Object

These joyous works are the most accomplished and varied of all
the multi-flower screens of the Rimpa school. They excel in
composition and technique the floral paintings produced by
Sōtatsu and his Inen studio, and in vigour and line the later
works of Hōitsu. The fact that they are done on paper and not on
gold leaf gives them a special flavour. The brilliance of Shikō's
pigments owes nothing to gold. Shikō had a strong interest in
painting from nature (see his sketch-book, no. 39), but he was
also entranced by the artificial brush techniques of Sōtatsu and
Kōrin, and there is a characteristic Edo period tension between
the two. Thus he has tried to give a natural movement and
growth to the maple on the left, while painting the boughs in
black and green splashed into each other in the *tarashikomi*

31

technique. He gives a less artificial feeling to the central flowers by
cutting off their stalks with the bottom of the picture, yet he has
some at the far right growing straight out of the paper in Inen
style. There is a basic tension between the careful detailing of the
individual plants and the unnaturalness of their all growing
together – in fact spring flowers begin on the right and move
through summer, autumn and winter at the far left. The
composition is elaborately devised to satisfy the eye across the
entire sweep of both screens.

Shikō combined an interest in naturalistic painting of birds and flowers with the extremely bold decorative methods of Ogata Kōrin (1652–1716). These very arresting screens depict the rounded hills of Yoshinoyama, now in Nara prefecture, which in April and May are covered with wild cherry-trees in blossom and have been a tourist attraction since at least the seventh century AD. Out of the simple forms of the hills (not very much exaggerated from reality), the white cherry-blossoms and the gold-leaf background he has created a pattern of startling poetic power. The foreground gold suggests mist and it is significant that on these works alone Shikō used the art-name *Keiai*, 'landscape mist'.

FUKAE ROSHŪ (1699–1757)

35 *The Narrow ivy road*

F/G6 紙本金地著色蔦の細道図　深江芦舟筆

[repr. in colour on pp. 164–5]
Ink and colours over gold leaf on paper
Sealed *Roshū*
Six-fold screen, 133 × 260 cm
UMEZAWA COLLECTION, Tokyo
Important Cultural Property

For the story of the Narrow Ivy Road see no. 19. Narihira and his companion are seen at the entrance to the pass. Ahead of them, and already climbing up it, is the man they will soon meet. Little is visible except his travelling priest's back-pack and his shaven head. This startling painting is in the simple and interesting stylised manner of Sōtatsu, whom Roshū seems to have preferred to Kōrin in spite of having studied with the latter in his youth. The hills are placed as great, decorative blocks on the gold-leaf ground. They are painted in the *tarashikomi* technique, where one colour is dripped on to another while still wet. The ivy is scattered irrationally across the picture, attached to nothing.

OGATA KŌRIN (1652–1716)

36 *Peacocks with plum-blossom and hollyhocks*

S/G6 紙本金地著色孔雀葵花図　尾形光琳筆

[repr. in colour on pp. 166–7]
Ink and colours over gold leaf on paper
s. *Hokkyō Kōrin* and sealed
Pair of two-fold screens, each 146 × 173 cm
After 1701
HINOHARA COLLECTION, Tokyo
Important Cultural Property

Kōrin's high decorative style is seen at its confident best in these expansive screens. As in all his greatest works, of which few remain, he has taken simple motifs from nature and placed them on a plain surface without depth, without much sense of movement, but with a simple perfection which makes him at his most inspired Japan's greatest decorative painter. In the right-hand screen the only hint of relative depth lies in the fact that the plum-bough falls behind the peacock. The rocky frame has none of the sense of depth and weight found in Sōtatsu or Roshū. The birds, though beautifully done, do not have Shikō's naturalistic liveliness, nor does the plum-bough; the group as a whole lacks the poetry of Hōitsu at his best. Rather, the painting relies on

32

WATANABE SHIKŌ (1683–1755)

34 *Flowering cherries at Yoshinoyama*

S/G6 紙本金地著色吉野山図　渡辺始興筆

[repr. in colour on pp. 162–3]
Ink and colours over gold leaf on paper
s. *Watanabe Shikō*; sealed *Shikō no in* ('Shikō's seal') and *Keiai*
Pair of six-fold screens, each 150 × 362 cm
PRIVATE COLLECTION, Japan

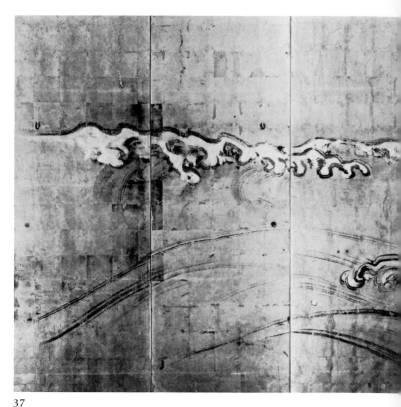

37

sheer inspiration of design. The left-hand screen is even simpler –
just seven stalks of red and white hollyhocks growing straight
upwards – yet an even more satisfying image than the more
lively floral works of Sōtatsu's Inen studio. These screens
represent the bold yet refined taste of the rich merchants of the
Genroku era for whom Kōrin was even in his day an artistic hero.

SAKAI HŌITSU (1761–1828)

37 *Waves*
F/G6 紙本銀地著色波図　酒井抱一筆

Ink and colour on silver leaf over paper.
s. *Hōitsu Kishin hitsu* ('by the brush of Hōitsu'; Kishin was the
name he took after becoming a Buddhist monk in 1798)
One of a pair of six-fold screens, each 170 × 369 cm
c. 1810–20
SEIKAIDŌ BUNKO, Tokyo

These screens, of which only the right-hand one is shown, reveal
Hōitsu at his strongest. They contrast with the more poetic and
subtle *Moon with autumn flowers* (no. 38). The source of their
strength of design is Hōitsu's obsessional interest in the works of
Kōrin, which he began to study with fanatical devotion around
1807. He published a book on Kōrin's designs in 1815 (*Kōrin
hyakuzu*) which includes the two-fold screens of waves now in
the Metropolitan Museum of Art, New York. The latter are
clearly the inspiration for these more expansive though less
intense works. Hōitsu's fondness for silver leaf is particularly
shown in these examples. Wave paintings on screens and doors
were a favourite subject in the Edo period and were done in
different styles by the Kanō, Maruyama and Rimpa schools.
Hokusai's famous 'Great Wave' print (no. 118) is in part a
summing-up of this tradition.

SAKAI HŌITSU (1761–1828)

38 *Moon with autumn flowers*
S/G6 紙本金地著色月秋草図　酒井抱一筆

[detail repr. in colour on p. 169]
Ink and colours over gold leaf on paper, with silver leaf
s. *Ukaan Hōitsu*. Sealed *Bunsen*
Six-fold screen, 140 × 309 cm
ASAHI OPTICAL CO., Tokyo
Important Cultural Property

Hōitsu was the son of the daimyō of Himeji. Nothing could
illustrate better the rise in social status of painting in the Edo
period. Certainly no Rimpa painter had before come from a
family of such status, painting having until then been a distinctly
middle-class activity. Hōitsu was deeply versed in both poetry
and the history of painting, especially that of Sōtatsu and Kōrin.
The latter he idolized. He is considered the last great Rimpa
master, although his pupil Kiitsu was an original and worthy
successor. Poetic feeling combined with the compositional
inspiration of Kōrin and the technical methods of Sōtatsu and his
followers produced in Hōitsu a unique flavour, at its best well up
to the standards he followed. This quiet theme recalls an *Inen*
screen designed by Kōrin and carried out by Hōitsu with a light
touch. The silver moon is a master's stroke. Hōitsu was fond of
silver leaf and extended the scope of Rimpa painting by using it.

WATANABE SHIKŌ (1683–1755)

39 *Sketches of birds*
FS/G6 紙本著色鳥獣写真図巻　渡辺始興筆

Ink and colours on paper
Hand scroll, 27 × 1758 cm
MITSUI TAKANARU, Tokyo

Shikō is considered a pioneer in western-style drawing from nature, which he did consummately well with the native brush, ink and colour washes. He probably did this series, now mounted as a hand scroll, for his patron Prince Konoe Ichiro, who was an enthusiast for western science. In it, almost for the first time in Japan, the structure of birds is visually analysed (though there is documentary evidence that Kanō Tan'yū may have tried the same several generations earlier) but the flowing, living line produced by the brush gives a sense of presence which is usually missing from western scientific drawings. Ōkyo knew these sketches and was much influenced by them.

OGATA KŌRIN (1652–1716)

40 *Willow*

F/G6　紙本金地著色柳図　尾形光琳筆

[repr. in colour on p. 168]
Colours over gold leaf on paper mounted on silk
Unsigned
Incense-wrapper now mounted as hanging scroll, 33 × 24.5 cm
c. 1700–1710
HOSOMI MINORU, Osaka

Kōrin was at his best painting on functional shapes – folding screens, fans, and a famous series of incense-wrappers (*kōtsutsumi*) of which this is one. Only one of them is signed (on

38

39

the reverse) but their perfection of design and the fact that they have been preserved at all make the attributions all but certain. The connoisseurship of incense (see no. 166) was one of the 'Ten Noble Accomplishments' which were affected by rich townsmen, and the wrappers for incense were expected to be of the same standards of elegance as were found in the brocade bags for tea ceremony utensils. The wrappers were folded in a standardised way – hence the square pattern of folds on them.

For incense wrappers (*kōtsutsumi*) see nos 40, 166. The surviving group are all said to have been done for a rich Edo merchant family called Fuyuki; such people were typical customers of Kōrin's.

OGATA KŌRIN (1652–1716)

41   *Ivy leaves*

S/G6   紙本金地著色蔦図　尾形光琳筆

Colour over gold leaf mounted on silk
Incense-wrapper, now mounted as a hanging scroll,
33 × 24.6 cm
c. 1700–1710
PRIVATE COLLECTION, Japan

OGATA KŌRIN (1652–1716)

42   *Young bracken*

F/G6   紙本金地著色蕨図　尾形光琳筆

Colours over gold leaf on paper
s. *Hokkyō Kōrin*; sealed *Kansei*
Uchiwa fan, now mounted as a hanging scroll, 23.6 × 23.4 cm
PRIVATE COLLECTION, Japan

It is not certain whether all Kōrin's fan-shaped paintings were intended for practical use. This example seems never to have been mounted on the solid frame which forms the basis of the

41

uchiwa fan. It may be that designs like this were too highly prized by their first owners to be exposed to the wear and tear of use. In any case some of Kōrin's most perfect designs appear on fan shapes and it is remarkable that he could produce designs of great power in this small format as well as on large-scale screens. The young bracken (*warabi*) which grows on the hills of Japan is a symbol of spring, and personal accoutrements such as fans were nearly always seasonal. *Warabi* was also a delicacy as a vegetable when gathered young.

OGATA KŌRIN (1652–1716)

43 *Camellia*

F/G6 　紙本金地著色椿図　尾形光琳筆

Colours on paper
Sealed *Kōrin*
Uchiwa fan, now mounted as a hanging scroll, 23.7 × 23.5 cm
PRIVATE COLLECTION, Japan

The paper for an *uchiwa* fan of this quality was finely grooved, with the lines radiating and diverging away from the base to which the handle was attached. The appearance was of minute folds and the surface was an attractive one for a decorative artist. The camellia, which bloomed in the snow, was a symbol of late winter. Kōrin has reduced the blooms and leaves to very simple patterns, but in the narrow confines of the stalks he has run several colours together in the *tarashikomi* technique. *Uchiwa* were less practical fans than folding ones and were very much used as a personal adornment.

42

43

75

OGATA KENZAN (1663–1743)

43a Hollyhocks, with calligraphic inscription

S/G6 　紙本著色立葵図　尾形乾山筆

Ink and colours on paper
s. *Kyōjō Shisui Shinsei*; d. 1741
Hanging scroll, 130 × 56 cm
HATAKEYAMA MEMORIAL MUSEUM, Tokyo

The simple but effective placing of the blossom on the paper reflects Kenzan's skill as a decorator of pottery, and also the example of his famous brother Kōrin.

OGATA KENZAN (1663–1743)

43b Bush clover, with a calligraphic poem

F/G6 　紙本著色秋萩図　尾形乾山筆
Ink and colours on paper
s. *Kyōjō Shisui Shinsei*
Hanging scroll, 130 × 52.5 cm
HATAKEYAMA MEMORIAL MUSEUM, Tokyo

The bush clover (*hagi*) is one of the 'Seven Flowers of Autumn'. The calligraphy of the *waka* poem is reminiscent of Kōetsu (nos 24, 94) to whom Kenzan's family was related by marriage.

OGATA KŌRIN (1652–1716)

43c Spear-flowers and water-ripples

F/G6 　絹本著色藪柑子図　尾形光琳筆

Colours on paper
Sealed Kōrin
Uchiwa fan, now mounted as a hanging scroll, 23.7 × 23.5 cm
PRIVATE COLLECTION, Japan

Kōrin makes a typical contrast between the dark water, taking up most of the fan, and the brilliant small blossoms.

ITŌ JAKUCHŪ (1716–1800)

44 Paintings from the series Dōshoku saie ('The Colourful World of Living Beings')

FS/G8 　絹本著色動植綵絵　伊藤若冲筆

Ink and colours on silk
Hanging scrolls, average size 143 × 80 cm
1757–1765
HIS MAJESTY THE EMPEROR OF JAPAN

Between 1757 and 1765 Jakuchū executed a great series of thirty paintings in elaborate colours on dyed silks. They were done for the Sōkokuji Temple in Kyoto, with which the artist as a professed Buddhist layman had close links. Their title is *Dōshoku saie*, which literally means 'coloured pictures of creatures and plants'. Jakuchū's intention was to make them a survey of living creation, that is, of the animal and vegetable kingdom, a naturalistic version of the Buddhist *mandara* paintings in which divinities and sometimes human beings and other creatures appeared in a semi-diagramatic form. His sympathies were very much with lower creatures – plants, fish, insects, reptiles and birds, and he depicts no large animals or human beings. Human life is, however, suggested by references to domesticated birds and to garden plants and crops, and when he presented the paintings to the Sōkokuji he added a triptych of Buddhist divinities by way of completion. The series was given to the imperial family in 1889. They form one of the great monuments of Japanese painting – exquisitely detailed, vigorously alive and well observed, and yet with a breadth and variety of design which are uniquely native.

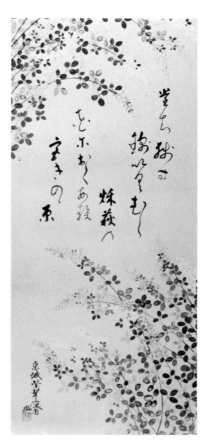

43a   43b   43c

a] *Chrysanthemums by a stream, with rocks*

[repr. in colour on p. 170]
Sealed *Tō Jokin in* ('The seal of Itō Jokin') and *Jakuchū Kōji*
('Jakuchū the Buddhist layman')
143 × 79 cm

This painting may claim to be the finest design of all the series
and the one with the least Chinese feeling. Indeed, in its brilliant
irrationality of design it is in the great tradition of Rimpa school
painting. The blue, green and gold rocks, distorted and
decorative, come through Rimpa from the native-style *Yamato-e*
painting of the middle ages, as does the stream meandering from
top to bottom of the painting on a plain silk ground without any
banks being shown. Yet the tendrils of chrysanthemum are
natural and detailed, in strong contrast to the unnaturally large
blossoms in white. In paintings like this Jakuchū raised
decorative art to high art.

b] *Maples, with small birds*

Sealed as (a)
142 × 79 cm

The colours of the maple-leaves in autumn, turning from green
gradually through yellow, orange, bright red and dark red, have
always been a favourite subject for Japanese painters and poets
(and even for musical composers). Artists, from mediaeval hand
scrolls and screens onward, approached the problem of depicting
them in two main ways – either an impressionistic blur of red on
a hillside, or a finely detailed depiction of one or more complete
trees. Jakuchū by contrast has taken his cue from Chinese
paintings of plum-boughs and painted part of a maple boldly
across the surface of the silk so that it dominates completely. A
few rocks and grasses at the bottom give some reference to the
large scale of the tree, but what is beyond is left, as in Chinese
models, to the imagination. Jakuchū has created a characteristic
tension between the finely detailed leaves, touched up with gold
wash, and the rugged, distorted, calligraphically drawn boughs.
These are in turn picked out with spots of green lichen, some
floating away from the branches altogether, in a tradition dating
from sixteenth-century screen-painting.

c] *Domestic fowl*

[repr. in colour on p. 171]
Sealed as (a)
142 × 73 cm

There are more cocks and hens in the series than any other sort
of creature. Jakuchū kept them in his yard in Kyoto and studied
them endlessly. In a context which is only linked to reality by a
few grasses at the left and bottom, he has created an amazingly
vibrant pattern of black, white and brown varieties in a perfectly
balanced group reminiscent of a textile design of the extravagance favoured at this period.

d] *White phoenix in an old pine-tree*

Sealed as (a)
142 × 79 cm

The phoenix is the only imaginary creature in the series. Jakuchū
is perhaps showing that the world of imagination is part of the
real world, and that there are no valid distinctions (a basic

44b

Buddhist sentiment). As in other paintings of the series he has
contrasted the delicacy of a bird with the rugged strength of a
gnarled pine-tree, twined with tendrils of morning glory. The
phoenix is drawn in shell-white with thousands of tiny strokes in
a surface resembling lace.

e] *Shells and water-creatures on the shore*

Sealed *Jokin* and *Kōji*
149 × 79 cm

This is the most advanced exercise in contrast of all the series. On
a beach left by the receding tide, the artist has spread many
varieties of shell and starfish, all done in such detail that they are
easily identifiable. The water, on the other hand, runs away into
long, white fingers which are like formal scrolling patterns, while
the blue rock at bottom right is more artificial than any distorted
decorative rock in a Chinese scholar's garden. The painting is
dominated by blue, white and shades of pink, gold and brown; its
palette, like all of the series, is unique to itself.

44d

44e

f] *Flock of sparrows descending on millet-heads*

s. *Kōji Jakuchū sei* ('made by Jakuchū the Buddhist layman');
sealed as (e)
d. in equivalence to autumn 1759
142 × 80 cm

The subject of small birds and millet in autumn was common in
Ming China, and was adopted by the Tosa school (no. 16). But
Jakuchū's treatment is very original, giving all the movement
and space to the birds in flight. He links the birds and the plants
by hanging one millet-head out into the advancing flock, among
which the artist has defeated monotony by the simple device of
making one bird white. The character *sei* used for 'painted' is a
conscious imitation of Chinese practice.

g] *Golden pheasants on a tree in the snow*

s. *Kingai Jakuchū sei* ('made by Jakuchū of Nishikimachi' – the
street in Kyoto where he was born); sealed as (e)
142 × 80 cm

44f

The artist was especially fond of the effects of snow, which he used with a decorative freedom which would have astonished the Chinese flower-and-bird painters he so admired. This is a very formal composition, the birds sitting directly in the centre of the 'S' shape formed by the snow on the tree. The holes in the snow, and the way it spreads to fill the whole corner of the painting, are quite irrational in Jakuchū's boldest vein. The camellia blooms add that element of riotous abundance which he favoured in his coloured paintings.

h] *Insects, amphibians and reptiles by a pond, with a gourd-plant*

s. *Tōbeian Jakuchū* (a reference to his never taking more than one *tō* of rice in payment for a painting); sealed as (a), with an extra comic seal describing himself as a *kami* (Shintō god) of coloured painting
142 × 80 cm

Fifty-two species of creature have been identified in this work, which is devoted to 'creeping things'. Jakuchū suggests a pond-

44h

edge without depicting any water, and frames the whole with a gourd-plant which houses most of the insects (and the snake). Yet water is indicated by the half-obscured tadpoles. The sense of cool, pale green is individual to the painting. Its circular movement is more strongly marked than in any other of the series.

MARUYAMA ŌKYO (1733–1795)

45 *Waterfall*

F/G8 紙本墨画瀑布図 円山応挙筆

[repr. in colour on p. 172)
Ink and light colour on paper
Large hanging scroll, 172 × 96 cm
1772
EMMAN'IN, Shiga

This enormous painting was commissioned by the abbot of the Emman'in, who is said to have felt the lack of a waterfall in his garden. Ōkyo, already preoccupied by the problems of depicting water in movement, responded to the challenge with one of his grandest works. In it he adopted an almost western method of putting an artificial frame round his composition, excluding any thoughts of what might be beyond. He concentrated the spatial interest on movement from the background to the foreground and boldly made his torrent pour out directly at the viewer. In this work, too, he added a strong sense of light and shade to the formal and rather dull Kanō school method of painting rocks in which he was trained; this is a landmark in his development of a grand style to revive the former glories of Japanese screen-painting.

44g

79

46

NAGASAWA ROSETSU (1754–1799)

46 *The Nachi waterfall and the Satta pass*

S/G8 絹本著色薩埵峠那智滝図　長沢芦雪筆

Ink and colours on silk
s. *Rosetsu sha* ('copied by Rosetsu'); sealed *Chō Gyo* and *Hyōkei*
Pair of hanging scrolls, each 145 × 55.4 cm
c. 1780
KISHIMOTO KŌICHI, Hyōgo

The two scrolls depict famous Japanese sights – Mount Fuji seen
from the Satta pass in Suruga province and the Nachi waterfall
in Kii province. Though widely separated in distance, both are
very holy places of the Shintō religion, each thought to be
inhabited by a *kami*. Rosetsu had already by this date surpassed
his master Ōkyo in the fluency of his ink brushwork, and the
colours are wedded to the ink with an ease which Ōkyo never
achieved. On the other hand, Rosetsu never quite achieves the
grandeur of his teacher.

AŌDŌ DENZEN (1748–1822)

47 *A true view of Mount Asama*

F/G8 紙本著色浅間山図　亜欧堂田善筆

[repr. in colour on p. 173]
Ink and colours on paper
Sealed
Six-fold screen, 149 × 342 cm
c. 1790
TOKYO NATIONAL MUSEUM

Denzen adopted the art-name Aōdō, which means 'Hall of Asia
and Europe'. It symbolizes his determination to bring the art of
Japan and Europe closer together – a marked contrast to Shiba
Kōkan (no. 48) whose western studies led him unjustly to
despise Japanese native styles. Denzen developed copper-
engraving, which he learned partly in Nagasaki and partly from
Kōkan, and he attempted paintings in western style, but differing
from Kōkan in generally not trying to copy oils. This fine screen is

perhaps the greatest Japanese painting in the European manner done before the Meiji period, and by far the artist's best. It is successful because it uses a Japanese format, paper and pigments, while imitating the 'blue-and-brown' palette favoured in European eighteenth-century landscape. The great Kyushu volcano is shifted to one side in the classic Japanese style, and the mists between the foreground and far distance are also a traditional Far Eastern device. Again, the point of view over the foreground is high and differs from much western practice. It is perhaps mainly the blue sky with smoke rising into it, together with the tones of pigment, that give the work its compellingly hybrid quality, though the absence of ink line, almost universal in native paintings, is also a major factor.

SHIBA KŌKAN (1747–1818)

48 Picture of the Seven-League Beach at Kamakura in Sōshū

S/G8 紙本著色七里ヶ浜図 司馬江漢筆

[repr. in colour on p. 174]
Oil colours on paper
s. *Seiyō gashi tōto Kōkan Shiba Shun byōsha* ('drawn and copied by Shiba Kōkan Shun, the western-style artist from the eastern capital'), also s. 'Sia Kookan, Ao 18' in European handwriting
Two-fold screen, 95.6 × 178.5 cm
d. 'twenty-fourth day of the sixth month of the year hinoe tatsu in the Kansei era' (1796)
KOBE NAMBAN MUSEUM, Hyogo

Kōkan was a leading student of western mathematics and science, as well as an artist who could paint in Japanese *Ukiyo-e* style, who studied Chinese painting at Nagasaki, designed for popular wood-block prints and did copper-plate etchings and engravings in the European manner. He also made many attempts to copy European styles of art, especially oil-painting, and his admiration for them led him to an unreasonable contempt for the art traditions of Japan.

This screen is his most ambitious landscape. In it he attempts a grand scheme of receding space and logical construction. The painting is done in oil-based pigments on paper, but the effect is western enough. The most European features are the carefully done sky, the low horizon and the shading on Mount Fuji, which can be seen to the left. The semi-island of Enoshima to its right, in contrast, is executed in a flat, traditionally Japanese way. The waves along the famous beach, too, though based on European models, have an intense stylisation which is almost the opposite of the sense of movement he intended.

Kōkan presented the painting to the Atagoyama shrine in Edo, following a common practice of artists, but it was removed in 1811 for fear that its foreign taste would bring trouble on the shrine. Kōkan then had it mounted on a hard backing in western style, but it was later remounted as a two-fold screen. The two inscriptions above it were added at that time. One is by the poet Ōta Nampo: 'This painting was hung before in the Atagoyama shrine south of Edo castle, but was taken away because it is in European style; it is now owned by Seizandō (a bookseller and poet). Using western methods, Kōkan has painted this picture of Enoshima. Within the limits of one picture he has admirably managed to confine and catch the feeling of the long, misty panoramic stretch of beach at Shichirigahama.' The other is an appreciation, even more enthusiastic, by Nakai Kundō Takayoshi, another writer.

NAGASAWA ROSETSU (1754–1799)

49 a] Shōki, the demon queller
   b] Toad

a] F/G8 紙本墨画蝦蟇鐘馗図 長沢芦雪筆
b] S/G8

Ink on paper
s. *Rosetsu ga* ('painted by Rosetsu') and sealed *Gyo*
Pair of hanging scrolls, 165 × 89 cm
c. 1787
OKAMOTO MASANORI, Wakayama

These dashing *suiboku* paintings were probably done on the artist's long visit to Kii province in 1787. They show his absolute mastery over brush and ink, and his lively sympathy for living beings. Unlike his master Ōkyo, who could achieve a sense of vibrant life only in his sketches (no. 53), Rosetsu was at home with human figures, animals, fish or birds in either ink or colour. His figure of Shōki, the mythical ridder of demons in Tang China, is full of movement and tension. Shōki was a favourite subject for paintings, prints and *netsuke* in the Edo period, and was usually depicted humorously as in Rosetsu's painting. The very essence of the toad seems to have been captured in a few skilful washes of ink. It is unlikely that this, one of the world's most lifelike animal paintings, took more than a few minutes to execute.

49b

49a

50a

50b

50d

MORI SOSEN (1747–1821)

50a,b] *Apes, deer and pines*

F/G8   絹本著色猿猴図　森狙仙筆

Ink and colours on silk
s. *Sosen hitsu* ('by the brush of Sosen'); two seals
Pair of hanging scrolls designed as for sliding doors,
each 165 × 136 cm
TOKYO NATIONAL MUSEUM
Important Art Object

c] *Apes in a persimmon-tree*
d] *Apes by a waterfall*

S/G8   絹本著色猿猴図　森狙仙筆

[(c) repr. in colour on p. 179]
Ink and colours on silk

s. *Reimyōan Sosen*; two seals, one of them *Sosen-in* ('Sosen's
seal')
Pair of hanging scrolls, each 127 × 54 cm
TŌYAMA KINENKAN FOUNDATION, Saitama

Sosen is the best-known painter of the Japanese ape, which he
studied at length in its native forests. He became celebrated
for the liveliness with which he depicted its movements and the
refined delicacy of his brushwork in its fur. He also excelled in
other furry animals, especially deer and wild boar, but he
attempted very little else. He learned to paint in the Kanō School,
but in his decision to observe nature itself instead of other
paintings he was at one with other eighteenth-century artists
such as Shikō and Ōkyo. Inferior copies of his paintings are very
common, especially in the west, where they have always been
popular for their subject-matter. But only his artistic descendants
Mori Tessan (1775–1841) and Mori Ippō (1798–1871) can be
shown to have equalled his skill.

MATSUMURA GOSHUN (1752–1811)

51 *Carp in a pond overshadowed by a pine-tree*

F/G8 絹本淡彩松下鯉魚図　呉春筆

Ink and light colours on silk
s. *Goshun*: sealed *Goshun no in* ('Goshun's seal')
One of a pair of hanging scrolls, 130 × 71 cm
c. 1800
ITSUŌ MUSEUM, Osaka

This painting (with its pair, which is of a peacock on a rock) is in Goshun's late style which was very much influenced by the work of Ōkyo. The contrast of finely washed water, the naturalistic and gleaming carp and the rugged pine-bough done in calligraphic ink-strokes is a synthesis of styles such as Ōkyo favoured. There is, however, a delicacy of atmosphere which comes from Goshun's more poetic temperament. This is only to be expected from a man who was an important *haiku* poet and the pupil of Buson, who was considered second only to Bashō in *haiku* verse.

MATSUMURA GOSHUN (1752–1811)

52 *Hibiscus and blue heron on a tree-stump*

S/G8 絹本著色木芙蓉鳰鶍図　呉春筆

[repr. in colour on p. 175]
Ink and light colours on silk
s. *Kure no kōri Goshun* ('Goshun from the district of Kure');
sealed *Hakubō*
Hanging scroll, 126 × 60 cm
d. ninth month of 1782
KUROKAWA KOBUNKA KENKYŪSHO, Hyōgo

Goshun's closeness to his master Buson is extremely clear in this very poetic summer scene. The long, rounded strokes of the rock are a feature of Buson's work derived from Chinese scholar painting. The use of pale washes to suggest atmosphere and vegetation blown by the wind also recalls Buson, but there is a poetic clarity and softness which are Goshun's individual contribution. The painting suggests the sort of moment in nature which inspired a *haiku* poem, a form of verse in which Goshun was a leading figure.

MARUYAMA ŌKYO (1733–1795)

53 *Fire and flood*

F/G8 紙本淡彩七難図画稿　円山応挙筆

Ink on paper
Hand scroll, 31.2 × 1541 cm
1768
EMMAN'IN, Shiga
Important Cultural Property

These are sketches for the set of coloured hand scrolls known as *Shichifuku shichinan* ('Seven happinesses and seven disasters') which are among the greatest treasures of the Emman'in. Ōkyo had a special association with Prince Yūjō, who was hereditary abbot of the temple and with whom he shared an interest in the theory of painting. The finished works made Ōkyo's reputation, but the best of the ink sketches made as preliminaries are perhaps even finer in their dashing sense of movement and their virtuosity with the brush. In them Ōkyo shows himself perhaps unexpectedly as one of Japan's greatest ink painters. The disastrous side of life, as perhaps to be expected in a country subject to earthquake, fire and typhoon, seems to have captured his imagination more and these sketches underline the fragile nature of the apparently stable world in which artists like Ōkyo could flourish.

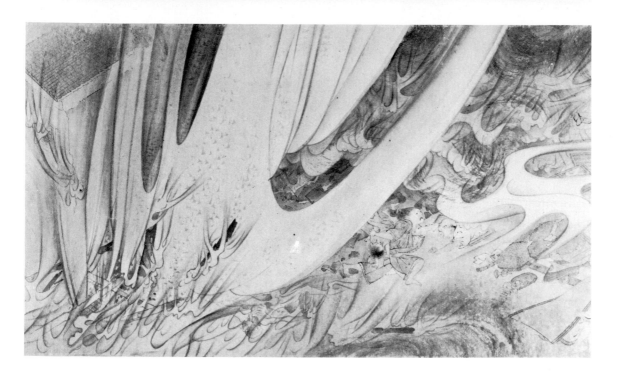

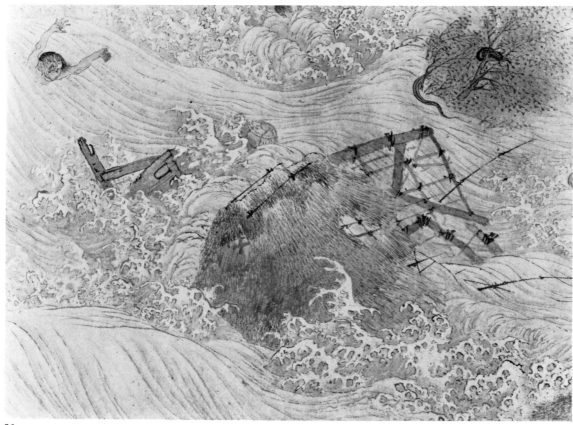

53

NAGASAWA ROSETSU (1754–1799)

54 *Birds, plants and fish*

S/G8 絹本著色花鳥遊魚図　長沢芦雪筆

[details repr. in colour on p. 178]
Ink and colours on silk
Hand scroll, 37 × 1130 cm
c. 1790
YASUDA NAKAZŌ, Hiroshima
Important Art Object

Painted in his late years for a family in the Hiroshima area he so loved, this scroll expresses both Rosetsu's skill and his poetry. The section with red maples floating across the moon is one of the most lyrical moments in Japanese painting, while the sparrows have all the sharp vivacity which distinguishes his hand from any copyists, each bird quite different in expression and character from every other one. Every part of this wonderful work is filled with Rosetsu's love of the natural world and his sympathy for all living creatures. The supreme skill of his technique seems to be

55

put entirely at the service of this passion. The clarity and
sharpness of the scroll images, most of them laid down on a plain
silk ground, is unwavering. The artist shows himself a subtle
colourist, throughout blending one pigment almost unnoticed
into the next, or shading a passage in ink with an imperceptible
touch of green or red. Unlike the toad (no. 49), this scroll must
have taken weeks or even months to plan and carry out.

KAWAHARA KEIGA (*fl.* early 19th century)

55 *Views of the Chinese and Dutch settlements
at Nagasaki*

FS/G8 紙本著色唐蘭館内図　川原慶賀筆

Ink and colours on paper
Pair of hand scrolls, *h* 22 cm
c. 1810
NAGASAKI MUNICIPAL MUSEUM
Important Art Object

Little is known of Keiga as a person, but he is known to have got permission to live and work in Nagasaki where he associated with the foreigners confined to that city and apparently made a good living from his detailed paintings of them and their activities. There was an inexhaustible demand in isolationist Japan for information about the outside world, but more particularly about the Europeans, whose increasing technological and military strength was becoming a source of real worry to thinking Japanese. Keiga indeed provided some illustrations for Franz von Siebold for his book on Japan which indirectly increased outside pressure on that country. He is also known to have fabricated works by Hokusai which Siebold took back to Holland. Although his work is influenced by European methods the scene is still viewed from high above the foreground in the traditional Japanese manner.

56h

56e

56g

MARUYAMA ŌKYO (1733–1795)

56 *Views of Kyoto in perspective style*

FS/G8 紙本版画著色眼鏡絵　円山応挙筆

Wood-block prints with hand-colouring, on paper
Each print 24 × 36 cm
c. 1760
YABUMOTO KŌZŌ, Hyōgo

After training with the Kanō artist Yūtei (1721–1786) the young Ōkyo worked for a Kyoto toy dealer called Nakajima Kambei, who sold the *nozoki karakuri*. This was a peep-show device, originally imported from Holland to Nagasaki, into which views done in strict perspective were fitted. When these were seen through the glass viewers of the machine, a three-

56f

dimensional effect was achieved. They were called *megane-e* ('pictures seen with spectacles'). Kambei got Ōkyo to use his artistic skill to devise new views for the machine. A fairly large number have survived, some of Chinese views copied from Suchow prints (themselves very westernised) and some of views around Kyoto. The latter are of higher quality, since Ōkyo was handling very familiar subjects.

The prints are done in wood-block, but they copy some western engraving devices such as the use of thick parallel lines to express recession or the surface of water, and cross-hatching for light and shadow. Since a *megane-e* had to be done in reverse image in order to be seen correctly in the machine, the blocks must have been cut with the design pasted down facing upwards (instead of downwards as with standard wood-block prints). They made exaggerated use of recession to a vanishing point in classic western style, since this aided the illusion given by the machine. Hand-colouring was added, on the whole of high quality, possibly done by Ōkyo himself or under his direction.

The effect of designing these prints was to awaken Ōkyo's interest in western art, and the influence, in modified form, on his later work was considerable (see particularly his *Waterfall*, no. 45, and *Pines in the snow*, no. 70).

a] *Archery contest at the Sanjūsangendō*

[repr. in colour on p. 176]

This famous building, known as 'The Hall of the Thirty-three Bays', is over 100 metres long and remains one of the great sights of Kyoto. It houses a thousand life-size images of the Bodhisattva Kannon. Its great length made it a natural subject for perspective. The *engawa* (verandah) was used for an annual archery contest lasting twenty-four hours.

b] *Summer night by the Kamo river at Shijō*
[repr. in colour on p. 176]

In late summer parts of the Kamo would dry up and booths for entertainment would be set up there. In the hot weather the night became the most popular time to visit the fair, and this is the scene Ōkyo has portrayed. He in fact lived very near, in Shijō street. The riverside restaurants and the hills surrounding the city are clearly visible. The use of a dark night sky and of figures silhouetted crossing the bridge are very westernised, and the print is quite untypical of standard Japanese art of the period.

c] *Shijō street by day*
[repr. in colour on p. 177]

The main street of Kyoto is seen looking east to the nearby hills beyond Gion. This was Ōkyo's own district. The writing on the shops is all reversed (see above).

d] *The Kiyomizu temple*
[repr. in colour on p. 177]

This famous temple on the eastern hills is built on stilts, which can be seen to the right. From them there is a splendid view across Kyoto to the western hills. Ōkyo has rather exaggerated the distance, and filled the valley with parallel lines which in a western engraving would represent water, but which he seems to have intended as low-lying mist.

e] *The Golden Pavilion (Kinkakuji)*

The three-storeyed pavilion covered with gold leaf in the north-west of Kyoto was and is its most famous landmark. Ōkyo has greatly magnified the lake and the openness of the scenery.

f] *Village in the hills near Kyoto*

This is probably a view of the Hozu river gorge, which Ōkyo knew well since he would have had to travel along it from his native village to Kyoto. The wild nature of the almost unin-habited hills near Kyoto is well conveyed.

g] *The bridge at Uji*

Uji, on the Uji river a few kilometres east of Kyoto, was always thought a most romantic and picturesque town. It is at the head of a gorge, and there stood in the Edo period a very scenic temple on an island in the middle of the fast-flowing waters. To capture the grandeur of the scene, Ōkyo has used the very high point of view traditional in Far Eastern painting.

h] *The torii of the Kamo Shrine*

At the right can be seen refreshment stalls for visitors. The shrine was the scene of the horse-race festivals. The artist has used a very western style of composition, drawing the viewer in towards the gate as if he were on the level of the actual visitors, whose shadows are depicted in a further concession to European effects.

NAGASAWA ROSETSU (1754-1799)

57 *Bounding tiger*

FS/G9   紙本墨画虎図   長沢芦雪筆

Ink on paper
s. *Hei Hyōkei sha* ('copied by Hyōkei of Kyoto'); sealed *Gyo*
Set of six sliding doors, four measuring 184 × 116 cm and two measuring 180 × 87 cm
1787
MURYŌJI, Wakayama
Important Cultural Property

Rosetsu was the most naturally talented of all Japanese *suiboku* artists, and this painting has claims to be his finest work, full of vigour and originality. This set of doors and a companion set of a dragon were painted for the *shoin* of the Muryōji on the artist's journey to the Kii peninsula in 1787. On this trip he did splendid paintings in a number of Zen temples. There is no precedent for Rosetsu's tiger. It bears little resemblance either to traditional images derived from Chinese paintings (see nos 13, 14) or to any real tiger which the artist might have conceivably seen in a private zoo (for tigers are known to have been imported from China in the Edo period). Rather it is a creature of Rosetsu's joyous imagination, which seemed to take over his hand when he grasped the brush loaded with ink of which he was a natural master. His sympathy with animals and birds is obvious from all his works, and here he seems to have converted into huge size and power the playful ferocity of a domestic kitten. With an audacity which is typical of this artist, he has reserved for the last door on the left the tips of the tiger's whiskers. The rocks on the right-hand two screens are fine examples of his dynamic brushwork in the landscape elements of paintings.

57 (detail)

58   left-hand screen

59   left-hand screen

YOSA BUSON (1716–1783)

58 Scholars riding and walking in the country

F/G10 紙本淡彩山野行楽図　与謝蕪村筆

[detail repr. in colour on p. 180]
Ink and light colours on paper
s. *Sa Shunsei sha* ('copied by (Yo)sa Shunsei') and sealed
Pair of six-fold screens, each 154 × 356 cm
c. 1770–1780
TOKYO NATIONAL MUSEUM
Important Cultural Property

Chinese scholars were thought of as always enjoying themselves. Buson has shown two parties of them – on the right riding out to enjoy the moonlight, on the left staggering home, with much help from their attendants, after a drinking-bout. In both cases the scenery is very Japanese. In the moonlit scene, Buson has indulged his love for moving foliage, expressed in flexible brushstrokes over wash. On the left, he has depicted a more rugged scene with long, curving strokes like hemp-fibres which he had copied from Chinese models and greatly exaggerated. The figures are in the comic, abbreviated *haiga* style, a type of quick sketching used to illustrate *haiku* poems, of which Buson was a master. Indeed, he is considered second only to Bashō (1644–1699) as a *haiku* poet.

58   right-hand screen

59   right-hand screen

YOSA BUSON (1716–1783)

59 *Country cottage in a bamboo grove, and riding back along the willow-shaded lane*

S/G10 紙本著色竹林茅屋柳蔭騎路図　与謝蕪村筆

[left-hand screen repr. in colour on pp. 180–1]
Ink and light colours on paper, with one gold-leaf panel on each
s. (a) *Sha Buson*, (b) *Shain*; sealed
Pair of six-fold screens,
each 134 × 309 cm
c. 1777–1783
YABUMOTO KŌZŌ, Hyōgo
Important Cultural Property

Although these scenes are peopled with Chinese scholars, the lyrical, quiet spring landscapes are entirely Japanese. The paintings are in fact vehicles for Buson to express his deep love of the spring-time greenery of his native land. For him, technique was more a means to an expressive end than the end in itself which it was for most *Nanga* artists. In both screens he gives structure by means of a linking path and bridge, but the real interest lies in the delicate handling of foliage, which he expresses with dots and short strokes in many different shades of colour over washes of pale green and yellow. This almost *pointilliste* technique was derived from conventions used in wood-block print copies of Chinese paintings, but Buson developed it (in common with his contemporary Taiga) into a style of its own. The fresh colours are set off by the darker gold-leaf panel which Buson has boldly added to each screen, and on each of which he has written in his own calligraphy a Chinese poem of the Tang dynasty.

93

60

Anonymous

60 *Okuni's Kabuki performance*

F/LR 紙本金地著色阿国歌舞伎図

Ink and colours over gold leaf on paper
Six-fold screen, 148 × 357 cm
Early 17th century

YAMAMOTO COLLECTION, Hyōgo
Important Cultural Property

The scene is a shrine, perhaps the Kitano shrine in Kyoto. Okuni is seen performing her entertainment of song and dance (*Kabuki*). Around the stage sit spectators of the samurai class with picnic boxes and refreshments. Other spectators can be seen in special booths. The freshness of the figures and the overall organisation of the composition point to a very competent artist of the Kanō school. The variety is given by adding blue clouds to the conventional gold ones which link parts of the composition. Okuni was a Shintō priestess whose performances of a somewhat suggestive nature became immensely popular. They are considered the beginning of the *Kabuki* theatre.

Anonymous

61 *A dance celebrating the New Year*

S/LR 紙本金地著色正月風俗図

Ink and colours over gold leaf on paper
Six-fold screen, 82 × 275 cm
17th century

SUNTORY ART MUSEUM, Tokyo

The New Year was the greatest festival in Japan and was celebrated over a period of at least a week. In this scene a group of women are performing a dance. They stand in a circle in the usual formation for group dances. Within the circle a group of less disciplined entertainers are cavorting. In the large building on the left various amusements are being pursued. Screens of popular subjects like these had a great vogue in the seventeenth century, but declined in the eighteenth. Their place seems to have been gradually taken over by the popular wood-block prints of the *Ukiyo-e* school.

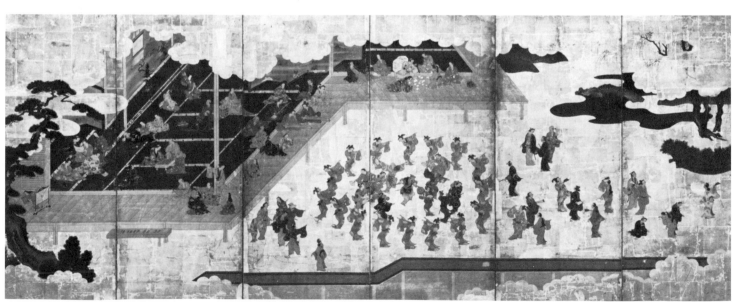

61

left-hand screen

62

right-hand screen

Anonymous

62 *Kabuki performed by young men, and women's amusements*

F/LR 紙本金地著色 野郎歌舞伎図
婦女子遊楽図

Ink and colours on paper with gold leaf
Pair of six-fold screens, each 155 × 343 cm
Second quarter of 17th century
ŌTSUGA YOSHIMITSU, Toyama
Important Cultural Property

In 1629 Okuni's *Kabuki* performances (*cf.* no. 60) and similar ones by Kyoto prostitutes were banned by the government and for a while the entertainment was carried on by young men (*wakashu*) dressed as women. One of their performances is shown in this unique screen. It takes places at a shrine in spring-time. The young men's *Kabuki* was in turn suppressed in 1652, and the emerging popular drama was taken over by more mature men who have carried it on ever since. The companion screen shows women of the same time walking in the streets and enjoying various relaxations, such as playing *go*. They show the comparative social freedom which women enjoyed in Edo period Japan.

left-hand screen

63   right-hand screen

Anonymous

63 *Women's amusements*

S/LR   紙本金地著色婦女子遊楽図

Ink and colours over gold leaf on paper
Pair of six-fold screens, 125 × 278 cm
17th century
SUNTORY ART MUSEUM, Tokyo

These screens have a strong element of fantasy about them. They are peopled entirely by women enjoying themselves in a series of idyllic and rather improbable buildings set around waterways. The feeling of unreality is emphasized by the very extensive gold-leaf clouds which obscure much of the screens. However, the variety of amusements and entertainments open to women in the large towns in the Edo period was large and their way of life compared favourably with that of women in most Asian countries at that time.

KATSUKAWA SHUNSHŌ (1726–1792)

64 *Snow, moonlight and flowers*

F/LR   絹本著色雪月花図　勝川春章筆

[repr. in colour on pp. 183, 184, 185]
Ink and colours on silk
Three hanging scrolls, 92.5 × 32 cm
After 1780
KYŪSEI ATAMI ART MUSEUM, Shizuoka
Important Cultural Property

Of all the artists of the *Ukiyo-e* school who became well known for their wood-block prints, Shunshō is the most skilful as a painter. In his paintings he specialised in subjects of beautiful women in elegant surroundings, although as a print designer he had been best known for his powerful portraits of *Kabuki* actors. He turned to painting late in his life, and these works date probably after 1780. They illustrate the classic poetic triad of snow, moon and flowers put into easily understood contemporary terms.

HOSODA EISHI (1756–1829)

64a   *Heads of nine beauties in a roundel with plum-blossom*

F/LR   絹本著色円窓九美人図　細田榮之筆

[repr. in colour on p. 182]
Ink and colours on silk
Hanging scroll, 87.3 × 34.5 cm
KYŪSEI ATAMI ART MUSEUM, Shizuoka

Like Shunshō, Eishi gave up a successful career as a print artist to concentrate on paintings. In his case there seems to have been some disillusionment with the declining standards of taste of the print medium, at least in the *Ukiyo-e* school, after around 1800. In his prints he had always tried to raise standards of elegance and subtlety and he clearly found this impossible to maintain except in paintings. This very elegant work uses the device of the round window, of which he was particularly fond. The plum-blossom bough suggests the youthful freshness of the fashionable women depicted and no doubt reflects the time of year when the painting was done. The woman with long hair is a poetess of the classic type. The others are Eishi's contemporaries.

KATSUKAWA SHUNSHŌ (1726–1792)

64b   *Entertainers at the riverside, a courtesan with her apprentice, and seven beauties in a bamboo grove*

S/LR   絹本著色 吾妻風流図 竹林七妍図　勝川春章筆

Ink and colours on silk
Three hanging scrolls, 94.5 × 34.8 cm
After 1780
TOKYO NATIONAL UNIVERSITY OF FINE ARTS

In these works Shunshō depicts two subjects which appear frequently in wood-block prints, although he himself rarely did prints on such themes. On the left two entertainers are apparently leaving a tea house or house of entertainment or restaurant on the banks of the Sumida River. They are seen walking on to the boat landing. One of them is carrying a box which holds her *shamisen*, a three-stringed instrument used by most entertainers by the eighteenth century. On the right a courtesan of the first rank accompanied by her *kumuro* (apprentice) is seen parading at blossom-time in the height of

64   64   64

64b

64b

fashion. The third subject is more of a semi-literary fantasy and may be compared with his *Snow, moonlight and flowers* (no. 64). He has taken the traditional Chinese motif of the Seven Sages in the Bamboo Grove and peopled it with contemporary beauties. Apart from the lady reading a love letter there seems to be no strong literary interest. The work is simply a charming joke for a connoisseur.

KATSUSHIKA HOKUSAI (1760–1849)

64c *The beauty Yotaka*

S/LR 紙本著色美人図　葛飾北斎筆

Ink and colours on paper
s. *Hokusai Sōri ga* ('painted by Hokusai Sōri') and sealed
Hanging scroll, 101 × 28.6 cm
c. 1800
HOSOMI MINORU, Osaka

64b

Hokusai is not best known for his paintings or prints of *bijin* (beautiful women) though he produced a number of fine works in the free, undetailed style seen in this example. It shows a famous beauty of the day parading on a wet evening. Her head is covered and she carries folded a waxed paper umbrella. She wears *geta* (high wooden shoes) to protect her from the wet ground. Two bats high up by the willow bough show it is evening. The liquid brushwork of the descending willow-branch gives the sense of dampness. Hokusai paints with his usual economy of means.

64c

Anonymous

65 *The dog-chasing event*

F/LR 紙本金地著色犬追物図

Ink and colours over gold leaf on paper
Pair of six-fold screens, each 152 × 349 cm
Second quarter of 17th century
TOKIWAYAMA BUNKO, Kanagawa
Important Cultural Property

Dog-chasing (*inu-ou mono*) was a samurai sport developed in the mediaeval period to improve the standards of archery of mounted warriors. The objective, basically, was to hit a dog let loose in a fenced enclosure with blunted arrows shot by a group of mounted contestants. It was suppressed in the Muromachi period but revived in the early Edo period, perhaps as a means of encouraging martial skills in peace-time. Screens depicting this event survive in moderate numbers from the seventeenth century and must have been very popular. The early ones, of which this is the earliest and finest, always have a division into two aspects. On the right is the parade of contestants, who ride in a circle round the dog and his handler. Other contestants stand and wait their turn. On the left, the contest is shown in progress. In this version the spectators are not numerous, being restricted to people of samurai class. These screens have been attributed to Kanō Sanraku. While the case is not proved, they must certainly have been painted by an artist well used to organising large-scale compositions and also a master of human figures and horses in movement.

left-hand screen

right-hand screen

left-hand screen

66

right-hand screen

Anonymous

66 *The dog-chasing event*

S/LR 紙本金地著色犬追物図

Ink and colours over gold leaf on paper
Pair of six-fold screens, each 130 × 353 cm
Mid 17th century
HOSOMI MINORU, Osaka
Important Art Object

For dog-chasing see the preceding. In this version, the two parts are, rather strangely, almost mirror-images of the enclosure. One shows the scene before the event, with dog-handler and samurai milling about in a great crowd. The other shows the event in progress. There are far more spectators than in the earlier screens, divided into samurai and the commoner people. This probably records the revival of the event in Edo in 1646 and after, when it became a great spectator sport.

HISHIKAWA MORONOBU (d. 1694)

67 *Scenes in the Yoshiwara*

FS/LR 紙本著色吉原風俗図　菱川師宣筆

Ink and colours on silk
Hand scroll, 53.6 × 1756 cm
c. 1680–1690
PRIVATE COLLECTION, Japan

The Yoshiwara in the Asakusa area of Edo was the district licensed by the Tokugawa government for prostitution. It was isolated on low-lying ground and had to be reached by a road along a dyke. Yet it became the centre of the city's social life. Within it the great establishments became centres of entertainment, gastronomy and social meeting as well as providing a sexual and even romantic outlet for men confined in a rigid family system with early arranged marriages. Many artists made paintings and prints of Yoshiwara activities (see no. 100). Of these Moronobu is the first whose name is widely known. Originally a textile designer, he became perhaps the first important *Ukiyo-e* artist in the city where that school of painting was to reach its greatest heights. This long scroll shows the artist's early familiarity with the licensed district.

101

MIYAGAWA CHŌSHUN (1683–1753)

68 *Scenes of popular entertainment*

F/LR 紙本著色風俗図　宮川長春筆

Ink and colours on paper
s. *Nihon-e Miyagawa Chōshun hitsu* ('by the brush of Miyagawa
Chōshun, the Japanese artist')
Hand scroll, 37 × 388 cm
c. 1720
TOKYO NATIONAL MUSEUM

Chōshun is perhaps the best of the *Ukiyo-e* painters who never designed for prints. His work has great freshness and he uses pigments of the highest quality. He represents the rise in standards of elegance and quality of life of the townsmen of Edo which is such a feature of the second half of the Edo period. His signature on this work points to his pride in the Japanese quality of his work and amounts to a protest against the supposed Chineseness of the ever more numerous and dominant official Kanō painters. In this famous work, which is one of the masterpieces of *Ukiyo-e*, he depicts the world of popular entertainers working in private houses and for small gatherings, including private semi-theatrical performances. Chōshun seems to have had little interest in the more public world of theatres, streets and restaurants and popular spectacles.

SUMIYOSHI GUKEI (1631–1705)

69 *Scenes of popular life in and around Nara*

S/LR 紙本著色都鄙図巻　住吉具慶筆

Ink and colours on paper
Hand scroll, 33.3 × 1273 cm
KOMBUIN, Nara

Although Nara ceased to be the capital of Japan in AD 784, and all its great temples had been founded by that date, it is a misconception that the town was in a state of decayed historical gentility after its great days. It was in fact a centre of vigorous popular culture. Gukei, who was son of Jokei, founder of the Sumiyoshi school, which took the Tosa style into a new life at Edo, nevertheless knew enough about Nara to be entranced by its life. In this delightful hand scroll he has produced a detailed and jewel-like account of the street life of the late seventeenth century. Its style, racy in detail, owes much more to the spirit of a new age than to the models of the past.

MARUYAMA ŌKYO (1733–1795)

70 *Pines in the snow*

F/G9 紙本墨画雪松図　円山応挙筆

[repr. in colour on pp. 186–7]
Ink and gold wash with some gold leaf on paper
s. *Ōkyo sha* ('copied by Ōkyo'); sealed *Ōkyo no in* ('Ōkyo's seal') and *Chūsen*
Pair of six-fold screens, each 156 × 362 cm
c. 1780
MITSUI HACHIRŌEMON, Tokyo
National Treasure

These famous works are Ōkyo's masterpieces. With the use of only ink-strokes and gold wash, and with a little flecking of gold leaf, he has caught a sense of space and atmosphere as the sun gleams at dawn or evening on the snow. The low, rather startling point of view of the onlooker seems to derive from western ideas, but the brushwork is the result of the artist's study of Chinese Ming models, while the format of the screen and the use of gold are very Japanese. The work is thus a typical putting together of styles by this great synthesizer. The right-hand screen represents the strong 'male' element, the left the more passive 'female'. These paintings are the culmination of Ōkyo's power as the last great decorator in the Momoyama tradition.

69

69

MARUYAMA ŌKYO (1733–1795)

71 *Wistaria in blossom*

S/G9 紙本金地著色藤花図　円山応挙筆

Ink and colours over gold leaf on paper
s. *Ōkyo*; sealed *Ōkyo no in* ('Ōkyo's seal') and *Chūsen*
Pair of six-fold screens, each 156 × 360 cm
d. autumn 1776
NEZU ART MUSEUM, Tokyo
Important Cultural Property

The wistaria screens are among the most original of Japanese paintings in this format. Their design is triumphantly simple and new. The twisting boughs of the creeper are starkly laid on the gold-leaf ground with no reference to the trellised arbour which would have had to hold them up in reality. On the left is the gentle, insinuating 'female' plant, on the right the more thrusting 'male' wistaria. This duality is deeply engrained in the popular philosophy of Japan, and is derived from Chinese ideas. Ōkyo has created a vivid contrast of two styles, one 'artistic' the other 'realistic', and he probably got this notion from the work of Shikō (no. 33), whom he so admired. Here the contrast is between the twisting, calligraphic line of the boughs, which are done in a wash of black ink through which the gold shines, and the brilliant, thick pigments of the leaves and blossoms laid on top. The blooms are delicately detailed and gleam out brilliantly from the subdued gold. Ōkyo was no calligrapher, but in the subtle lines of the boughs he has expressed his personality in the way that calligraphy was supposed to do. He has especially made use of the technique of loading the brush with unequal strengths of ink, so that one edge of the line is dark and the other light, with many variations between.

left-hand screen

right-hand screen

RYŪ RIKYŌ (1706–1758)

72 Bamboo

F/GIO 絹本著色彩竹図 柳里恭筆

[repr. in colour on p. 190]
Green pigment on dark blue ground; signature in gold; on silk
s. *Kien shai* ('the essential idea rendered by Kien'); two seals,
one *Kōbi*
Hanging scroll, 94.5 × 25.7 cm
c. 1740–1750
PRIVATE COLLECTION, Japan

The artist is often known in the west by the name Yanagisawa
Kien, but the more 'Chinese' adopted name of Ryū Rikyō is
preferred in Japan and seems more appropriate to this pioneer of
the revival of interest in Chinese scholar painting, which he
introduced to the Edo area. He was more of an intellectual and
connoisseur than a painter; most of his works are rather stiff and
academic, except for his finger-paintings of bamboo, for which he
was famous. He taught this technique to Taiga (no. 76). This
painting, however, is done with the brush and is his most
successful work. Although it is a fine calligraphic exercise in
bamboo, the first of the 'Four Noble Plants' favoured by Chinese
scholar painters, its success derives from its closeness to the
Japanese tradition of decorated paper. It is painted in a lightened
malachite pigment on a ground of *kon* (a deep blue). The
signature in gold and the seals in red complete a pattern of simple
beauty, like the painted end-papers of hand scrolls which it so
much resembles.

GION NANKAI (1677–1751)

73 Plum-bough in blossom

S/GIO 紙本墨画梅図 祇園南海筆

Ink on paper
s. *Genyu shiga hei rei* ('Genyu composed the poem, painted the
picture and did the clerical script')
Hanging scroll, 96.2 × 52.6 cm
1740–1750
PRIVATE COLLECTION, Japan

Nankai was a Confucianist from Wakayama in Kii province, one
of the centres of Tokugawa loyalty. He was a pioneer of the
Nanga school of painting, which he learned mainly from wood-
block books imported from China. In this restrained work he has
come close to understanding the calligraphic nature of Chinese
ink-painting of the 'Four Noble Plants' – plum, bamboo, orchid
and chrysanthemum. The painting is a landmark in the change
of sensibility away from native aesthetic ideas in the mid-
eighteenth century, for although the flowering plum had always
been a symbol of early spring in Japan, its depiction in art had
usually been more poetic and colourful than its serious treatment
in China.

IKENO TAIGA (1723–1776)

74 The Eight Views of the Xiao-xiang Rivers, with accompanying calligraphy

FS/GIO 紙本墨画瀟湘八景図 池大雅筆

Ink on paper
Various signatures and seals, including *Kyūka Sanshō*
Folding fan paintings, 20 × 52.5 cm
PRIVATE COLLECTION, Japan

73

These works seem never to have been used as fans, and are now
mounted as double album sheets with a painting backed to a
poem. They clearly belong to Taiga's last period, but they are not
dated. Each painting refers to one of the traditional Eight Views
(no. 15), but in a very abbreviated style, close to the *haiga*
paintings done to accompany *haiku* verses. The poems, however,
are Chinese, and in each of them Taiga imitated (or rather
recreated in his own imaginative way) the calligraphy of a
Chinese master. The paintings are entirely original and show
Taiga's complete mastery of brush and ink. The 'lingering snow
over sky and river', for example, consists of only five ink-strokes
done in *katabokashi*, a technique of loading the brush with ink of

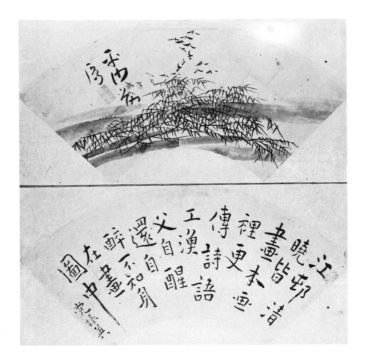

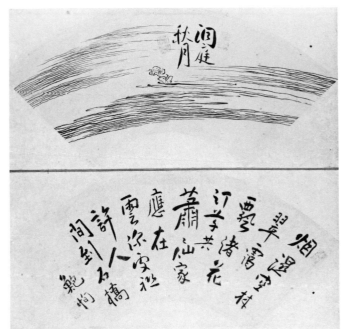

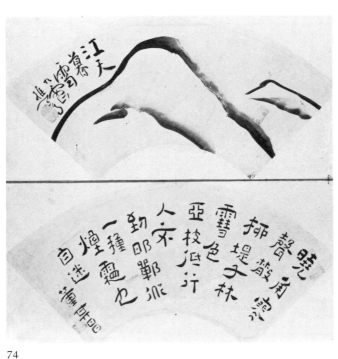

74

unequal strength; all the sky and the river are themselves omitted and merely suggested by two peaks. In the delightful 'Autumn moon on Lake Dongting' a fisherman plays his flute standing on a boat which is scarcely differentiated from the ripples of water. The waves of sound and of water seem to merge, and there is no need to paint the moon at all. In all of the paintings Taiga exploits the tension between the curve of the fan and the straighter lines of the horizon.

IKENO TAIGA (1723–1776)

75 Landscapes in the four seasons in Chinese styles

FS/G10 紙本著色四季山水図　池大雅筆

Ink and colours on paper
Each s. *Mumei*, with two seals
Set of four hanging scrolls, each 19.1 × 24.6 cm
c. 1753
PRIVATE COLLECTION, Japan

Four different Chinese scenes each represent one of the seasons, and each is done in a different Chinese style. All are painted with

75c

75d

76

an almost naive simplicity of construction and line which
suggests that Taiga copied his ideas from wood-block books
illustrating Chinese painting methods. Such books had been
allowed into Japan since 1720 and had been a major impetus to
the founding of the *Nanga* school. In spite of their apparent
crudity, Taiga has filled these little paintings with a poetry which
is all his own and resembles very little the cool rationalism of the
real Chinese paintings which he probably never saw. Taiga,
although eccentric, was typically Japanese in his ability to create
something exciting and new out of borrowed and only partly
understood ideas. The subjects are:

a] Spring. A scholar sits in a pavilion overlooking a lake.
[repr. in colour on p. 188]

b] Summer. Verdant hills in the foreground and, beyond, a
distant village under mountains.
[repr. in colour on p. 188]

c] Autumn. Scholars set out in a boat under willows for a
moon-viewing expedition.

d] Winter. Pavilions nestle almost invisible among jagged,
snowy peaks above the cloud-line.

IKENO TAIGA (1723–1776)

76 *A nightingale on a plum-bough*

F/G10 紙本墨画淡彩梅花黄鳥図　池大雅筆

Ink and light colours on paper; finger-painting
s. *Kyūka Tsutomu shiboku* ('by Kyūka Tsutomu with fingers and
ink') and sealed
Hanging scroll, 111 × 55 cm
c. 1740
PRIVATE COLLECTION, Japan

The young Taiga made his name when he visited Edo by his
ability to paint with his fingers, fingernails and hands. This
technique (*shitōga*) was one of the accomplishments of Chinese
scholars, and Taiga learned it from Kien (see no. 72). In spite of
its limitations, he has produced a painting of a lyricism and
sensitivity which excel the brush-painting of a plum-bough by
his senior Gion Nankai (no. 73). The sharpness of the plum-
blossoms and of the thinner twigs is astonishing.

IKENO TAIGA (1723–1776)

77 *Dragon of the storm*

S/GIO 紙本著色起龍図　池大雅筆

Ink and light colours on paper
s. *Ike Tsutomu*; two seals
Hanging scroll, 148 × 41 cm
d. 1746, 'at the *Raishōkan*'
PRIVATE COLLECTION, Japan

This youthful work by the exuberant Taiga is an exercise in agitated brushwork and in the 'piled up' method of composition favoured by many Chinese artists. At the bottom a bridge over a river gorge leads to a group of houses built precariously on rocks. From a window a scholar looks out at the storm raging above. The dragon itself, often associated in Japan with storms over Mount Fuji, is painted so small that it is almost invisible, a typical Taiga joke. All the elements in the painting would be easily understood by those interested in Chinese painting and ideas. Like most Nanga paintings, therefore, it is addressed to those who know and not to the general public.

URAGAMI GYOKUDŌ (1745–1820)

78 *Old man singing in the mountain*

F/GIO 紙本墨画山翁嘯咏図　浦上玉堂筆

Ink on paper
s. *Gyokudō*
Hanging scroll, 165 × 92 cm
c. 1810
PRIVATE COLLECTION, Japan
Important Art Object

77   78

Gyokudō was an extreme individualist. Most of his landscape paintings can be thought of as personal, expressing his own feelings rather than trying to record any sort of exterior reality. Thus the old man 'singing' in his hut is Gyokudō himself, the centre of a circling mass of foliage, mountains and rocks which seem in motion round him. Gyokudō was one of Japan's greatest composers on the *koto*, of which he was also a master player. The musical reference in the title is therefore not an accident. The

79

80

artist's interest, too, in the unorthodox and officially disapproved Wang Yangming school of Confucian philosophy gave him a powerful sense of the harmony of men, their activities and nature. This unity is achieved on paper by the use of brush and ink with no additional means of expression.

URAGAMI GYOKUDŌ (1745–1820)

79 *Sheer cliff in the deep forest*

S/G10 紙本著色深林絶壁図　浦上玉堂筆

Ink on paper
s. *Gyokudō kinshi* ('Gyokudō the koto master')
Hanging scroll, 177.5 × 64.8 cm
c. 1810
PRIVATE COLLECTION, Japan
Important Art Object

This great painting is an extreme example of the wild composition and excited brushwork of Gyokudō at his most inspired. According to contemporary accounts, the inspiration was often released by alcohol. A tiny figure in Chinese dress crosses a bridge over a rushing mountain stream at the bottom of the picture. He is moving towards a hut almost hidden in the welter of ink strokes of trees and rocks in the middle ground. Above them the cliff seems to dissolve into the sky. Strange, irrational shapes appear in the cliff. Gyokudō's vision is of a man alone in the mystery of the natural world, yet part of it. Like most of the artist's greatest paintings, this is on a large scale, for he felt the need to expand his painting surface as his excitement increased.

TANOMURA CHIKUDEN (1777–1835)

80 *Boating on the Inagawa river*

F/G10 紙本淡彩稲川舟遊図　田能村竹田筆

[detail repr. in colour on p. 189]
Ink and light colours on paper
s. *Chikuden Seiken* and sealed
Hanging scroll, 133 × 47 cm
d. 1829
KATAOKA COLLECTION, Yamaguchi
Important Cultural Property

The inscription records the events which led to the painting of this delightful work. Chikuden and Rai Sanyō (1780–1832), the calligrapher and poet, had been staying with a rich patron, a saké brewer, called Sakagami Tōin, whose house was by the Inagawa river at Itami. When Chikuden left by boat, his friends came to see him off. Chikuden himself may be the figure in the dress of a Chinese scholar pushing off his boat in the foreground. The construction of this painting is typical of the Nanga school in its fragmentation, consisting of exquisitely executed poetic vignettes. In the trees the artist uses dots and other strokes in very pale pigments which blend into a haze of misty colours.

OKADA HANKŌ (1782–1846)

81 *Rain in the deep mountains*

S/G10 絹本著色満山豊雨図　岡田半江筆

[repr. in colour on p. 191]
Ink and colours on silk
s. *Hankō Shuku ga* ('painted by Hankō Shuku') and sealed
Hanging scroll, 141 × 46.4 cm
d. autumn 1841
PRIVATE COLLECTION, Japan
Important Art Object

Hankō's reputation has risen in recent years. His finest works, of which this is one, combine a tightly-knit and carefully thought-out organisation of landscape elements with a soft, glowing, intensely poetic use of colour washes. Here these washes magically suggest the damp misty atmosphere of rain in the mountains in summer. The scene is of course meant to be Chinese, but Hankō, like every other Nanga artist until the late nineteenth century, was confined to his own country by the isolationist laws and what he paints is an ideal, dreamy world of happy scholars in an idyllic landscape.

TANI BUNCHŌ (1763–1840)

82 *Evening view of Matsushima*

F/G10 絹本墨画松島晩景図　谷文晁筆

Ink on dyed silk
s. *Bunchō*; sealed *Bunchō*
Hanging scroll, 42 × 125.4 cm
d. 1826
PRIVATE COLLECTION, Japan

The many islands of Matsushima near modern Sendai in north-east Honshu were one of the 'three great sights' of Japan. The other two were Ama no Hashidate ('the Bridge of Heaven') and the Itsukushima shrine. Bunchō has achieved a startlingly atmospheric account of the islands' receding into the sea with a most skilful use of graded ink. Bunchō, with Rosetsu, is one of the great masters of Japanese *suiboku* painting, although he was able to turn his hand to almost any style.

TANI BUNCHŌ (1763–1840)

83 *Landscape with a Chinese gentleman and his attendant crossing a bridge*

S/GIO 絹本著色寒林晩帰図 谷文晁筆

[repr. in colour on p. 193]
Ink and colours on silk
s. 'Bunchō at Shazanrō' (his studio) and sealed
Hanging scroll, 67.8 × 28 cm
d. 1793
TOKYO NATIONAL MUSEUM

In this fresh, early work, Bunchō, possibly the most diverse of all Japanese painters, has combined the structural methods of Chinese Song dynasty painting with a cheerful use of colour washes which is all his own. This work nicely illustrates the Japanese conception of the Chinese scholar, seen wandering in the lonely mountains accompanied by a boy who carries his *koto* on which he would stop to play as the fancy took him. The life of the Japanese so-called 'scholar painter' was very different. Without hereditary income, he would have to earn his living by teaching, by selling his paintings, or by being adopted by a rich patron of the merchant class. But it was not an unpleasant life and artists like Bunchō who led it enjoyed both freedom and prestige.

HAYASHI JIKKŌ (1777–1813)

84 *Dragonfly*

F/GIO 紙本墨画蜻蛉図 林十江筆

Ink on paper
s. *Chōu ga* ('painted by Chōu'); sealed *Jikkō*
Hanging scroll, 79 × 56.2 cm
HANAWA KŌSUKE, Ibaragi

84

This dashing ink painting is a rare example of a large-scale depiction of an insect. It is done with complete assurance. Jikkō was a Confucian scholar from Mito (in modern Ibaragi prefecture), a castle town and centre of a major branch of the Tokugawa family. He was a friend of Tani Bunchō, from whom he probably acquired his skill in *suiboku*. The best of his known paintings are of insects, fish, animals and mythical creatures.

HAYASHI JIKKŌ (1777–1813)

85 *Karasu Tengu*

S/GIO 紙本墨画烏天狗図 林十江筆

Ink on paper
s. *Jikkō*; sealed *Hayashi Chōu*
Hanging scroll, 116 × 51.5 cm
YAMAZAKI KINTARŌ, Ibaragi

The 'Crow Tengu' was a mythical bird-like creature of the woods and mountains. Though fierce of aspect, it was not considered particularly unfriendly. Jikkō has shown it in a storm which allows him to show his skill in ink-washes. He has spattered the whole painting with dots of ink to represent snow or hail.

AOKI MOKUBEI (1767–1833)

86 *Landscape in autumn*

F/GIO 紙本淡彩秋景山水図 青木木米筆

[repr. in colour on p. 192]
Ink and light colours on paper
s. Ryūbei
Hanging scroll, 105 × 27.9 cm
d. 1827
PRIVATE COLLECTION, Japan
Important Art Object

Mokubei was not a full-time artist and spent more of his later years in the study of the Chinese tea ceremony (*sencha*) and in making pottery for it (nos 227, 228). His works are few and highly prized in Japan for their individual flavour. His later paintings, though broadly based on landscapes by various Chinese artists, are very Japanese in their lack of rational composition. This example is typical. Like most of his landscapes it is tall and narrow. The elements of trees, rocks, river, waterfall and mountain peaks are a sort of shorthand pattern meant to recall the essence of landscape to the recipient of the painting. The unifying factor is the warm washes which Mokubei liked to blend with his ink and which give a poetic atmosphere.

AOKI MOKUBEI (1767–1833)

87 *Mount Penglai (Hōraizan)*

S/GIO 紙本淡彩蓬来山図 青木木米筆

Ink and colours on paper
s. *Kempitsu Mokubei* ('a presentation painting by Mokubei') and sealed
Hanging scroll, 138 × 29 cm
d. New Year 1811
SEIKADŌ BUNKO, Tokyo
Important Art Object

The mythical Happy Mountain of China is an appropriate present offering good wishes for the New Year. For this reason, perhaps, the pine trees which dominate the lower ground and which symbolize the New Year in Japan are given more prominence than in Mokubei's other paintings. Growing from the rock to the left of them is the *reishi*, the magical fungus, which is way out of proportion and confirms the symbolic nature of the work. In this

relatively early painting (for Mokubei took up the art late) he has not developed his typical use of warm colour washes, but the tall, narrow format and the distorted planes give a sense of reconstructed reality which is almost akin to Cubism.

85

87

88

89

UKITA IKKEI (1795–1859)

88 *The web of government*

F/G11　紙本著色蜘蛛巢図　浮田 ·恵筆

Ink and very light colours with gold washes on paper
s. *Gain seito Ka-i hitsu* ('painted by the student of the painting academy Ka-i'). Sealed *Ukita Ikkei*
Hanging scroll, 168 × 58.9 cm
KISHIMOTO KŌICHI, Hyōgo

Ikkei was a loyalist of the imperial family, whom he wished to see restored to political power. For his views he was imprisoned by the Tokugawa government. This seemingly innocent and delicate painting, done mostly in ink over gold washes, is a fierce satire on the shōgunate. The spider is the shōgun, the web his government, with helpless, delicate insects caught in it. The web overshadows the moon, which is a symbol of the emperor. Such a painting was as direct an expression of political opposition as the artist dared paint. Ikkei worked for the court, but he did not live to see the Restoration. However, his enthusiasm for the ancient courtly culture and painting of Japan was part of an intellectual movement which eventually removed the shōgunate.

WATANABE KAZAN (1793–1841)

89 *Portrait of Satō Issai*

S/GII 絹本著色佐藤 ·斎像 渡辺崋山筆

Ink and colours on silk
Sealed
Hanging scroll, 80.7 × 50.2 cm
d. 1821
KAWADA AKIRA, Saitama
Important Cultural Property

This is one of Kazan's finest portraits in the semi-western style he made his own. Although he studied European engravings, the shading and modelling of the faces is more powerful than followed from such sources, and he surely learned directly from the Ōbaku school how to achieve such effects in Japanese materials. The Ōbaku painters had had since the seventeenth century a tradition of portraying their priests in a Chinese/European style similar to Kazan's, but lacking his intensity.

Satō Issai (1772–1859) added his own inscription, dated 1824, when no doubt the two were mounted together. A very respectable Confucianist, he became head of both the bakufu official college and the Hayashi college of Confucianism. He nevertheless questioned much about Japan's future and was a secret adherent of the instinctive and colourful Wang Yangming school of Confucianism. Such a man naturally appealed to Kazan, who was deeply concerned about Japan's position in the world and who eventually committed suicide in prison where he was sent by the Tokugawa government.

WATANABE KAZAN (1793–1841)

90 *Five studies for the portrait of Satō Issai*

FS/GII 紙本墨画佐藤 ·斎像画稿 渡辺崋山筆

Ink on paper
Unsigned
Sketches now mounted as hanging scrolls, 39.4 × 19 cm
c. 1820–1821
PRIVATE COLLECTION, Japan

Kazan made a number of ink sketches for the portrait of Issai (no. 89) which show a lively perception of the differing moods of the man and which may get closer to his personality than the formal finished work. They also show the artist's extremely easy use of brush and ink to express subtleties of facial expression seldom attempted by artists of East Asia.

90

91

91

WATANABE KAZAN (1793–1841)

91 *Four studies for the Ukō kōmon*

FS/G11 紙本墨画于公高門図画稿　渡辺華山筆

Ink with pale washes of colour on paper
s. *Ukō kōmon zu Kazan Gaishi* (picture of the great gate of
Count Yu by Kazan the unofficial historian')
Mounted as four hanging scrolls, 132 × 50 cm
TOKYO NATIONAL MUSEUM

These are preliminary studies for a highly finished silk painting.
The story, briefly, is that Count Yu of the Chinese Han Dynasty,
sure that his military achievements would make his successors
wish to build a castle, decided to build himself a great gateway for
it. It was big enough for a four-horse carriage with a high roof.
Kazan's superficial reason for painting this scene was his interest
in all matters technical. But there is an underlying message in
the story. Kazan has worried about Japan's lack of preparedness
for the future, especially in coastal defences capable of keeping at

91

91

bay the advanced naval power of Europe and North America, and in Yu's foresight in planning for a big future he saw an example for his own country. These sketches have a freedom which is more attractive than the finished work. They are lightly washed in with pale colours in Kazan's most relaxed manner. The details of construction of the great roofed gate are described with enthusiasm and knowledge. The scaffolding of bamboo poles is still used on smaller buildings in the Far East.

REIZEI TAMECHIKA (1823–1864)

92 *Nenjū gyōji ('Events of the year at the imperial court')*

FS/GII 紙本著色年中行事図巻　冷泉為恭筆

Ink, colours and gold on paper
From a set of hand scrolls, 37.8 × 1154 cm
HOSOMI MINORU, Osaka
Important Art Object

Tamechika, a fervent supporter of the imperial house, adopted the attitudes of *Fukko Yamato-e* (revival of *Yamato-e* painting) from Tanaka Totsugen (1760–1823) and Ikkei (no. 88). He had to flee the wrath of the shōgunate and was eventually murdered in the troubles leading up to the Restoration. A passionate copyist of early courtly paintings, his great set of reinterpretations of mediaeval hand scrolls on court events is a monument to his skill and industry. They are unwavering in their attention to detail and the pigments are of the highest quality. In spite of his revivalist convictions, the scrolls are easily recognisable as of their true period in the mid-nineteenth century. The two scenes exhibited are (1) Nobles floating poems in cups down a stream, and (2) the New Year festival for exorcising demons. An archer is seen shooting a courtier in demon disguise.

92 (2)

92 (1)

118

Calligraphy

Calligraphy in Japan has never lost the status which it acquired when writing was first introduced into the country from China, where it was held to be the first of the arts. In China the square character, *kaishu*, was regarded as the most noble and difficult of execution, but alongside it from the start there existed more cursive forms of writing, of which the so-called 'grass character' was the most fluent and the most abstracted from the basic structures. When the writing was adopted in Japan means had to be found to express the multitudinous grammatical endings of the language, in addition to the roots of nouns and verbs, a problem which the nature of their language had spared the Chinese. So Japanese scribes, taking certain characters for their purely phonetic value, gradually simplified them in the spirit of the grass character, attaining a flexibility which had a particularly native flavour. This form of writing, known as *hiragana*, could be used either in conjunction with the fully formed substantive characters, or alone. The latter style was specially favoured for poetry and romances composed in a Japanese which owed little to imported Chinese vocabulary. The tension between *hiragana*, full characters written in similar fluent style, and fully formed characters has remained one of the expressive resources of Japanese calligraphers until the present day.

Comparatively few examples of calligraphy have been included in this exhibition, for much study and illustration is needed to afford any significant insight into the complexities and subtle allusiveness of the art. Some pieces shown illustrate the two extremes of style described above, and one piece represents the middle-of-the-road 'going hand' which was also popular in the Edo period. This is a pair of hanging scrolls by the Emperor Goyōzei, who was a great patron of arts and was contemporary with the three great calligraphers of the early seventeenth century. Two of these, Hon'ami Kōetsu and Konoe Nobutada, revived in a more dynamic form the *hiragana* calligraphy of the tenth- to twelfth-century Heian period (nos 24, 96, 96a). The third, Shōkadō, is much more individual and cannot be easily defined (no. 93). At the other extreme is the character calligraphy of the Zen priest Hakuin, whose apparently rough brushwork conceals considerable power (nos 97, 98). No Japanese calligrapher ever attained greatness in the classical square-character style of China. But Hakuin adapted it into something more Japanese and completely individual. Between these extremes of liquidity and square power fell many styles of writing. Most of them derived from China. The scholar painters of the eighteenth and nineteenth centuries made many attempts to follow these examples, with more or less success; but none of them can claim to be the equal of their models. Some examples of these attempts can be seen in the catalogue, for example, the Tang period poems written by Yosa Buson on his screens (nos 58, 59).

In the end the most attractive forms of Japanese calligraphy are in the *hiragana* style over decorated papers, a tradition going back to the Heian period. The scrolls of thirty-one-syllable poems known as *waka* written by Kōetsu over gold and silver designs by Sōtatsu (no. 24) are among the most beautiful of Japanese works of art.

The influence of calligraphy permeates all of Japanese art. As children learn to write they acquire the sense of balance and *mise en page* which is basic to all varieties of Japanese painting and design. Some feeling for the writing is important to any understanding of the art in general. A fine hand was formerly considered to be so important that it was difficult for anyone to be taken seriously if he did not possess one.

LRHS

SHŌJŌ SHOKADŌ (1584–1639)

93 *Poems of the Thirty-Six Poets (Sanjūrokkasen)*

FS/G3 松花堂昭乗筆三十六歌仙色紙帖

Ink over paper decorated with gold and silver
Folding album, each sheet 19.8 × 17.3 cm
TOKYO NATIONAL MUSEUM

The monk Shōkadō was one of the 'Three Great Brushes' of the early seventeenth century. Like the other two, Kōetsu and Nobutada, he returned to the *hiragana* calligraphy of earlier periods and aimed at an expressive liquidity of style. In this elegant album he has written over sheets elaborately prepared with silver and gold in the form of gold leaf and blown-on gold dust. The *Sanjūrokkasen* is a medieval anthology of thirty-six *waka* poems, each by a famous poet of earlier times. The verses were so familiar to educated Japanese that the point of any version lay in the calligraphy and in the decorative papers used.

94 *Texts for the Nō drama printed by movable type*

FS/G3 版本謡本（光悦本）

Ten volumes, Saga, *c.* 1605
24.1 × 18 cm
TOKYO NATIONAL MUSEUM

At a time when Japanese printing by wood-block was comparatively simple and just beginning to spread outside the Buddhist temples which had monopolized it. Kōetsu produced a number of magnificent art books at Takagamine and Saga in the

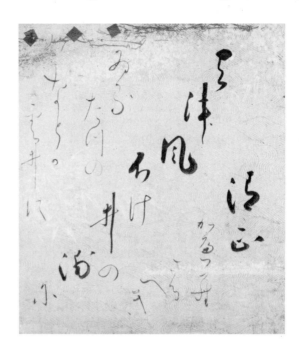

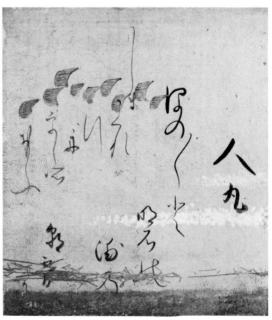

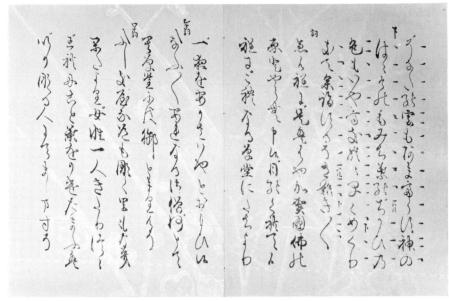

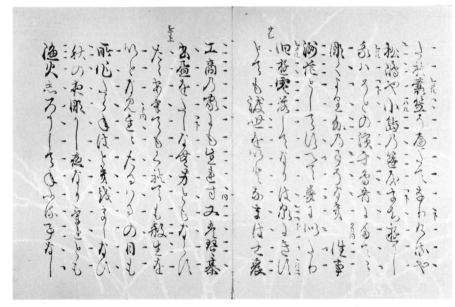

94

northwest of Kyoto. He often used movable type cut in wood, a vogue of the late sixteenth and early seventeenth centuries which was soon to die out. These texts for the Nō drama are masterpieces of book production. They are from a set of over ten, intended for a select market of connoisseurs among the rich Kyoto merchant class. The print is based on Kōetsu's own very distinguished calligraphy and the books are printed on coloured paper with under-designs in powdered mica of silver or pale green colour. The covers are decorated in the same way. The designs are the result of Kōetsu's collaboration with Sōtatsu and have much in common with their calligraphic handscrolls (no. 24). The Play titles are:

Hyakuman, Nonomiya, Bashō, Kantan, Sesshōseki, Sekidera Komachi, Ominaeshi, Hotoke no hara, Ukon, Rashōmon.

The dots and dashes in the text are the special expression-marks used in the Nō drama, which in the early seventeenth century was becoming a taste of the merchant and samurai class instead of an aristocratic and courtly entertainment.

The Emperor GOYŌZEI (1571–1617)

95 *Calligraphy: 'Dragon, tiger' and 'Plum, bamboo'*

FS/G3   後陽成天皇宸翰二大字

Ink on paper
Unsigned
Pair of hanging scrolls, each 145 × 52 cm
c. 1600
HŌKONGŌIN, Kyoto

Goyōzei reigned during the rise to power of Hideyoshi and then of Ieyasu, and saw the complete disappearance of any imperial power. He was a major patron of the arts, especially calligraphy, and encouraged Karasumaru Mitsuhiro (no. 19) and Konoe Nobutada (nos 96, 96a). These expansively brushed characters are in the semi-cursive *gyōsho* style which was particularly favoured in Japanese official circles and was practised by many

CALLIGRAPHY

95

emperors. The characters are full of traditional associations – the dragon and tiger are often painted together in pairs and so are the plum and bamboo. Further, tigers are often shown in groves of bamboo, and dragons sometimes contrasted with the delicacy of plum-blossom.

KONOE NOBUTADA (1565–1614)

96 *Calligraphy: poetry from the Shinsen Rōeishū*

FS/G3 近衛信尹筆新撰朗詠集抜書

Ink over paper decorated with gold and silver designs
Hand scroll, 35.7 × 493 cm
c. 1600
YŌMEI BUNKO, Kyoto

This anthology, *A New Collection for Recitation*, consists of *waka* poems and Chinese poems selected from much earlier periods. From very early times the elegant writing of poems over decorated papers had been much admired. Nobutada revived this practice with his virile version of the old cursive, flowing style. He was much encouraged by the Emperor Goyōzei, who contributed some of the sheets to this scroll, as did Konoe Maehisa. Nobutada is the most traditional of the three great calligraphers of the early seventeenth century and the decorated backgrounds he favoured were more restrained than those of Kōetsu. His combination of calligraphy and background is dignified and integrated.

96

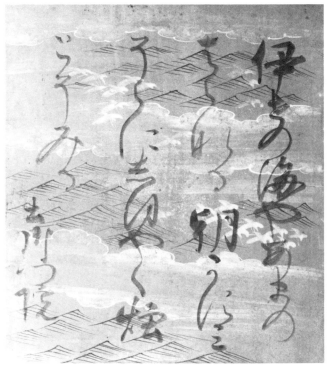

96a

KONOE NOBUTADA (1565–1614)

96a *Poems of the Thirty-Six Poets (Sanjūrokkasen)*

F/G3　近衛信尹筆三十六歌仙色紙帖

Ink over coloured paper decorated with designs in gold and silver
Folding album, each sheet 21.1 × 18.6 cm
TOKYO NATIONAL MUSEUM

The anthology of thirty-six *waka* poems each by a famous poet had been popular since the Heian period and was a favourite subject for fine calligraphy. Nobutada has revived the Heian tradition of coloured papers with delicate designs of the natural world in gold and silver, over which to impose his strong cursive calligraphy.

97a

97b

S

b] *Shibaraku fuzai shinin no gotoshi*
('Let your thoughts wander for an instant and you are
no better than a dead man')
Unsigned
113 × 50 cm
1754

Apart from one-character works, Hakuin liked to write the shorter sayings of Zen Buddhism, like this one by Gantō Wakō, in which the balance between the heavy characters and their interplay of meaning became crucial. He tended to write such texts with a well loaded, thick brush, giving the characters that even density of ink which was admired in China. By contrast, the native *kana* style tends to emphasize the coming and going as the brush is loaded and then exhausted.

The Priest HAKUIN (1675-1768)

98 *Calligraphies: four solemn characters*

G5 紙本墨書寿・刻・中・死字　白隠慧鶴筆

Ink on paper
Hanging scrolls
EISEI BUNKO, Tokyo

F a] *JU* ('Long life')
s. *Hakuin Sō sho* ('written by the old man Hakuin')
124 × 56 cm
d. 1757

Ju or *kotobuki* is known as 'the character with a hundred forms', since it appears so frequently as a symbol of good fortune. Hakuin wrote it many times, giving it a flowing weight which it often lacks. Here he has placed it at the centre of a semi-comic text of a typically Zen type; it also forms the final character of the text. He

The Priest HAKUIN (1675-1768)

97 *Calligraphies: two maxims*

G5 紙本墨書欽山一鏃語・巖頭語　白隠慧鶴筆

Ink on paper
Hanging scrolls
EISEI BUNKO, Tokyo

F a] *Ichizoku sanseki wo yaburu*
('One arrow breaks three barriers')
Sealed.
127 × 28 cm
c. 1735

Here Hakuin allows his ink to lighten out towards the ends of the strokes. The trickle from the left of the first character 'one' shows the vigour with which he began it, for it moves from left to right, and therefore the trickle precedes the first stroke. Hakuin's style, based on Ōbaku-sect calligraphy imported from China and on certain Chinese eccentrics of the early seventeenth century, is nevertheless completely his own. He is the best of Edo calligraphers in the 'square style' (*kaisho*).

98a

98b   98c

98d

has emphasised its power by releasing it from the grid in which he has placed the other characters – a reference to the ruled grids within which Buddhist scriptures were often written. But Hakuin has strayed outside the limits of the grid in any case, because his calligraphy depends on overall balance and not on the geometrical balance basic to the square hand.

S   b] *KOKU*

('Time')
Unsigned
130 × 19 cm

Hakuin has extended the third character of the inscription downwards to dominate the whole of the paper. The problem of balance is quite acute, for it is the right-hand stroke of the character which is written last and is therefore the only one which can be extended. Hakuin has solved the problem by slanting the stroke gradually inwards so that the first two characters have room at the right.

S   c] *CHŪ*

('The middle')
Sealed
120 × 28 cm
c. 1760

The text reads 'Strength in work is a hundred thousand times better than a quiet heart'. Hakuin makes the character *chū*, which is in fact the second in order of the text, dominate the whole surface. *Chū* is the 'middle way' of Buddhism. By a characteristic Zen paradox, he disparaged the 'quiet heart', sought in more conventional Buddhism, in favour of more ordinary things.

F   a] *SHI*

('Death')
Sealed
115 × 28 cm
c. 1760

To Hakuin calligraphy was one means to Enlightenment. He liked endlessly to brush certain key characters, giving them each time a slight variation of emphasis in the placing. Here the character is of such weight that it seems to have sunk to the bottom of the paper under its own gravity. The inscription above is mainly in the lightweight *kana* syllabary, and is executed in much paler ink. To the left of 'death' is a horizontal trail of ink which Hakuin deliberately let happen as if to emphasize how heavily his brush was loaded at that point.

125

Wood-block prints

All items are printed by a combination of line-block in ink with separate colour-blocks on *kōzō* paper, unless otherwise stated. Additional features, such as the absence of colour-blocks or the use of metallic powders or blind-printing, are mentioned under individual items.

KAIGETSUDŌ ANCHI (*fl. c.* 1710–1720)

99 *An oiran parading*

FS/AR 花魁図銘安知図

Printed in ink only
s. 'a picture by Anchi, follower of Kaigetsudō, for amusement, in the Japanese style' (i.e. not in the Chinese style)
59.8 × 33.3 cm
c. 1715–1720
BRITISH MUSEUM

The parades of the grand courtesans of Edo in the licensed quarter of the Yoshiwara were one of the great sights of the city, both for the glamour of the women themselves and for the new fashions of which they were important promoters. The Kaigetsudō studio artists painted these women in all their finery with a broadness of treatment and yet with a detailed and rich depiction of their clothes which the Edo public found fascinating. As a result, large prints, in black and white only, done as a cheap way of disseminating their work, are among the biggest and grandest of Japanese wood-block productions. They are also among the rarest and therefore cannot have been produced in very large numbers.

TORII KIYOTADA (*fl. c.* 1720–1750)

100 *The Daimojiya in Naka no chō, Shin Yoshiwara*

FS/LR 新吉原仲ノ町大文字屋座敷図銘清忠画

s. 'by the brush of the painter Torii Kiyotada'
48 × 69 cm
c. 1730–1740
BRITISH MUSEUM

The Yoshiwara (*cf.* no. 67), the licensed pleasure quarter of Edo, was originally established near Nihombashi in 1618 but after the great fire of 1657 it was moved to an area north of Asakusa and was renamed Shin ('new') Yoshiwara. It was a square enclave built on a grid plan and separated from the rest of Edo by a moat. Courtesans were forbidden to leave it without a special pass and pleasure-seekers who wished to visit it had to enter through the main gate (*Ōmon*) which led directly into Naka no chō, which was the principal thoroughfare. The open-plan architecture (the sliding *fusuma* screens have been for the most part pulled back to give a better view) and the garden at the rear seem, to judge from other contemporary prints, to be typical of the larger houses in the Naka no chō. Two courtesans are playing backgammon (*sugoroku*), a pastime introduced from Europe.

KITAGAWA UTAMARO (1754–1806)

101 *Portrait of the oiran Hanaōgi*

FS/LR 花扇花魁図銘歌麿筆

s. 'by the brush of Utamaro'
38.4 × 25.9 cm
c. 1798
BRITISH MUSEUM

This is an *ōkubie* or 'large head' of one of the most famous Yoshiwara courtesans, who was depicted by several other print artists including Koryūsai, Kiyonaga, Shunchō, Eishi and Eishō. She held her place as one of the leading lights of those circles for an exceptionally long period, *c.* 1773–1800. The development of

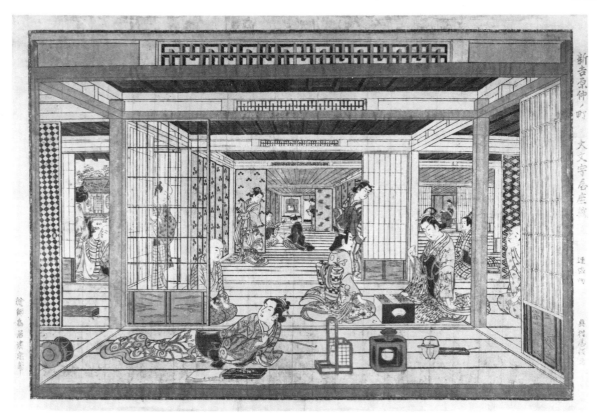

100

101

102

ōkubie reflects increasing confidence by print artists, especially Utamaro, in the portrayal of a living celebrity.

SUZUKI HARUNOBU (1724–1770)

102   *Osen's tea-stall*

FS/LR   お仙茶屋図銘春信画

s. 'painted by Harunobu'
27.8 × 20.1 cm
c. 1769
BRITISH MUSEUM

Osen was a celebrated beauty who served tea and sweetmeats at a stall by the Kasamori shrine in Edo. The *torii* of the shrine dominates the scene. Osen is seen serving a young samurai, who has discreetly lowered his head so as not to be too obviously seen in frivolous pursuits. However, to be seen at Osen's was also a social necessity, and prints of her by several other artists prove her popularity. Harunobu, in this early example of a popular multi-block colour print, has imposed his doll-like ideal of feminine beauty upon her.

103

Suzuki Harunobu (1724–1770)

103 *A blow-pipe parlour (fukiya-mise)*

FS/LR 吹矢見世図　春信画

Diptych print
Unsigned
Each sheet 26 × 20 cm
c. 1766–1768
BRITISH MUSEUM

The *fukiya-mise* was a sort of amusement arcade in which both men and women tried to hit a target with darts from a blow-pipe. The prizes, clearly of little value except as souvenirs, are shown above the targets. As in other fashionable places of amusement, the elegance of the female attendants seems to have been an important factor and this is what has attracted Harunobu, who rarely designed a print without a woman in it. However, other prints by the artist suggest that he saw women as major customers for his work and, relatively free as they were in

contemporary Edo, they probably did buy works depicting the more respectable amusements they could indulge in. This is a rare example of a multi-sheet print by the pioneer artist.

Torii Kiyonaga (1752–1815)

104 *Enjoying the blossom at Asukayama*

FS/LR 飛鳥山花見図銘清長画

Triptych print
s. 'painted by Kiyonaga'
Each sheet 37.5 × 24 cm
c. 1787
BRITISH MUSEUM

For those Edo dwellers who found the teeming city oppressive there were local beauty-spots and open spaces in which the air and scenery could be enjoyed and people dressed in the height of fashion could see and be seen. Viewing the cherry-blossom at

104

105

Asukayama, in the slightly hilly country near the city, was one of the favourite occasions. Kiyonaga's ladies are very like each other, and it is clear that they represent an ideal of face and fashion. But the composition has an extraordinary freshness and sense of space, and in this and a few other multi-sheet works the artist proved himself the true founder of the *Ukiyo-e* landscape print.

TORII KIYONAGA (1752–1815)

105   *A pleasure-boat on the Sumida river*

FS/LR   遊船図銘清長画

Triptych print
Each sheet s. 'painted by Kiyonaga'
Each sheet approximately 38 × 26 cm
1780s
BRITISH MUSEUM

The Sumida river, which ran through Edo into Edo Bay, was a

major source of recreation. Along its banks were restaurants, tea houses, and houses of entertainment, and on it plied pleasure-boats which might have on board not only food, but also hostesses, musicians and entertainers. River-parties on summer evenings were particularly popular. Kiyonaga, the pioneer of the triptych and of prints with even more than three sheets, used these formats to expand very greatly the scope of *Ukiyo-e*; multi-sheet compositions of river-parties are fairly common among his works.

KUBO SHUMMAN (1757–1820)

106   *The Shikian restaurant on the Sumida river*

FS/LR   料理屋図銘俊満画

Diptych print
s. 'painted by Shumman'
Each sheet approximately 38 × 26 cm
BRITISH MUSEUM

106

Shumman, a poet and *bon vivant* as well as a designer of sheet-prints, *surimono*, books and albums, was more concerned with the elegance of life in general than with female beauty in particular. His work reflects the very high standards of taste of Edo townsmen at their most cultivated, but lacks the human passion of Utamaro. The *Shikian* ('Hut of the Four Seasons') overlooks the river. Beyond it are warehouses and a fire-tower, on which a warden watches for the ever-present danger of conflagration. On the balcony, clients smoke and are served food and drink, while entertainers dance and sing.

107

UTAGAWA TOYOHARU (1735–1814)

107 *The festival of Benten at the Itsukushima shrine*

FS/LR 厳島弁天祭図銘豊春画

s. 'painted by Utagawa Toyoharu'
25 × 38 cm
c. 1775–1780
BRITISH MUSEUM

Tourism and pilgrimages within Japan were one of the major diversions open to Japanese who were not of the peasant class and therefore not legally bound to their land. The great shrine at Itsukushima, in Aki province (now Hiroshima prefecture) was one of the 'three great sights', and the *torii* built in the sea was its most famous feature. It is shown thronged with visitors at one of its great festivals.

Toyoharu was founder of the Utagawa school, which dominated *Ukiyo-e* prints, apart from landscape subjects, from *c.* 1800 until the end of the Edo period. Curiously, he himself contributed most to the landscape print, making use of exaggerated western style perspective and often attempting night-scenes, for which before him there were no firm artistic conventions. These westernised features are seen in this print, as well as his dramatic use of the *torii* as a foreground gateway to the picture.

KITAGAWA UTAMARO (1754–1806)

108 *Young women visiting the seashore at Ise*

FS/LR 伊勢二見ケ浦婦女子遊楽図銘歌磨画

Triptych print
s. 'by the brush of Utamaro'
Each sheet 37.7 × 25 cm
c. 1800
BRITISH MUSEUM

The twin rocks at Ise were one of the most sacred places of the Shintō religion. The sun, one of the central Shintō symbols, rose directly between them at the New Year and they were joined by the straw rope which marks the precincts of the gods. The beach was thus a major tourist centre, and many thousands of people flocked there every year. Utamaro, characteristically, has chosen a group of beautiful young women as his tourists. Prints like this were sold mainly in the enormous city of Edo, and must have done much to stimulate the internal tourist industry which provided diversion for the city-dwellers.

108

This unusually large and vigorous print shows the actor Ōtani Awaji I, as the gigantically strong Asahina, dragging the actor Ichikawa Danzō, as Soga no Gorō, into a room by the lappets of his armour. This is from one of the many plays about the thirteenth-century story which were immensely popular, but reference to the actual context of a *Kabuki* theatre is very slight and there is clearly much exaggeration of how the actors appeared. Parts of the print are hand-coloured with a hot red mineral pigment known as *tan*, which added interest to the design of plain ink-prints.

109

TORII KIYOMASU (*fl.* 1696–mid 1720s)

109 *Actors in a scene from the 'Revenge of the Soga Brothers'*

FS/AR 曽我歌舞伎図銘鳥居清倍

Printed in ink only, hand-coloured in *tan*
s. *Torii Kiyomasu*
53.4 × 32.2 cm
c. 1717
BRITISH MUSEUM

OKUMURA MASANOBU (1686–1764)

110 *Interior of a Kabuki theatre*

FS/LR 歌舞伎座図　政信画

Printed in ink only, with hand-colouring. Originally s. on the right-hand margin, now trimmed off
44 × 63.7 cm
c. 1740
BRITISH MUSEUM

By the early eighteenth century, the popular *Kabuki* theatre had become the dominant public entertainment in Edo. This *ukie* print (using western-style perspective) shows another play about the Soga brothers (see no. 109). The scene shows the play as also a social occasion, with eating, drinking and conversation during its performance. From the ceiling hang lanterns bearing the *mon* of the main actors, on a pillar at the left hangs the title of the play and at the right are titles of *Sambasō* dances to be performed. This unusually large print is composed of two sheets of paper joined up and more than one block had to be used. The hand-colouring, quite common at that period, is contemporary and was almost certainly done to standard instructions by the publisher.

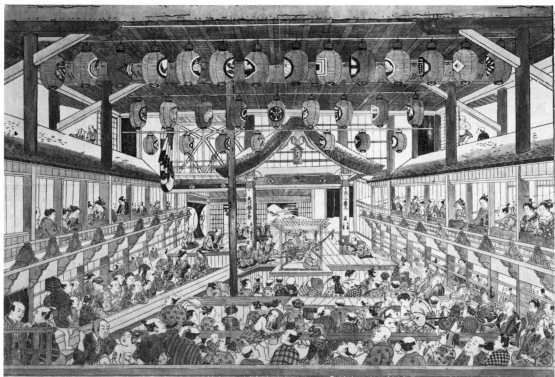

110

111

112

KATSUKAWA SHUNSHŌ (1726–1792)

111 *The actor Ichikawa Danjūrō V as Sakata Kintoki*

FS/LR 五代市川団十郎図銘春章画

s. 'painted by Shunshō'
31 × 14 cm
1781
BRITISH MUSEUM

The Danjūrō actors specialised in highly dramatic roles, and favoured the powerful brick-red costumes of which an example is seen here. On it is the character *kin* ('golden') representing Kintoki. He was a legendary warrior who as a boy was brought up by his mother in the mountains and was noted for deeds of fantastic strength. He later became a retainer of the eleventh-century general Minamoto no Yorimitsu. Shunshō, the most prolific of eighteenth-century designers of actor prints, favoured this narrow format, which he often designed in diptych or triptych form.

TŌSHŪSAI SHARAKU (*fl.* 1794–1795)

112 *The actor Ichikawa Ebizō as Takemura Sadanoshin*

FS/LR 市川海老蔵図銘写樂画

s. 'painted by Tōshūsai Sharaku'
36.5 × 24.5 cm
1794–1795
BRITISH MUSEUM

Sharaku is unknown except for the fewer than two hundred *Kabuki* actor prints he produced in the years 1794–1795, after which nothing more is heard of him. All his prints were published by Tsutaya Jūsaburō, who was also Utamaro's main publish

TŌSHŪSAI SHARAKU (*fl.* 1794–1795)

113 *The actors Ichikawa Komazō II and Nakayama Tomisaburō as the lovers Chūbei and Umegawa*

FS/LR 二代市川高麗蔵中山富三郎図銘写樂画

Printed with a mica ground
s. 'painted by Tōshūsai Sharaku'
36 × 24 cm
1794
BRITISH MUSEUM

The story of the passionate and illicit love of Chūbei and Umegawa, ending in their execution, was the subject of many plays, one of which gave rise to this print made in the eighth month of 1794. They are shown setting out on their flight from arrest. Stories of this sort were eagerly watched by the Edo public, who could strongly identify themselves in the conflicts of love and duty they so often described. Sharaku has uncannily caught the flavour of the man Nakayama underneath the make-up, dress and mannerisms of the woman he was impersonating.

UTAGAWA TOYOHARU (1735–1814)

114 *The bunraku puppeteer Yoshida Bungo II*

FS/LR 二代 吉田文吾図銘豊春画

s. 'painted by Utagawa Toyoharu'
31.5 × 14 cm
c. 1780
BRITISH MUSEUM

113

114

The puppeteer is shown operating a puppet of a *shakkyō* dancer. This was a popular dance with a lion's head and body. *Bunraku* puppet plays and performances were often as popular as *Kabuki* plays, and the top operators were as celebrated as actors. This performance is described as taking place at the Satsumaza theatre. However, this form of drama was more common in Osaka than Edo and does not appear very frequently in the prints of the latter. For *Bunraku* puppets see nos 188, 189.

KATSUKAWA SHUN'EI (1762–1819)

115 *The sumō wrestler Tanikaze and attendant*

FS/LR 谷風図銘春英画

s. 'painted by Shun'ei'
37.7 × 25 cm
1793
BRITISH MUSEUM

The best wrestlers, like Tanikaze ('Wind of the Valley'), became as celebrated as the great *Kabuki* actors, and prints like this, of them off duty, were produced for their supporters. He is attended by a lesser fighter from the same 'stable', named Takinooto ('Sound of the Waterfall') who carries the bow which is a symbol of the *yokozuna* or highest rank of wrestler. Both have the traditional long hair, arranged in a distinctive 'bun'.

KATSUKAWA SHUN'EI (1762–1819)

116 *Parade before a sumō tournament*

FS/LR 土俵入り図銘春英画

Triptych print
s. 'painted by Shun'ei'
Each sheet 37.5 × 25.5 cm
1796
BRITISH MUSEUM

Sumō wrestling, once confined to local shrines and temples,

115

116

became a professional sport in Edo in the mid-eighteenth century and acquired the passionate following it still commands in Japan. Two tournaments a year were held and as can be seen from this vivid print of the autumn event of 1796, a large and elaborate temporary stadium was put up at the Edoin temple to hold many spectators. The *dohyō-iri*, or parade of wrestlers in their formal aprons, was and still is one of the great moments of the tournament. In the centre is the raised ring, and over it the traditional shrine-roof. Shun'ei, who specialised in actor and *sumō* prints, has depicted the admittedly bulky wrestlers even larger than life, following a popular convention.

KATSUSHIKA HOKUSAI (1760–1849)

117   *Fuji in clear weather*

FS/AR   凱風快晴富士山図銘北斎筆

s. 'by the brush of Hokusai, changing his name to Iitsu'
26.2 × 38.3 cm
Early 1830s
BRITISH MUSEUM

It is not known for certain when Hokusai started work on his great series *Thirty-six Views of Mount Fuji*, although it appears that he may have conceived the idea of such a project as early as 1821. This is one of the most famous sheets of the series, and its graphic simplicity and brilliant use of colour have represented the quintessence of Japanese art to many westerners for over a century, in spite of the fact that the clouds and other features betray considerable European influence.

KATSUSHIKA HOKUSAI (1760–1849)

118   *Fuji seen through the waves off Kanagawa*

FS/AR   神奈川沖浪裏富士山図銘北斎筆

s. 'by the brush of Hokusai, changing his name to Iitsu'
24.6 × 36.5 cm
Early 1830s
BRITISH MUSEUM

An announcement by the publisher of the Fuji series, Nishimura Eijudō, made in 1831, speaks of the 'Thirty-six views of Mount

117

118

Fuji by Hokusai, decorated with prussian blue' and it seems likely that the availability of this new pigment, imported via the Dutch trading post at Deshima, was one of the stimuli which inspired Hokusai to embark on the series. He started experimenting with this design in a self-consciously western-style series which he produced around 1800; thirty years later western influence is still evident in the use of perspective and shading, but this print has nonetheless become a world-wide symbol of Japanese art in general.

YASHIMA GAKUTEI (c. 1786–1868)

119 *Moonlit night at the Suehiro bridge, Tempōzan, Osaka*

FS/AR 天保山末広橋月夜の図銘五岳

> s. *Gogaku*
> 24.8 × 37.2 cm
> 1834
> BRITISH MUSEUM

Gakutei lived in Osaka during the 1830s and he celebrated its scenery in a series of six designs entitled *Fine Views of Mount Tempō*, referring to a small mound at the mouth of the Aji river. Pleasure-boats were especially popular in Osaka, a city of many rivers and canals, and their delights are extolled by the great Osaka writer Ihara Saikaku (1642–1693) in his novel *The Life of*

119

an Amorous Man (*Kōshoku ichidai otoko*, 1682): 'On the cruising boats were makeshift bathrooms and barrels of sea-bream and sea-bass. . . . Verily, there is more fun in this pleasure-boat cruising than in playing in the mountains of Kyoto. . . .'

UTAGAWA TOYOSHIGE (TOYOKUNI II, 1777–1835)

120 *Evening rain at Ōyama*

FS/AR 大山夜雨の図銘豊国筆

> s. 'by the brush of Toyokuni'
> 26.2 × 37.7 cm
> Early 1830s
> BRITISH MUSEUM

Toyoshige, a pupil of the great designer of actor prints Toyokuni, whose name he took, is one of a number of minor nineteenth-

century artists whose landscape designs very occasionally rival those of Hokusai and Hiroshige. Hokusai's influence is apparent in the boldness of the overall design; it would be tempting to ascribe the effective use of the driving diagonal rain to the influence of Hiroshige's famous print of Shōno in the Tōkaidō series, but considerations of date make it impossible to be certain of this.

120

121

ANDŌ HIROSHIGE (1797–1858)

121 *Ōi*

FS/AR 大井図銘広重画

> s. 'painted by Hiroshige'
> 25.1 × 37.3 cm
> Late 1830s
> BRITISH MUSEUM

This print, number forty-seven in the Kisokaidō series (see also nos 122, 123), is perhaps the best-known of all Hiroshige's atmospheric snow scenes and is typical in its sympathetic depiction of the travellers lowering their hats for protection against the blizzard. The Kisokaidō (also called the Nakasendō, 543 km long), parted from the Tōkaidō (see no. 124) at Kusatsu, not far from Kyoto, to turn inland and wind its way through the mountainous provinces of Mino, Shinano and Kōzuke, eventually terminating, like the Tōkaidō, at Nihombashi in Edo.

122

ANDŌ HIROSHIGE (1797–1858)

122   *Seba*
FS/AR   洗馬図銘広重画

s. 'painted by Hiroshige'
24.4 × 37 cm
Late 1830s
BRITISH MUSEUM

Like many *Ukiyo-e* artists, Hiroshige received some training early in his life from a member of the Kanō school and something of this Kanō background is revealed in the extensive use of uncoloured line in this unusual print from the Kisokaidō series. As so often in Hiroshige's work, the composition is so contrived as to draw the viewer's attention to the human figures, in this case by placing trees in the middle ground which bend at the same angles as the toiling boatmen.

IKEDA EISEN (1790–1848)

123   *The Inagawa bridge at Nojiri*
FS/AR   野尻伊奈川橋図銘溪斎画

123

s. 'painted by Keisai'
24.2 × 35.4 cm
Late 1830s
BRITISH MUSEUM

Eisen is best known for the twenty-three prints which he contributed to the landscape series *Sixty-nine Stations on the Kisokaidō*, the rest of which was designed by Hiroshige. The present print, number forty-one in the series, has justly been called 'Hokusai foreground, Hiroshige background', the graphic depiction of the waterfall (probably derived directly from Hokusai's 1831–1832 series of waterfalls) contrasting vividly with the homely detail of the journeying figures. The Inagawa bridge, in Shinano, is famous for its outline which recalls the shape of Mount Fuji itself.

124

ANDŌ HIROSHIGE (1797–1858)

124   *Morning scene at Nihombashi*
FS/AR   日本橋朝之景銘広重画

s. 'painted by Hiroshige'
23.8 × 36.3 cm
c. 1833–1834
BRITISH MUSEUM

This view of the head of a daimyō procession leaving the Nihombashi bridge early in the morning is the first print in the well known series *Fifty-three Stations on the Tōkaidō (Eastern Sea Road)* by which Hiroshige established his reputation as a designer of landscape prints. The Tōkaidō was the principal artery of land communication between eastern and western Honshu; the Nihombashi bridge in Edo, built in 1602, was the centre of the system of roads which developed under the Tokugawa shōgunate and all distances were, in theory, measured from its central post.

125

KATSUSHIKA HOKUSAI (1760–1849)

125 *Snowy morning at Koishikawa*
FS/AR 礫川雪の旦図銘為一筆

s. 'from the brush of Iitsu, formerly Hokusai'
25 × 37 cm
Early 1830s
BRITISH MUSEUM

Koishikawa was a popular pleasure-resort on the outskirts of Edo and this print might, therefore, perhaps be more appropriately entitled 'The Morning After at Koishikawa', although it is impossible to say whether the ladies looking at Mount Fuji have just emerged on to the viewing-platform after an all-night party or have made a special dawn trip to admire the mountain in the morning light.

KATSUSHIKA HOKUSAI (1760–1849)

126 *Watching the sunset over Ryōgoku bridge from the Ommaya embankment, Edo*
FS/AR 御厩川岸から両国橋夕陽富士山図銘為一筆

s. 'from the brush of Iitsu, formerly Hokusai'
24.8 × 38 cm
Early 1830s
BRITISH MUSEUM

The sight of Fuji in the distance catches the attention of a group of early evening pleasure-seekers as they make their way by ferry across the Sumida river (see nos 105, 106). Hokusai uses the unusual and much illustrated form of Ryōgoku bridge to draw the viewer's eye towards the distant peak.

126

ANDŌ HIROSHIGE (1797–1858)

127 *A drapery store in Edo*
FS/AR 江戸呉服屋図銘広重画

Triptych print
s. 'painted by Hiroshige'
Each sheet approximately 37 × 25 cm
c. 1850
BRITISH MUSEUM

Drapery stores were among the most successful commercial enterprises of the Edo period and one of them survived the Meiji restoration to become the modern industrial giant Mitsui. The present triptych, one of a number of such views of Edo which Hiroshige produced around this time, gives us a glimpse of the daily life of urban Japan on the eve of the arrival of Commodore

127

Perry. Outside the shop, which is hung with dark blue curtains (*noren*) emblazoned with the *mon* (in this case acting as a trademark) of the company, samurai wearing two swords jostle with women passers-by and porters whose uniforms bear the same *mon*; inside customers examine lengths of cloth. The geometrically precise perspective of this design is a sign of the considerable influence of western painting techniques at the period.

ANDŌ HIROSHIGE (1797–1858)

128 *The precincts of the Kinryūzan temple, Asakusa, Edo*

FS/AR   淺草金龍山境内の図銘広重画

Triptych print
s. 'painted by Hiroshige'
Each sheet approximately 37.5 × 25.5 cm
1854
BRITISH MUSEUM

The Kinryūzan temple, also called Sensōji and Asakusa Kannon, was and is one of the most popular religious buildings in Edo and the centre of an important entertainment area. Pilgrims can be seen making their way from the entrance gate to the main hall, round whose raised verandah they circulate. Hiroshige has employed two methods of perspective: the bird's eye view of the temple precincts is constructed on western principles but the spatial relationship between the precincts and the rest of Edo is

128

blurred by the introduction of Tosa-style clouds which create an effect of greater distance.

GOUNTEI SADAHIDE (1807–1873)

129 *Englishman sampling cloth*

FS/GII 英吉利人分色図銘貞秀画

s. 'painted by Gountei Sadahide'
36.9 × 25 cm
1861
BRITISH MUSEUM

As in the other prints from this series, which depict Russian, Dutch, American and French as well as English merchants, the subject's spouse is shown in a cartouche, possibly intended to represent an oil painting but also recalling the insets popular in the landscape sets of the 1840s and 1850s. The merchant, seated in a western-style chair, is examining a length of cloth which appears to be dyed in *kanoko shibori*, tie-dying yielding a 'deer dappling'.

129

UTAGAWA YOSHITORA (*fl. c.* 1850–1880)

130 *Englishman on horseback*

FS/GII 英吉利人図銘芳虎画

s. 'painted by Yoshitora'
36.7 × 25.6 cm
1861
BRITISH MUSEUM

The inscription at the top is typical in its wide-eyed admiration and its bewildering mixture of the general and the none too accurate particular: 'England or Britain is a great island nation in the continent of Europe. Its capital is London and its people are intelligent, strong and skilled in gunnery. They are at present ruled by a Queen. When a noble comes into the presence of the sovereign he places his hand upon her knee and when the Queen has shaken his hand the noble withdraws and ?kisses the place which she has touched.'

130

IPPŌSAI YOSHIFUSA (*fl. c.* 1837–1860)

131 *An English soldier*

FS/GII 英吉利人図銘芳房画

s. 'painted by Ippōsai Yoshifusa'
36.4 × 24.9 cm
1860
BRITISH MUSEUM

Portraits of soldiers in uniform are particularly common among the *Yokohama-e* and their long firearms are frequently depicted. Not surprisingly, given the importance of the sword in Japan as an item of personal decoration, the artist has gone to some trouble to show the Englishman's weapon in detail, giving

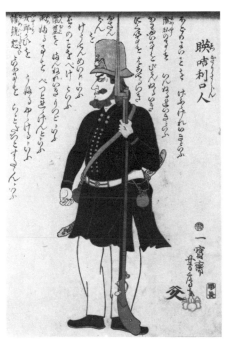

131

viewers an opportunity to compare Japanese and foreign fashions. The inscription gives English phrases (in transliteration) and their Japanese equivalents.

132

UTAGAWA YOSHITORA (*fl. c.* 1850–1880)

132 *English couple with an umbrella*

FS/GII 英吉利人図銘芳虎画

s. 'painted by Yoshitora'
37 × 25.4 cm
1860
BRITISH MUSEUM

The grotesque features of the man and the exaggerated peculiarities of his wife's clothing recall the *netsuke* and *namban* screens of earlier times. The man's face strongly resembles that of the rider in no. 130, suggesting that in order to keep up with the heavy demand for portraits of the foreigners the *Yokohama-e* artists sometimes did no more than ring the changes on a stock range of subjects. Very often no attempt is made to distinguish between the different expressions of merchants from different countries, although these must surely have been evident to Japanese observers of the Yokohama scene.

GOUNTEI SADAHIDE (1807–1873)

133 *Foreign families on the harbour front at Yokohama*

FS/GII 外商人遊行図銘貞秀画

Triptych print
Each sheet s. *Gountei Sadahide*
Each sheet approximately 36.5 × 25 cm
1861
BRITISH MUSEUM

The right-hand sheet shows an English family, the centre sheet a Dutch family and the left hand sheet a Russian family. As usual in *Yokohama-e*, they are suitably equipped with exotic equipment

133

134

such as telescopes and concertinas. The faces of the women, with long, sharp noses, are of interest in that they are clearly an adaptation of the standard type adopted for Japanese women by the members of the Utagawa school in the mid-nineteenth century.

SUZUKI HIROSHIGE II (SHIGENOBU, 1826–69)

134 *The British Legation on the Bluff at Yokohama*

FS/G11 横浜高台英役館の全図銘喜斎立祥筆

Triptych print
s. 'by the brush of Kisai Ryūshō', English insc.
'Plan of English Legation at Bluff land in Yoko-hama, Benten dohi, Morohcaya'; Japanese insc. 'Complete view of the English Legation on the Yokohama Bluff, printed by Morookaya of Benten-dōri go-chōme'
Each sheet approximately 36 × 24 cm
c. 1867
BRITISH MUSEUM

When the Japanese were forced to agree to the opening of a Treaty Port the choice naturally fell, not on Yokohama, but on the thriving town of Kanagawa on the opposite side of Yokohama bay. The Japanese, however, fearing that this might lead to clashes between travellers on the Tōkaidō, including daimyō processions, and foreigners, insisted that the merchants should live in the insignificant fishing village of Yokohama, where they moved in 1858. A fire in 1866 destroyed most of the buildings and in 1867 the Bluff was leased for building purposes. The British legation, which was built at that time, is seen here to be inappropriately equipped with a Japanese-style garden.

Wood-block books and albums

From the enormous number of fine illustrated books and albums published from the mid-seventeenth century onwards, a selection of eight has been made to supplement the theme of entertainment and leisure.

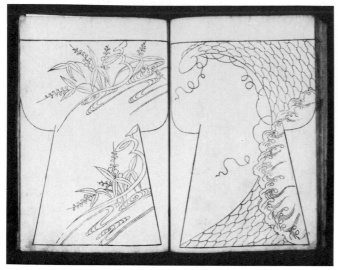

135

136

TAKE HIRATSUGI (*fl. c.* 1690)

135 *Fashionable kimono patterns*

FS/LR 御前雛形

From *Gozen Hiinagata* ('Patterns for Noble Ladies'), published in Edo, I volume
Printed in black ink only
23 × 16.2 cm
c. 1690
BRITISH MUSEUM

Fashion was one of the preoccupations of the townspeople of the Edo period and its pursuit served as a major diversion as well as an industry. Prostitutes and actors were among the leaders of fashion, but in this book the middle-class townswomen are being flattered into believing they can follow the styles of the nobility. In fact, these extravagant designs have both the daring and the slight vulgarity typical of urban taste in the Genroku era.

NISHIKAWA SUKENOBU (1671–1750)

136 *Tea-house scene*

FS/LR 百人女郎品定　西川祐信

From *Hyakunin jorō shina sadame*, volume II
Printed in ink only
28.5 × 19.5 cm
1723
BRITISH MUSEUM

The serving girls of the Izumiya tea-house are hard at work: on the right one of them carries a tray of smoking utensils, a tiered

food box and a kettle while in the kitchen her colleagues are grilling bean-curd (*tōfu*) and drying up the teacups. The work of Sukenobu, an immensely productive artist, consists almost entirely of illustrated books, printed in ink only, of which this is perhaps the finest. His influence was great and it spread from his native Kyoto to Edo and affected the style of Harunobu and Shunshō.

SUZUKI HARUNOBU (1724–1770)

137 *Two girls smoking*

FS/LR 吉原美人合　鈴木春信

From *Yoshiwara bijin awase*, volume V
26 × 17 cm
1770
BRITISH MUSEUM

Tobacco-smoking, which was introduced from Europe during the late sixteenth century, became immensely popular in Edo period Japan, not only among the sophisticated urban *demi-monde* but also, as we see from the prints of Hiroshige, among the rural population. The bowl of the pipe was extremely small and only a few puffs could be had from each 'fill'; as a result it was necessary to have a constant source of fire and an ashtray. The tray by the girl on the left contains an ashtray (*haifuki*) formed from a bamboo tube, as well as a *hi-ire*, a miniature ceramic brazier filled with ash topped with glowing charcoal.

137

138

KATSUKAWA SHUNSHŌ (1726–92) and IPPITSUSAI BUNCHŌ
(fl. c. 1765–1792)

138 *The actors Ichikawa Benzō and Azuma Fujizō*

FS/LR　絵本舞台の扇　勝川春章一筆斎文調

From *Ehon butai no ōgi*, volume III
With the *Mori-shi* seal of Bunchō
27 × 17.5 cm
1770
BRITISH MUSEUM

This very popular work had a considerable effect on the
development of the actor print, not only in illustrated books but
also in independent sheet form, and is particularly celebrated for
the skill with which the individual actors are vividly
characterised.

KITAO SHIGEMASA (1739–1820) and KATSUKAWA
SHUNSHŌ (1726–1792)

139 *Girls of the Echizen-ya playing cards*

FS/LR　青楼美人合姿鏡　北尾重政勝川春章

From *Seirō bijin awase sugata kagami*, volume II (autumn and
winter)
28 × 18.5 cm
1776
BRITISH MUSEUM

This justly celebrated book consists, as the title, 'A Mirror of
Beautiful Women of the Green Houses Compared', implies, of
scenes in the pleasure houses of the Yoshiwara. The present
opening shows a game of cards in progress: the inscriptions give
the calls made during the course of the game, and in the left
background a minor dispute is in progress. For card-games in the
Edo period see no. 170.

139

140

KITAGAWA UTAMARO (1754–1806)

140 *Women playing the shell game*

FS/LR 汐干のつと　北川歌麿.

From *Shioi no tsuto*
26 × 19 cm
c. 1790
BRITISH MUSEUM

The seven other openings of this masterfully printed album show a scene of shell-gathering and six scenes of shells on the seashore. The present print however shows the shells in use with a container of the type which became standard for the shell game (see no. 169). The meticulous arrangement of the shells suggests that, as with other Edo period games, it was the style of play rather than any question of winning or losing which was uppermost in the minds of the participants.

UTAGAWA TOYOKUNI (1769–1825)

141 *The actors Hagino Isaburō, Arashi Sanzō, Iwai Kiyotarō and Nakamura Kan'emon by the entrance to a dressing room*

FS/LR 俳優三階興　歌川豊国

From *Yakusha sangaikyō*, volume I
21.8 × 15.6 cm
1801
BRITISH MUSEUM

The practice of showing actors off stage as well as on was popularised by Katsukawa Shunshō and this book, entitled 'Amusements of Actors on the Third Floor', is entirely devoted to such scenes. In the dressing room the actor's chest of drawers, make-up brush and wash-tub are clearly depicted.

AOI SŌKYŪ (*fl.* early 1800s)

142 *A boating party*

FS/LR 葵氏艶譜　葵双鳩

From *Kishi empu*, volume II
25.8 × 18.1 cm
1803
BRITISH MUSEUM

Nothing is known about the creator of this superbly economical and humorous series of Shijō-style designs of scenes in the Osaka entertainment quarters.

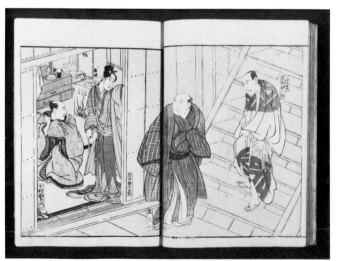

141

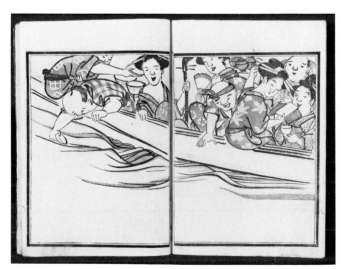

142

3 ANONYMOUS *Portrait of Tokugawa Ieyasu* After 1642

5   ANONYMOUS *Water-wheel and bridge with willow-trees in the moonlight* Late 16th/early 17th century

left hand screen

right hand screen

7   *Attr.* KANŌ EITOKU *Hawks, pines and rocks* (details) Late 16th century

9b TOSA MITSUYOSHI *Scene from the Tale of Genji c.* 1610–1613

8   KANŌ SANRAKU 1559–1635 *Dragon of the storm, tiger with bamboo*

left hand screen

right hand screen

16   TOSA MITSUOKI 1617–1691 *Quail, millet and foxtail, with autumn flowers*

left hand screen

right hand screen

18 KANŌ TAN'YŪ *Pine-trees in the four seasons c.* 1640–1650

left hand screen

right hand screen

22 SCHOOL OF SŌTATSU
   Flowering plants c. 1630–1640 (one of four doors)

23   TAWARAYA SŌSETSU *Flowering plants of autumn* (right-hand screen) *c.* 1640–1650

24   TAWARAYA SŌTATSU/HON'AMI KŌETSU *Scroll of waka poems* (section) *c.* 1610

33   WATANABE SHIKŌ 1683–1755 *Flowers and trees of the four seasons*

left hand screen

right hand screen

28   KUSUMI MORIKAGE c. 1620–1690 *Staying cool under an arbour of 'evening glory'* (detail)

29   HANABUSA ITCHŌ *The Four Accomplishments* (detail) *c.* 1720

34   WATANABE SHIKŌ 1683–1755 *Flowering cherries at Yoshinoyama*

left hand screen

right hand screen

35   FUKAE ROSHŪ 1699–1757 *The narrow ivy road*

36 OGATA KŌRIN *Peacocks with plum-blossom and hollyhocks c.* 1701–1710 (also opposite)

40 OGATA KŌRIN *Willow* c. 1700–1710

38   SAKAI HŌITSU 1761–1828 *Moon with autumn flowers* (detail)

44a ITŌ JAKUCHŪ *Chrysanthemums by a stream, with rocks* c. 1760

44c   ITŌ JAKUCHŪ *Domestic fowl c.* 1760

45 MARUYAMA ŌKYO *Waterfall* 1772

47   Aōdō Denzen 'A true view of Mount Asama' c. 1790

48 SHIBA KŌKAN *'Picture of the seven-league beach at Kamakura in Sōshū'* 1796

52 MATSUMURA GOSHUN
Hibiscus and blue heron on a tree-stump 1782

56a   MARUYAMA ŌKYO *Archery contest at the Sanjūsangendō c.* 1760

56b   MARUYAMA ŌKYO *Summer night by the Kamo river at Shijō c.* 1760

56c MARUYAMA ŌKYO *Shijō street by day c.* 1760

56d MARUYAMA ŌKYO *The Kiyomizu temple c.* 1760

54   NAGASAWA ROSETSU *Birds, plants and fish* (detail) *c.* 1790 (also below)

50a MORI SOSEN 1747–1821 *Apes in a persimmon-tree*

58 YOSA BUSON
Scholars riding and walking in the country (detail) *c.* 1770–1780

59 YOSA BUSON *Country cottage in a bamboo grove c.* 1777–1783

擱木功橋遮小村繁華羊偹竹

蓽紫門白頭不識王俟車

閑旭牛經教子孫

觀富書於雪堂

64a HOSODA EISHI 1756–1829 *Heads of nine beauties in a roundel with plum-blossom*

64 KATSUKAWA SHUNSHŌ *Snow, moonlight and flowers* (central scroll) After 1780

64 KATSUKAWA SHUNSHŌ *Snow, moonlight and flowers* (left-hand and right-hand scrolls) After 1780

70   MARUYAMA ŌKYO *Pines in the snow c.* 1780

left hand screen

right hand screen

75   IKENO TAIGA *Landscape in the four seasons in Chinese styles c.* 1753   above: Summer   below: Spring

80   TANOMURA CHIKUDEN *Boating on the Inagawa river* 1829 (detail)

72 Ryū Rikyō *Bamboo c. 1740–1750*

81 OKADA HANKŌ *Rain in the deep mountains* 1841

86 AOKI MOKUBEI *Landscape in autumn* 1827

83   TANI BUNCHŌ *Landscape with a Chinese gentleman and his attendant crossing a bridge* 1793

145   *Screen with design of chrysanthemums and paulownia badges* Late 16th/early 17th century

147   *Set of table and bowls with design of reeds with chrysanthemum and paulownia badges c.* 1593–1598

opposite: 144   *Bookrest with design of chrysanthemums, autumn grasses and paulownia badges* Late 16th century

156   *Box with design of scenes from court life, known as the van Diemen box c. 1630–1645*

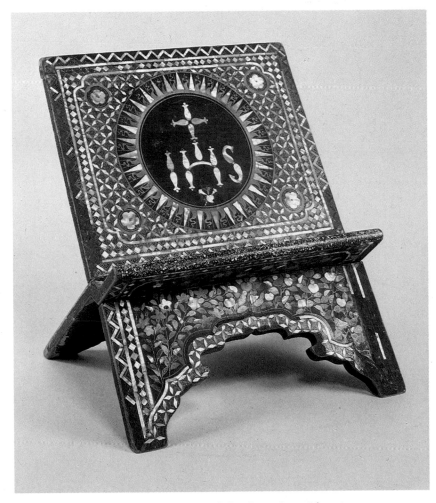

151 *Lectern with geometric and plant designs* Late 16th century

overleaf left: 158 *Writing box with design of a moored boat, reeds and plovers* Design *attr.* HON'AMI KŌETSU Early 17th century

overleaf right: 162 *Writing box with wave design* Designed by OGATA KŌRIN after HON'AMI KŌETSU Genroku period

160 *Set of lacquered furniture and utensils with design of peonies, karakusa scrolls and the double crane badge of the Nambu family* Late 17th/18th century

169 *Set of equipment for the shell game* 17th century

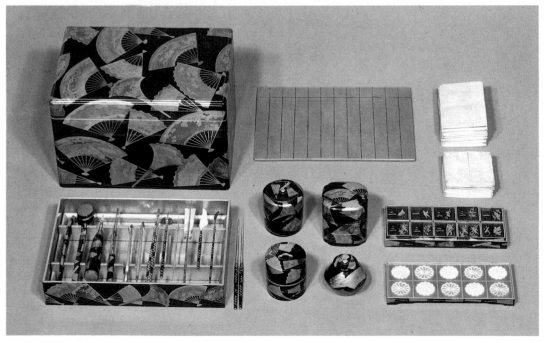

166   *Set of utensils for the incense game with design of scattered fans* Middle Edo period

198   *Set of five mukōzuke fan-shaped cups with green glaze and iron slip decoration* Late 16th/early 17th century

195   *Tea bowl called Hashihime* Late 16th century

opposite: 206   *Jar for leaf tea with design of Mount Yoshino* NONOMURA NINSEI Mid-17th century

224   *Water jar in the shape of a wooden bucket with inglaze decoration of waterplants and a stream* OGATA KENZAN 18th century

opposite: 225   *Set of five dishes* OGATA KENZAN 18th century

215 *Large dish with overglaze decoration of a string of aubergines against a wave pattern on
dark green ground in underglaze blue and overglaze enamel* Late 17th century

208   *Large deep bowl with landscape design in underglaze blue c. 1640–1650*

209   *Squared dish with celadon glaze and underglaze blue c. 1640–1650*

opposite: 217   *Chinese lion dog decorated in overglaze enamels 1692*

214　*Large dish with decoration of peony and butterfly in underglaze blue and overglaze enamel* Late 17th century

222　*Saucer dish with linked wheel pattern in underglaze blue and overglaze enamel* Early 18th century

228   *Set of implements for the green tea ceremony, pottery and porcelain* AOKI MOKUBEI Early 19th century

230   *Suit of armour in ōyoroi style* Early 18th century

opposite: 233   *Suit of armour in nimaidō gusoku style* Late 16th century

241 *Helmet in the form of a conch-shell* Momoyama or early Edo period

opposite: 237 *Helmet in the form of a court cap* Momoyama period

254   *Mounting for a pair of swords (daishō) with design of the mon of the Nabeshima family* Middle Edo period

257   *Mounting for a pair of swords (daishō) with striped design* Late 17th/early 18th century

top: 263 *Sword guard with design of the moon reflected in flooded rice fields* NISHIGAKI KANSHIRŌ 1709–1710

above: 262 *Sword guard with grapevine and trellis design* UMETADA MYŌJU Early 17th century

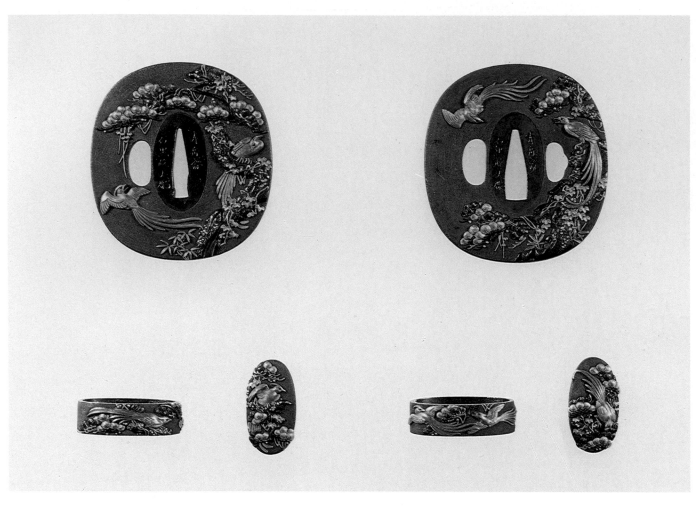

269 *Set of fittings for a pair of swords with design of long-tailed birds and pine-trees* ISHIGURO MASAYOSHI Late 18th/first half of 19th century

below left: 265 *Sword guard with stylised crane design* TSUCHIYA YASUCHIKA 1730–1744

below right: 258 *Sword guard with design of broken fans and falling cherry blossoms* HAYASHI MATASHICHI 17th century

a

b

c

d

INRŌ: a] 174   *with design of the three apes* SHIOMI SEISEI *Late 17th/early 18th century*
       b] 175   *with design of horses at pasture and monkeys* YAMADA JŌKASAI *Late 17th century*
       c] 181   *with design of chrysanthemums and butterflies* SHIBAYAMA SCHOOL *Late 18th or early 19th century*
       d] 182   *with design of dragon and phoenix medallions Late 18th century*

186   *Ceremonial palanquin (norimono) with design of peony, bamboo and hollyhock and peony mon* KŌAMI CHŌHŌ 1661–1663

337   *Jimbaori of blue and red woollen cloth* Momoyama period

350 *Kosode in white silk painted with a plum tree by* SAKAI HŌITSU Late Edo period

342   *Uchikake of purple silk with crane and trellis pattern* Middle Edo period

353 *Kosode of white figured satin with hats and maple leaves* Middle Edo period

354 *Kosode of white figured satin with wood-grain, clematis and wistaria* Middle Edo period

359 *Kosode of silk with hanging columns of straw hats and fans* Late Edo period

360   *Kosode of light yellow silk with the Eight Views of Lake Biwa in Yūzen dyeing* Late Edo period

361 *Kosode in green crêpe with windows and flowering plum beside a waterfall* Late Edo period

362   *Kosode in green crêpe with scattered plum blossom and characters above a bamboo trellis* Late Edo period

369 *Lined kariginu for Nō performance in gold brocade on indigo silk* Middle Edo period

375   *Nuihaku of silk for Nō performance on tea-coloured ground with butterflies, pine trees and wistaria* Early Edo period

380   *Karaori of silk for Nō performance, dangawari with autumn grasses* Middle Edo period

382 *Suō of dark purple silk for Kyōgen performance with waves and reeds in resist dyeing* Middle Edo period

381 *Kataginu for Kyōgen performance in pale blue hemp with gourds and half-wheels* Late Edo period

383   *Kataginu of silk for Kyōgen performance with windows, bamboo and flowering plum in resist dyeing* Early Edo period

387   *Banded atsuita of black silk for Nō performance with coloured triangles and windmills, cloud-roundels and floral squares in gold* Middle Edo period

404 *Katsugi with design of blinds and peonies in blue ground on linen* Late Edo period

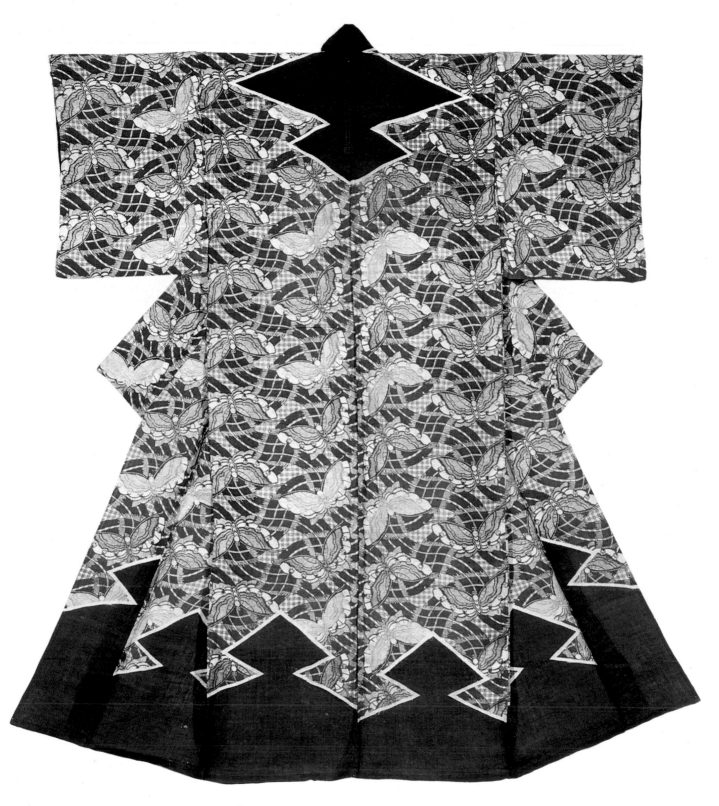

405   *Katsugi of linen with stencil-dyed butterflies on espaliered branches* Late Edo period

388   *Atsuita of silk for Nō performance with dyed paulownia and gongs on tortoise-shell ground* Middle Edo period

opposite: 277 vi)   *Wooden mask for Nō performance: Hannya, the female demon*

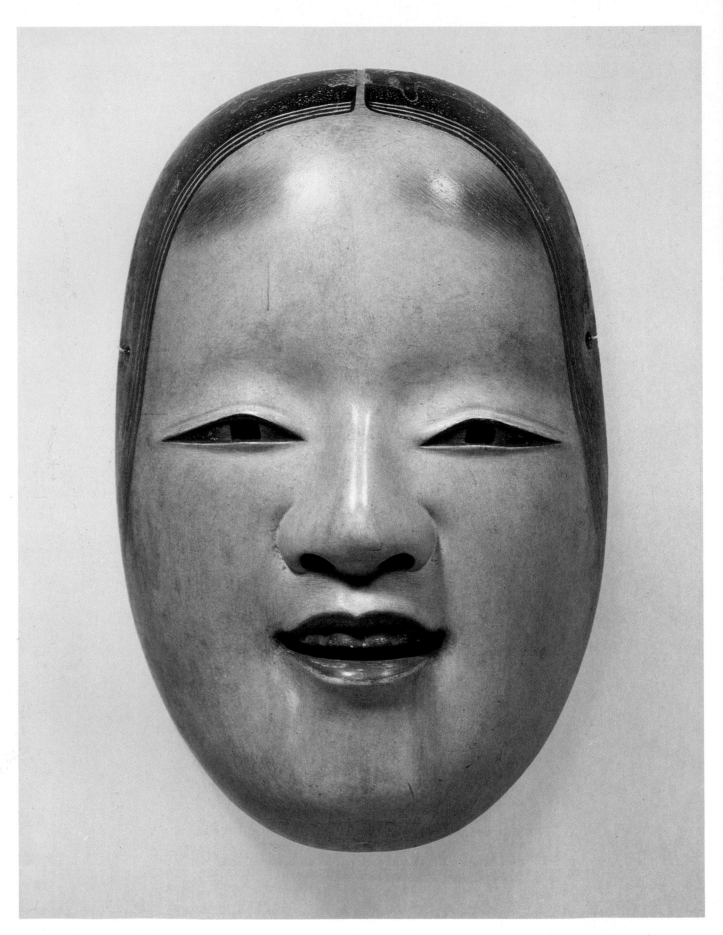

277 viii) *Wooden mask for Nō performance: Ko-omote, a young girl's mask*

Lacquer

In the middle of the first millennium BC wooden objects belonging to the Late Jōmon culture were painted with a substance that has all the appearance of the lacquer of later times, the sap of the lacquer tree, *Rhus verniciflua*. More advanced techniques of lacquering, applied to a wood or textile base, came from China in the sixth century AD, when Buddhism, together with many other elements of Chinese culture, including craft techniques, was introduced from the Asian mainland. At first lacquer was used chiefly in religious sculpture, but before long it had become a leading medium of decoration on a wide variety of objects ranging from sword scabbards to boxes for religious garments; from the tenth century onwards we find frequent examples of and literary references to *maki-e*, which, although of Chinese origin, was to become the most characteristic of Japanese lacquering techniques. The word *maki-e* means literally 'sprinkled picture' and the essence of *maki-e* is that the design is sprinkled in metal (usually gold or silver) dust from a bamboo tube onto a coat of still-wet lacquer which has been painted over a previously-applied and dried lacquer ground. There are three main types: *hiramaki-e*, in which the design is raised above the ground only by the thickness of its coats of lacquer (see no. 146), *takamaki-e*, in which the design is built up and modelled in a mixture of lacquer and charcoal or clay dust (see no. 147), and *togidashi-e*, a complex technique in which the completed *hiramaki-e* design and its ground are covered in further layers of lacquer which are then polished down until the design reappears, flush with the new ground (see no. 171).

By the end of the Kamakura period all three types of *maki-e* were fully developed and there was also available the rich ground decoration known as *nashiji*, which is achieved by setting irregularly shaped flakes of gold at different angles in a bed of damp lacquer. During the succeeding Muromachi period and especially in the second half of the fifteenth century, at the court of the shōgun Ashikaga Yoshimasa (1436–1490), all four techniques were used in the creation of an intricate and luxurious style of landscape decoration which makes frequent allusion in its subject-matter to the themes of classical poetry and, in spite of a trend towards simplification of design in the sixteenth century, it was essentially this style which predominated, at least in work destined for the use of the aristocracy or the higher ranks of the samurai, at the dawn of the Momoyama period.

The most dramatic expression in lacquerwork of the bravura and immediacy of the Momoyama decorative style is the group of wares known collectively as *Kōdaiji maki-e* from the Kōdaiji temple in Kyoto, built on the orders of Hideyoshi's wife Kitano Mandokoro as a mausoleum for herself and her husband. Some of the interior architectural features of the temple building itself, completed in 1606, are decorated in the style, but inconsistencies in the design, alterations recently detected by X-ray and, most importantly, an inscription dated 1596 in the shrine containing Hideyoshi's image indicate that they must have been moved to the Kōdaiji from somewhere else, probably Fushimi castle. Researchers have now established that the style was in fact current as early as 1586; articles lacquered specifically in the Kōdaiji manner were last made around 1630, although its influence continued at least until the middle of the Edo period.

The Kōdaiji lacquers (nos 143–147), some of which are said by a temple tradition to have been used by Hideyoshi and Mandokoro during the former's lifetime, are distinguished both by their stylistic and technical features and by their subject-matter. Instead of the dense *nashiji* ground decorated with thick *takamaki-e* and precious metal inlays typical of the Muromachi period, we normally find a plain black lacquer ground with designs executed in the simpler and faster *hiramaki-e* technique and for greater speed and immediacy the final polishing of the *hiramaki-e* is often omitted. *Nashiji* is used not as a ground but as a method of decoration and a wide variety of effects is achieved by the application of gold flakes of differing degrees of purity over black- and red-coloured backgrounds. Another characteristic feature is *harigaki*, 'needle-drawing', in which a sharp tool is used to scratch lines in the lacquer before it has fully dried.

In Kōdaiji work of the classic period (approximately 1592 to 1615), the decoration is confined almost exclusively to the so-called *akikusa*, 'autumn grasses', of which the most common are the chrysanthemum, bush-clover (*hagi*), bellflower (*kikyō*), wild pink (*nadeshiko*) and pampas grass (*susuki*). These are drawn in a free and naturalistic manner and are frequently contrasted with formal *mon*, especially the chrysanthemum and paulownia much used by Hideyoshi; further contrasts are sometimes effected by a zigzagging diagonal line which separates areas of sharply differentiated surface treatment. Although many of these methods can be found in lacquers of the Muromachi period, it was not until the Momoyama that they were combined to form a coherent and distinctive idiom which appealed to the taste for striking visual appeal of Hideyoshi and his contemporaries.

The most original lacquer products of the early Edo period are the group of pieces associated with the name of Hon'ami Kōetsu (1558–1637). The extent and nature of his connexion with their manufacture can probably never be established but the arduous and time-consuming process of lacquering might well have been alien to his temperament, suited as it was to the more directly achievable effects of calligraphy and pottery. Documentary evidence, in the form of three letters by Kōetsu to a client and possibly to a *maki-e* craftsmen, tends to suggest that Kōetsu's rôle was akin to that of the art director, that is to say he was responsible not only for the general design of a piece but also for the choice of materials and techniques employed to achieve it. Such a rôle would be in keeping with Kōetsu's early training as a connoisseur (of swords) and there would have been no shortage of craftsmen to execute his designs at his artistic community in Takagamine.

The Kōetsu group of lacquers (nos. 150, 158) make use of many of the materials and techniques of the Muromachi *maki-e* masters but favour great strength and simplicity in place of the painstakingly detailed craftsmanship of the early period. Instead of delicately modelled applied gold and silver details there are broad sheets of dull base metal, lead or pewter, sometimes boldly engraved, contrasting with plain gold *hiramaki-e*; for the ground, *nashiji* is avoided in favour of plain black lacquer. The emphasis is on overall design and, to draw attention to the design, the form of the writing box (*suzuribako*), a traditional vehicle for lacquer decoration which contains brush, water-dropper, inkstick and inkstone for grinding the ink, is altered: the formerly flat lid is given a domed profile, which encourages the eye to appreciate the totality rather than the detail. In subject-matter there is a marked preference for classical themes, just as we would expect from the example of the calligraphy and painting collaborations of Kōetsu and Sōtatsu.

Coming to the lacquer productions of Kōetsu's successor Ogata Kōrin (1658–1716), we encounter still greater difficulty in assessing the degree of his involvement in the works associated with his name. Of the four pieces in this exhibition (nos 162–165), one is stored in a box on which an inscription by Kōrin states that it is a copy by him after a (lost) piece by Kōetsu, one is constantly ascribed to him and its design appears in a later book of Kōrin designs and the other two, although quite likely to be of early eighteenth-century date and definitely in the Kōrin manner, cannot be confidently connected with him in any way. Although there can be no doubt of Kōrin's indebtedness to the Sōtatsu-Kōetsu tradition, his lacquerwork, even in the supposedly copied Sumino-e writing box (no. 162), has a lightness and grace which is considerably removed from the assertive boldness of the early Edo period.

The arrival of the Portuguese brought new furniture shapes and new decorative techniques to Japan and these gave rise to a new type of lacquerware inspired by European models and mostly made for the European market. The new shapes included the domed coffer (no. 155) and the chest of drawers with fall front; the latter is the scriptor of English furniture, derived from the *escritorio* of Spain. In the mid-sixteenth century these shapes were new to Japan and were immediately copied. By the mid-seventeenth century the fall-front of the chest of drawers was replaced by a pair of doors opening at the sides and this is the familiar export lacquer chest that was to become a feature of so many great houses throughout Europe and was quickly imitated in China and then in Europe itself. It was probably the early type of these chests that are referred to in a letter of 1569 by the Jesuit Luís Fróis which says 'Nobunaga . . . has twelve or fifteen chests like those of Portugal'.

At first, these pieces were decorated in a new technique. This was the inlay of relatively large pieces of shell in patterns or pictures into a matrix of coarse dark lacquer, which was then lacquered over with details in gold. This technique has some resemblance to earlier Korean technique but may have been derived from Gujarat 'japanned' (false-lacquered) chests imported by the Portuguese. There are examples of this style in European collections that can certainly be dated to before 1596 from inventory records. Also, there are pieces made for Christian use: Bible rests, Host boxes and triptych shrines (nos 151, 152), many of which bear the Jesuit monogram. This implies a date of manufacture before the most severe restrictions on Christianity in 1623. Probably the style was on the wane at the beginning of the century in favour of the new pictorial lacquer which decorated exported wares throughout the seventeenth century. Possibly such wares are referred to by Captain Saris, bringing the *Clove* into London in 1614 with 'Some Japan wares, as ritch Scritoires, Trunckes, Beoubes (*byōbu*, the Japanese word for 'screen'), Cupps and Dishes of all sortes, and of a most excellent varnish'. Few of these are of such high quality as the box especially made for Maria van Diemen, wife of the Governor of the Dutch East Indies (no. 156), but then most of them are trade goods and not special orders.

Of course some lacquers reached Europe at early times that were not made particularly for export – these belong to the 'Cabinet of Curiosities' rather than to the normal furnishing of a European house. Among the great quantity of mid-seventeenth century lacquer belonging to the Royal house of Denmark is the remarkable picnic set, with its associated teabowl and *cha-ire* (no. 157).

Important and interesting as the lacquerwares of the Kōetsu-Kōrin tradition and the export pieces are, they are somewhat removed from the main tradition of seventeenth-century lacquer, which is in essence a continuation of the Muromachi period style. This continuity was principally due to the strength of hereditary craft traditions, of which the Kōami family are the most distinguished and remarkable example. The first five members worked for the Ashikaga shōguns, the sixth and seventh worked for Hideyoshi and Ieyasu and successive generations until 1723 were official lacquerers to the Tokugawa shōguns. There were many subschools and other similar families were employed both by the shōgunate and by many of the daimyō. The traditional style is seen at its most conservative and luxurious in the famous wedding set made by the tenth master Chōjū (1599–1651) for a Tokugawa wedding in 1639 and in the tiered box (no. 161) in this exhibition: the decoration follows closely the Ashikaga style of idealised landscape but the technique is still more elaborate, the design more crowded. A variant, owing something to the Kōdaiji lacquers, which avoided the depiction of the landscape setting, is illustrated by the great *norimono* (no. 186) and the somewhat later wedding set (no. 160) in which bold plant designs often bearing some symbolic auspicious meaning are combined with family *mon*.

Such work offered a challenge more to the craftsmen's patience than to their artistic creativity and the traditionalism in design demanded by their clients combined with supremely confident technique could not but result in a trend towards over-ornateness and lack of originality. But the rise to popularity of the *inrō* during the seventeenth and eighteenth centuries presented lacquerers with a timely opportunity to give freer range to their imaginations and to experiment technically. The *inrō* was originally, as the name, meaning 'seal-basket', implies, a container for seals; the first such containers were imported from China during the early Muromachi period and later the *inrō* form was miniaturised as a set of interlocking compartments held together by a cord hung from the waist and used to hold a variety of herbal and other medicines. The popularity of *inrō* and the fact that they were commissioned as much by the merchant class as by samurai and daimyō and had no traditionally fixed style of decoration brought into being a wide range of new techniques or variations on techniques and these were used in the depiction of an enormous variety of subject-matter. The number of colours was increased, *togidashi-e* was greatly refined and frequently used on its own, sometimes even to imitate brushwork (no. 180), shell and other materials were applied (nos 181, 182) and the wood core could be made a feature of the design. The vogue for *inrō* led to the use of innovatory styles and techniques on other objects and the practice of hanging them from the belt increased the demand for *netsuke* (nos 278–336), which shared with *inrō* that love of the curious and exotic which is a feature of much of the lacquer of the eighteenth and nineteenth centuries.

JVE, ORI

143 *Document box with design of autumn grasses and bamboo*

F/G2 秋草蒔絵手文庫

Wood, decorated in black lacquer and gold *hiramaki-e* and *nashiji* lacquer
26.7 × 50.3 × 31 cm
c. 1593–1598
KŌDAIJI, Kyoto
Important Cultural Property

This box is one of a group of lacquer utensils still in the Kōdaiji temple which were probably made for Fushimi castle and are said to have been used by Toyotomi Hideyoshi and his wife Kitano Mandokoro. It exhibits many of the most characteristic technical and stylistic features of Kōdaiji lacquer: contrasted areas of plain black and gold *nashiji* lacquer are separated by a zigzagging diagonal line and the contrast is sharpened by the difference in treatment between the freely drawn flowers and grasses and the rigid bamboo. The metal fittings are decorated with the chrysanthemum and paulownia badges much used by Hideyoshi.

144 *Bookrest with design of chrysanthemums, autumn grasses and paulownia badges*

S/G2 秋草蒔絵見台

[repr. in colour p. 194]
Wood, decorated in black lacquer and gold *hiramaki-e* and *nashiji* lacquer
57 × 37.5 × 29.2 cm
Late 16th century
TOKYO NATIONAL MUSEUM

Somewhat unusually for Kōdaiji lacquer, the black ground is

decorated with a sparse overall sprinkling of gold *nashiji* flakes. Denser *nashiji* flakes, probably on a background of reddish lacquer, are used to depict some of the flowers and leaves; the other principal technique is gold *hiramaki-e*. The contrast characteristic of the Kōdaiji style is provided here by the combination of flowing chrysanthemums and autumn grasses with stiff and formal paulownia badges. The gilt copper mounts are engraved with chrysanthemum badges.

145 *Screen with design of chrysanthemums and paulownia badges*

F/G2 秋草蒔絵座屏

[repr. in colour on p. 195]
Wood, decorated in black lacquer and gold *hiramaki-e* and *nashiji* lacquer
63.2 × 60.5 × 25.3 cm
Late 16th or early 17th century
TOKYO NATIONAL MUSEUM

Because of the close similarity of the framework of this screen to that of a sword stand in the Kōdaiji, it has been suggested that it was converted into its present form from a sword stand by the addition of the decorated panel. The design is unusual: more attention than is normal with Kōdaiji lacquer is given to the ground from which the plants grow and chrysanthemums only are depicted to the exclusion of all other autumn grasses. The typical contrast of natural plant forms with stylised badges is echoed in the gilded *shakudō* mounts.

143

146

146 Travelling chest with design of dewy grasses and paulownia badges

S/G2 　芒に桐紋蒔絵旅箪笥

Wood, decorated with black lacquer and gold *hiramaki-e* and *nashiji* lacquer
50.2 × 38.9 × 30.8 cm
Late 16th or early 17th century
SUNTORY ART MUSEUM, Tokyo

This travelling chest with removable drop front is a remarkable demonstration of the variety of effects which can be achieved by using the *nashiji* technique in different ways. On the leaves of the *susuki* grasses and the paulownia crests the contrast between areas of sparsely and densely sprinkled *nashiji* is sharpened by the use of different coloured backgrounds. The metal mounts are engraved as usual with formalised heraldic badges.

147 Set of table and bowls with design of reeds with chrysanthemum and paulownia badges

F/G2 　芦辺蒔絵懸盤・椀類

[repr. in colour on p. 195]
Wood, decorated with gold *nashiji*, *hiramaki-e* and *takamaki-e* lacquer and gold and silver foil
Table 17.7 × 34.5 × 33.5 cm
c. 1593–1598
KŌDAIJI, Kyoto
Important Cultural Property

Although this set forms part of the group of lacquerwares which were probably made for Fushimi castle and used by Hideyoshi, its decoration is untypical of Kōdaiji lacquer in both technique and subject-matter. The entire ground is covered in dense *nashiji* and the design of reeds on a river bank is executed in thick *takamaki-e* instead of the more usual *hiramaki-e*. The use of gold and silver foil on the paulownia badges is another lavish technique more typical of the preceding Muromachi period.

148 Two-tiered octagonal food box and cover with design of squirrels and grapes

S/G2 　葡萄栗鼠蒔絵食籠

Wood, decorated in black lacquer and gold *hiramaki-e* and *nashiji* lacquer
26.4 × 25.2 × 25.2 cm
Late Momoyama or early Edo period
TOKYO NATIONAL MUSEUM

This box demonstrates the gradual refinement of style which characterized the Kōdaiji lacquer tradition during the first thirty or so years of the seventeenth century. The dramatic contrasts of the earlier pieces have given way to a refined virtuosity and, on the technical front, an even greater range of effects is achieved by the use of gold of varying purity and a wide range of densities in the *e-nashiji*. The shape of the box is of Chinese origin.

148

149 Set of shelves with design of the Kokei sanshō

F/G2 　虎渓三笑蒔絵棚

Wood, decorated in black lacquer, gold *takamaki-e* lacquer and gold and silver foil
65.2 × 73.3 × 32.7 cm
c. 1600–1615
TOKYO NATIONAL MUSEUM

Documentary evidence indicates that the tea master Furuta Oribe (1544–1615) commissioned Kōami Chōgen (1572–1607) to decorate a bookcase with the motif of the *Kokei sanshō* ('Three Laughers of Tiger Torrent'), but none of the surviving examples corresponds exactly with the detailed description given in Chōgen's biography. The *Kokei sanshō* motif is the final scene of the story of the Chinese recluse Hui Yuan, who was tricked by two guests into leaving his place of meditation and crossing the Tiger Torrent, something he had vowed never to do.

149

150

150 Set of shelves, called nenohi-dana, with design of Genji motifs

S/G2   子日蒔絵棚

Design traditionally attributed to HON'AMI KŌETSU (1558–1637) Wood, decorated in black lacquer and gold *takamaki-e* lacquer with applied tin, gold, silver and shell
65.5 × 72.5 × 33 cm
Early 17th century
HINOHARA COLLECTION, Tokyo
Important Cultural Property

This set of shelves takes its name from the motif on the top shelf of two young pine branches, which refers to an incident in Chapter XXXIII of the *Genji monogatari*. The other shelves also bear Genji motifs, of fans and an oxcart. Because of their striking similarity in form, size and decorative technique to the *Kokei sanshō* set (no. 149), it has recently been suggested that the Nenohi shelves are as likely to owe their inspiration to Furuta Oribe as to Kōetsu, to whom they have been traditionally ascribed.

151 Lectern with geometric and plant designs

F/G3   IHS七宝繋蒔絵螺鈿書見台

[repr. in colour on p. 197]
Wood, decorated with black lacquer, gold and silver *hiramaki-e* lacquer and shell inlay
35.8 × 34 × 46 cm
Late 16th century
TOKYO NATIONAL MUSEUM

This lectern follows closely the contemporary European folding pattern, even to the decorative outline of the foot in Baroque style. Like many of the Christian lacquers, it features the monogram of the Society of Jesus surrounded by a sunburst halo.

152 Portable shrine with design of trees and animals

S/G3   花鳥獣螺鈿蒔絵聖龕

Wood, decorated with black lacquer, gold and silver *hiramaki-e* lacquer and shell inlay, and with gilt copper mounts
49.5 × 30 × 4.8 cm
Late 16th century
TOKYO NATIONAL MUSEUM
Important Cultural Property

An Iberian or Flemish-style crucifixion is enclosed in a Japanese case with folding doors which are decorated on both sides in the rather coarse technique typical of these early Christian lacquerwares. It is an indication either of a shortage of religious paintings among the Jesuit missionaries or, perhaps, of the characteristically Japanese love of lavish decoration at this period that the wings, instead of containing paintings of saints or donors, should feature entirely secular designs of camellias, mandarin trees, monkeys, deer and an owl. The extensive use of the time-saving *harigaki* technique is a feature shared with the Kōdaiji lacquer group.

152

153

154

153 *Stationery box with design of Europeans*

F/G3 南蛮人蒔絵料紙箱

Wood, decorated in black lacquer and gold *takamaki-e* lacquer, with fragments of shell and traces of tin foil

13.6 × 32.9 × 41.1 cm
Late Momoyama period
PRIVATE COLLECTION, Japan

The arrival of Europeans in Japan excited the curiosity of craftsmen as well as painters and there is a large group of Momoyama period lacquers which testify to the contemporary fascination with the foreigners' strange clothes and grotesque features. The maker of this box contrived to draw the viewer's attention towards such exotic features as buttons and cap-feathers by the application of fragments of shell.

154 *Writing box with design of Europeans*

S/G3 南蛮人蒔絵硯箱

Wood, decorated in black lacquer and gold *takamaki-e* lacquer, with fragments of shell; the interior decorated with plum-blossom and pinks

4.3 × 21.2 × 22.8 cm
Late Momoyama period
OSAKA PREFECTURE

The very close similarities in style, technique and subject-matter between this writing box and the stationery box (no. 153) suggest that they both came from the same atelier. An interesting feature common to both is the device of indicating differences of rank by differences in height between the figures.

155

155 *Pair of lacquered wood coffers*

FS/G3 　扇面蒔絵螺鈿大櫃一双

Decoration of gold lacquered fans and cartouches with
rayskin and pearl-shell inlay on lacquered ground
62.9 × 131 × 55.9 cm
Late 16th or early 17th century
LORD METHUEN

A hint of the painted export lacquers that were to supersede these
namban-style pieces is visible in the cartouches of the one coffer
and the fans of the other. By the mid-seventeenth century the
painting had spread to cover the whole decorated surface and it
was these latter pieces that were exported from Japan in great
quantities in the second half of the century. They were quickly
imitated in China and, in 'japan', in Europe.

The letter of Captain Saris mentions 'trunckes. . .of a most
excellent varnish' in 1614. In Gripsholm Castle near Stockholm
there is a coffer, markedly similar to these, that is inventoried for
1613, and has been in the castle ever since.

One coffer will be shown in each half of the exhibition.

156 *Box with design of scenes from court life, called the van Diemen box*

FS/G3 　源氏絵蒔絵箱

[repr. in colour on p. 196]
Wood, decorated with black lacquer, gold and silver *hiramaki-e*
and *takamaki-e* lacquer and gold and silver foil
insc. inside the lid 'MARIA UAN DIEMEN'
16 × 48 × 36.7 cm
c. 1630–45
VICTORIA AND ALBERT MUSEUM

The van Diemen box is unique among Japanese exported
lacquers for the outstanding quality of its workmanship in which
none of the time-saving lacquer techniques encountered in most
other pieces is found and for the fact that it is essentially
Japanese in form, in contrast to the much-exported coffers and
escritorios of European inspiration. However, the avoidance of

Japanese compositional method, the formal decoration of the
borders and the shape of the cartouche on the interior suspended
tray all indicate that it was made with a European client in mind.

Probably the single most celebrated Japanese artefact to have
entered Europe in the pre-modern period, it was originally owned
by Maria, the wife of Anton van Diemen (*d.* 1645), ninth
Governor of the Dutch East Indies; her name is inscribed inside
the lid. It next comes to light in the posthumous *Inventaire* of the
collection of Madame de Pompadour (1765), by whom it was
probably acquired shortly before July 1753. Then it appears in
the sale of the collection of Pierre Louis-Paul Randon de Boisset
(1777), where it was bought for the sixth Duc de Bouillon at the
record price of 6,901 livres, and in 1797 it was bought for
William Beckford (1760–1844), the author of *Vathek* and
renowned collector of Japanese lacquer. It was later acquired by
his son-in-law the Duke of Hamilton (1767–1852), from whom
it passed, via the collection of Sir Trevor Lawrence, to the Victoria
and Albert Museum in 1916

157 *Picnic set with design of flowers and grasses*

FS/LR 　秋草蒔絵箱・椀類

Wood, decorated in black lacquer and gold and silver
hiramaki-e lacquer and with iron and copper mounts
The container 41 × 25 cm
Mid-17th century
NATIONALMUSEET, Copenhagen

This remarkable picnic set, which includes instruments for the
making of tea, comes from the Cabinet of Curiosities of the
Danish Royal House. As it was not realised in the seventeenth
century that the pieces belonged together, the various parts came
into the royal collection – and are hence inventoried – at different
dates. The earliest date for any part of the interlocking pieces is
1674, but because of the style of decoration, recalling the Kōdaiji
lacquers, its date of manufacture is clearly considerably earlier.

Associated with the set is not only a tea whisk but also a tea
bowl and tea jar. The bowl is metal-lined but is wooden and
decorated with lacquer which imitates Raku pottery. From an

155

illustration of this piece in Simon Paulli's *Commentarius de abusu tabaci . . . et herbae theé . . .* it is known that this tea bowl was in Europe before 1665. The jar is not inventoried until 1725 but its association with the set seems probable. It is made of bamboo, metal-lined, and is lacquered in close imitation of a Takatori tea jar, itself imitating a node of bamboo.

158 Writing box with design of a moored boat, reeds and plovers

F/G3 芦舟蒔絵硯箱

[repr. in colour on p. 198]
Design traditionally attributed to HON'AMI KŌETSU (1558–1637)
Wood, decorated in black lacquer and gold *hiramaki-e* and *takamaki-e* lacquer with applied lead
4.2 × 22.4 × 23.6 cm
Early 17th century
TOKYO NATIONAL MUSEUM
Important Cultural Property

After the well-known Bridge of Boats writing box, this is perhaps the most celebrated of the lacquer designs attributed to Kōetsu. The combination of gold *hiramaki-e* and *takamaki-e* with bold metal inlay and the distinctive contour of the lid are both innovations which were later copied by his follower Ogata Kōrin. Kōetsu's love of classical and literary tradition is illustrated by his choice of subject-matter, since the design of boat and plovers is very close to that on one of the famous Heian period handscrolls of the Thirty-six Poets in the Nishi Honganji, Kyoto.

159 Storage box for Nō drama texts with design of autumn grasses and calligraphy

S/G3 秋草蒔絵謡曲簞笥

Wood, decorated in black lacquer and gold and silver *hiramaki-e* lacquer and shell, with silver studs
27.7 × 40.4 × 26.3 cm
First half of the 17th century
SEIKADŌ BUNKO, Tokyo
Important Art Object

Although this is not one of the pieces closely associated with Kōetsu, there is strong evidence of his influence in the style of the calligraphy of the Nō drama titles and the decoration as a whole is reminiscent of the calligraphy scrolls with background painting by Sōtatsu (no. 24). The autumn grasses executed in gold *hiramaki-e* illustrate the lasting influence of the Kōdaiji manner.

160 Set of lacquered furniture and utensils with design of peonies, karakusa scrolls and the double crane badge of the Nambu family

FS/G4 牡丹唐草向鶴丸紋散蒔絵婚礼調度

[repr. in colour on p. 201]
Wood, decorated in black lacquer, gold *nashiji* lacquer and gold and silver *hiramaki-e* and *takamaki-e*, and with silver fittings
Kurodana 68.2 × 77.7 × 39.1 cm; *zushidana* 79.7 × 99.1 × 39.7 cm
Late 17th or 18th century
KŌZU KOBUNKA KAIKAN, Kyoto

157

161

159

In the early Edo period it became the practice for suites of this type, often made up of more than fifty pieces in all, to be commissioned for the trousseaux of brides of daimyō or other senior samurai families. The present set includes the standard three-shelved *zushidana* (with curved top) and *kurodana* (with flat top) which developed towards the end of the sixteenth century from the earlier two-shelved *tana*, a clothes-rack, bowls and a ewer for washing, mirror stands and mirror cases, equipment for blackening the teeth (a widespread practice among women) and burning incense, a stand for making offerings (*sampōdai*) and a writing box, as well as a wealth of other boxes of differing shapes and sizes, including the large and small *sumiakabako* with their distinctive areas of red lacquering standing out in sharp contrast to the otherwise uniform decorative scheme.

Half of the set will be displayed in each half of the exhibition.

161 *Two-tiered box and cover with design of landscapes and Tokugawa mon*

FS/LR 山水葵紋蒔絵二段重箱

Wood, decorated in gold *nashiji* lacquer and gold and silver *hiramaki-e* and *takamaki-e* lacquer with gold and silver foil; rims gold *fundame* lacquer; fittings gilt metal
13.1 × 24.1 × 16.7 cm
Late 17th or early 18th century
VICTORIA AND ALBERT MUSEUM

This tiered box, probably from an incense set, exemplifies the luxurious style of lacquer decoration which was current during and shortly after the shōgunate of Tokugawa Tsunayoshi (reigned 1680–1709). The idealised landscapes are essentially a revival of the Muromachi tradition, but the technique is yet more detailed and meticulous; the minute attention to detail extends even to the *mon*, each of which is executed in a slightly different combination of gold *hiramaki-e* and gold foil.

162 *Writing box with wave design*

F/G6 住江蒔絵硯箱

[repr. in colour on p. 199]
Designed by OGATA KŌRIN (1658–1716) after HON'AMI
KŌETSU (1558–1637)
Wood, decorated in gold lacquer and applied silver and lead
10 × 23 × 25.8 cm
Genroku period
SEIKADŌ BUNKO, Tokyo
Important Cultural Property

The storage box in which this piece is normally kept bears an inscription by Kōrin to the effect that it is a copy of one by Kōetsu. The shape is similar to Kōetsu's Boat and Reeds box (no. 158) and the design recalls his decorative style, but the subject-matter is treated in a more abstract fashion and the bold lines of the waves are a distinctive and original feature which is also found in Kōrin's paintings. The silver characters give the text of a poem from the *Kokin wakashū* anthology (*c.* 900 AD): 'Waves beat (*yoru*) on the shores of Sumino-e. Even at night (*yoru*), in the passageway of dreams, you try to avoid the eyes of the world.'

163

163 *Writing box with design of flying cranes and waves*

S/G6 群鶴蒔絵硯箱

After OGATA KŌRIN (1658–1716)
Wood, decorated in gold *hiramaki-e* lacquer and applied lead and silver
4.8 × 21.8 × 24.2 cm
18th century
TOKYO NATIONAL MUSEUM

It is impossible to establish the nature of Kōrin's involvement, if any, in the manufacture of this box. There appears to be no parallel in the wood-block printed books of Kōrin designs which appeared after his death, but he is known to have used the 'thousand cranes' motif on a decorated incense wrapper. The waves, too, are very much in the Kōrin manner and the box has many technical features in common with the rest of the Kōrin group.

164 *Writing box with design of Ariwara no Narihira on a fan*

F/G6 業平扇面蒔絵硯箱

Designed by OGATA KŌRIN (1658–1716)
Wood, decorated in gold *hiramaki-e* lacquer on black lacquer, with tin and silver
insc. inside with a later signature, *Hokkyō Kōrin*
5.3 × 19.8 × 27.6 cm
18th century
NEZU ART MUSEUM, Tokyo
Important Art Object

The design on this box, which shows the famous ninth-century poet Ariwara no Narihira, is included in the *Kōrin shinsen hyakuzu* (1864), a wood-block printed book of Kōrin designs. Although it cannot be definitely established that Kōrin actually supervised its production, it is known to have been owned and admired by the distinguished lacquer artist Koma Kansai II (1766–1835) (see no. 177) and his famous pupil Shibata Zeshin (1807–1891); it shares many of the stylistic features mentioned in connexion with the Sumino-e box (no. 162).

165 *Two-tiered writing box with design of deer and bush-clover*

S/G6 鹿萩蒔絵硯箱

Style of OGATA KŌRIN (1658–1716)
Wood, decorated in black lacquer with gold *hiramaki-e* lacquer, tin, lead and thick shell
13 × 17.2 × 29 cm
18th century
ISHIKAWA PREFECTURAL MUSEUM

The design spreads over the sides in a way reminiscent of the famous Yatsuhashi writing box, the best known of the Kōrin lacquers, which is similar in size and shape to the present piece, although the lid is of a different type. The materials used, too, are typical of the Kōrin group of lacquers and the literary allusions implied by the autumnal theme of deer and bush clover (*hagi*) are very much in the Sōtatsu-Kōetsu tradition. In a two-tiered box of this type, the lower half is used to store paper.

164

165

166 Set of utensils for the incense game with design of scattered fans

F/LR 扇散蒔絵十種香道具

[repr. in colour on p. 201]
Chiefly wood, decorated in black lacquer with
gold and silver *hiramaki-e* lacquer; metal fittings iron and silver
Box 15.5 × 23.6 × 17 cm
Middle Edo period
TOKYO NATIONAL MUSEUM

Although the sophisticated appraisal of incense in Japan dates back to the Heian period, it was not until the late fifteenth century that the incense game evolved as a formalised ritual with a fixed set of rules. In the Edo period the competitive element in the game became somewhat more pronounced but the beauty of the utensils remained a prime consideration. The present set is used for a version of the game in which four different incenses are used: first three of them are burnt and their smells memorised, then ten further pieces of incense, each made from one of the four incenses in the game, are burnt in turn in a random order and compared to the three memorised smells. The players indicate which incense they think is being burnt by placing one of four different wood tokens, marked in gold lacquer, in a circular box with a slot; the tokens are marked 'one', 'two', 'three', corresponding to the three incenses burnt at the beginning, and 'guest' (*kyaku*) corresponding to the fourth incense which was not burnt at the beginning. The small tools in the flat box are used in preparing the incense for burning, the papers are used to keep the incenses hidden from the players and the boards are used to record their scores and the progress of the game.

167 Markers for the incense game in the form of racing horsemen

S/LR 競馬香道具

Board wood; horsemen ivory with silk clothes
Board 11.8 × 73 cm; horsemen *h* 9.8 cm,
19th century
TOKYO NATIONAL MUSEUM

During the Edo period a number of highly ingenious means of scoring the incense game were devised, including one in which a model of a praying mantis is charmed by one or other of a pair of miniature lutes and moved towards it. The commonest markers, however, were horsemen which were moved towards a finishing post each time an incense was correctly identified.

168 Set of equipment for preparing incense for the incense game

S/LR 香割道具

Block, chisel, hammer, knife and saw
Lacquered wood with gold and silver foil and steel; the block oak
Block 7.3 × 14.5 cm, chisel *l* 14.3 cm, hammer *l* 19.6 cm,
knife *l* 21.3 cm, saw *l* 25.2 cm
Middle Edo period
TOKYO NATIONAL MUSEUM

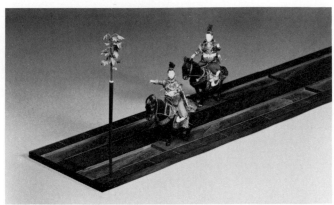

167

168

169 Set of equipment for the shell game

FS/LR 貝合わせ具

[repr. in colour on p. 200]
Boxes wood, painted, lacquered and decorated with gold paper; clam shells painted in colours and gold
Boxes 34.6 × 32.3 cm, shells *dm* 10 cm
Middle Edo period
KŌZU KOBUNKA KAIKAN, Kyoto

The shell game was another popular Edo period pastime and its equipment often formed part of the suites of lacquer furniture presented to daimyō brides. The present set is in the standard form, with octagonal containers decorated with gold paper stuck over relief diaper designs (*kikkōmon*) executed in *gofun*, and painted with conventional court scenes in Tosa style. The object of the game, which originated in the Heian period, is simple: a number of shells, sometimes as many as 360, are divided into their two halves, one set of halves going in one box and the other in the other box. One set of halves is put out and halves from the other set are withdrawn one at a time and united with their matching half. To make it easier to form pairs, the matching halves are painted with related scenes from the *Genji monogatari* and other medieval romances.

170 Set of poem cards

FS/LR 百人一首かるた

Cards gold-edged, painted in colours, ink and gold
Each 8.5 × 5.6 cm
Middle Edo period
TOKYO NATIONAL MUSEUM

The poem card game is believed to have been devised at the imperial court in Kyoto by the poet Nakanoin Michimura (1588–

170

1653) as a combination of the recently introduced European playing cards with the traditional Japanese practice of inscribing pairs of shells with two halves of a poem in a version of the shell game. The game is based on the *Ogura hyakunin isshu*, an anthology of a hundred poems by a hundred poets compiled by Fujiwara Teika (1162–1241). Half of the full pack of two hundred cards is decorated with portraits of the hundred poets and their poems, and the other half with the last words of their poems. The object of the game is to unite the poets with the last words of their poems.

171 *Picnic set with design of autumn grasses*
F/LR 秋草蒔絵提重

Wood, decorated with black lacquer and gold *togidashi-e* lacquer: bottles silver
29.3 × 28 × 19.8 cm
Middle Edo period
SUNTORY ART MUSEUM, Tokyo

The picnic set, which combines saké bottles, a tiered box for food and other utensils in a convenient carrying case, is one of the most practical of the many new lacquer forms devised during the Momoyama and Edo periods.

172 *Picnic set with striped design and bottle in the form of an eggplant (nasubi)*
S/LR 変塗蒔絵提重

Wood, decorated with gold *nashiji* lacquer and multicoloured *hiramaki-e* and *takamaki-e* lacquer
29.8 × 32.7 × 15.9 cm
18th or 19th century
PRIVATE COLLECTION, Japan

During the later eighteenth and nineteenth centuries many of the innovatory lacquer techniques and styles which had at first been confined to *inrō* were applied to other objects. The maker of this piece has used the ribbed form of the tiered box (which conceals the divisions between the layers) as a vehicle for an extravagant display of technical virtuosity.

171

172

173 Inrō with design of doves on a peach tree

F/G11 桃鳩蒔絵印籠銘梶川作

Gold *fundame* lacquer ground decorated in gold and coloured *takamaki-e*; *ojime* coral, *netsuke* lacquered wood, as a *sennin* with a gourd.
Inrō s. 'made by Kajikawa'
8.5 × 5.2 cm
18th century
TOKYO NATIONAL MUSEUM

The Kajikawa, one of the families of lacquerers which worked for the shōguns throughout the Edo period, specialised in the manufacture of *inrō* and were proficient in a wide variety of styles and techniques. The unobtrusive and yet luxurious combination of dull *fundame* (made from fine gold dust) and *takamaki-e* in restrained colours would have appealed to the sober tastes of the samurai class.

173

174 Inrō with design of the three apes

S/G11 猿蒔絵印籠銘塩見政誠

[repr. in colour on p. 219]
SHIOMI SEISEI (1647–1722)
Black lacquer ground decorated in multi-coloured *togidashi-e* and *takamaki-e*; *ojime* coral, *manjū netsuke* ivory carved with chrysanthemum and paulownia badges
Inrō s. *Shiomi Seisei*
7.9 × 6.3 × 2.8 cm
Late 17th or early 18th century
TOKYO NATIONAL MUSEUM

Shiomi Seisei, a painter as well as a lacquerer, was noted for the great refinement of his technique, especially in *togidashi-e*, and for his skilful depiction of animals. The motif of the three apes, who see, hear and speak no evil, derives from the fact that one of the classical negatives of the verb, *zaru*, is similar in sound to the word *saru*, monkey.

175 Inrō with design of horses at pasture and monkeys

F/G11 牧馬猿蒔絵印籠銘常嘉斎作

[repr. in colour on p. 219]
YAMADA JŌKASAI (active *c*. 1681–*c*. 1704)
Gold *fundame* ground decorated in gold, silver and coloured *takamaki-e*; *ojime* coral, *netsuke* ivory, as Jurōjin, one of the Seven Gods of Good Fortune, accompanied by a bird
Inrō s. 'made by Jōkasai'

9.1 × 4.8 × 2.8 cm
Late 17th century
TOKYO NATIONAL MUSEUM

Yamada Jōkasai was a member of the Kajikawa family (see no. 173), who specialised in the manufacture of *inrō* and incense boxes. There is documentary evidence that in 1682 or 1683 he received a commission from the Tokugawa family to produce a large number of such pieces in collaboration with Chōho, a member of the Kōami family of official lacquerers (see no. 186).

176 Inrō with design of cherry blossoms and maples

S/G11 楓桜蒔絵印籠銘古満巨柳

KOMA KORYŪ (active 1764–1789)
Black lacquer ground decorated in multi-coloured *togidashi-e*; *ojime* metal with a design of gourds and flowers, *netsuke* with a lacquered frame and a bamboo panel with a design of two cranes in lacquer
Inrō s. *Koma Koryū*
8.2 × 5.5 cm
Late 18th century
TOKYO NATIONAL MUSEUM

Like Shiomi Seisei, Koryū, a member of the Koma family of lacquerers, was famous for the quality of his *togidashi-e*. The depiction of contrasting scenes on either side of the *inrō* is a favourite device of *inrō* artists.

176

177 Sheath inrō with cicada design

F/G11 蟬蒔絵印籠銘寛哉

KOMA KANSAI II (1766–1835)
Bamboo decorated in black and gold *takamaki-e*; *ojime* metal, as Daikoku, god of wealth, with his rice bales and mallet, *netsuke* ivory as a fat sparrow (*fukura suzume*) carved with waves and leaves
Inrō s. *Kansai*
6.2 × 4 × 1.9 cm
Late 18th or early 19th century
TOKYO NATIONAL MUSEUM

The sheath *inrō* is a variation on the usual *inrō* construction: the outer case, of bamboo, contains a smaller *inrō* made up in the usual way from a number of compartments. The unconventional form and the striking contrast of materials are both appropriate for the master of that great innovator, the famous nineteenth-century lacquerer Shibata Zeshin (1807–1891).

177

178 Inrō with design of folded papers

S/GII 畳紙蒔絵印籠 長谷川重美作

HASEGAWA SHIGEYOSHI (*fl.* late 18th century)
Red ground with large gold flakes decorated in gold
takamaki-e; *ojime* gold as a bale of rice straw, *netsuke* stained
ivory as lotus leaves and a seed-pod
Inrō s. 'inscribed by Tosa no kami Fujiwara, chief artist of the
Office of Painting, of the lower first grade of the fifth rank'
6.9 × 4 × 2 cm
Late 18th century
TOKYO NATIONAL MUSEUM

During the later Edo period *inrō* artists were constantly devising
new technical effects and searching for unusual subject-matter.
The use of large gold flakes of varying sizes on a red ground is a
technical innovation. The motif of *tatamigami*, folded pieces of
paper used for sketching poems, is taken from a painting by the
court artist Tosa Mitsusada (1738–1806), whose assistance
Shigeyoshi acknowledges in the signature.

178

179 Inrō with design of dewy grasses and paulownia badges

F/GII 芒桐紋蒔絵印籠銘 羊遊斎

HARA YŌYŪSAI (1772–1845)
Plain wood ground decorated in gold *takamaki-e* and *hiramaki-e*;
ojime metal, *netsuke* painted wood as a figure with a fan
Inrō s. *Yōyūsai*

8.9 × 4.3 × 2.2 cm
Late 18th or early 19th century
TOKYO NATIONAL MUSEUM

The motif of dewy *susuki* grasses and paulownia badges was used
as early as the Momoyama period (see no. 146), but is here
transformed by a lightness of touch which recalls the painting of
Sakai Hōitsu, whose designs Yōyūsai is known to have copied.

179

180 Inrō with design of geese by a stream

S/GII 芦雁蒔絵印籠銘観松斎

IIZUKA TŌYŌ (active second half of the 18th century)
Fundame ground decorated in shaded black *togidashi-e*; *ojime*
silver, as a tortoise, *kagamibuta netsuke* with ivory frame and
metal plate decorated with flowers and grasses
Inrō s. *Kanshōsai*
7.7 × 6.9 × 2.3 cm
Second half of the 18th century
TOKYO NATIONAL MUSEUM

The *sumi-e togidashi-e* technique was used, like *katakiri* in
metalwork, to imitate the effects of ink painting (*sumi-e*). A
varying mixture of camellia charcoal and silver dust produces
differing shades of grey and black.

180

255

181 *Inrō with design of chysanthemums and butterflies*

F/GII 菊蝶嵌装象牙印籠 芝山細工

[repr. in colour on p. 219]
SHIBAYAMA school
Inrō, *ojime* and *netsuke* all ivory, decorated in shell, coloured horn and coral; 8.6 × 5.7 cm
Late 18th or early 19th century
TOKYO NATIONAL MUSEUM

The work of the Shibayama family, who were active from the late eighteenth century onwards in the production of *inrō*, combs and other accessories, represents the culmination of the trend towards increasingly lavish decoration in unusual and expensive materials which characterizes the second half of the Edo period.

182 *Inrō with design of dragon and phoenix medallions*

S/GII 蟠龍鳳凰青貝印籠 根付銘杣田造

[repr. in colour on p. 219]
SOMADA school
Inrō, *ojime* and *netsuke* all decorated in shell and metal inlay; *ojime* with diaper designs, *netsuke* with long-tailed birds, s. 'made by Somada'; 7.3 × 5 × 2 cm
Late 18th century
TOKYO NATIONAL MUSEUM

The Somada family, lacquerers to the wealthy Maeda daimyō family of Kaga, were active from the middle of the eighteenth century onwards and specialised in minutely detailed shell inlay work. They are said to have copied this technique from the shell-inlaid lacquers of Ming dynasty China and they show a marked preference, as here, for subject matter of Chinese origin.

183 *Group of ornamental combs and hairpins with embroidered cases*

FS/GII 櫛笄簪・箱迫 櫛銘羊遊斎

Silver, ivory, wood and tortoiseshell decorated with designs in lacquer
One comb s. *Yōyūsai* (Hara Yōyūsai, 1772–1845, see no. 179)
combs *w* 12.1–16.9 cm; hairpins *l* 13.3–29.1 cm;
cases 8–15 × 16–21 cm
Chiefly 19th century
TOKYO NATIONAL MUSEUM, NOMURA COLLECTION

During the Momoyama and early Edo periods it became the practice among women of all classes to wear the hair up and it is known from literary references and from a series of apparently ineffectual sumptuary edicts that gold, silver and tortoiseshell were in use for hair ornaments by the end of the seventeenth century. During the eighteenth century, ivory, glass and other foreign materials were imported for the same purpose and it can be seen from *Ukiyo-e* prints that there was greater and greater extravagance in the number, size and decoration of the ornaments, of which the most important were the *kushi*, similar in form to the western comb from which it may be derived, the *kōgai*, a thick hairpin which narrows towards its centre, and the *kanzashi*, a thinner metal hairpin with pendant decorations at one end. Displayed alongside the *kanzashi* are their brocade cases with *netsuke* and silver chains to enable them to be worn, like *inrō*, from the waist.

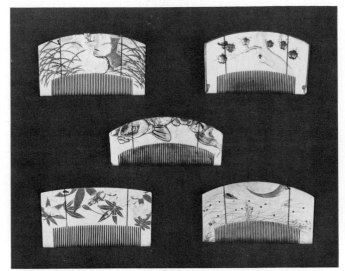

183

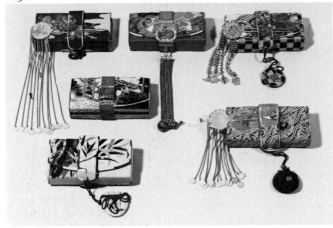

183

184 *Set of interlocking picnic boxes*

S/AR 漆塗組弁当

Lacquered wood
21 × 35 cm
19th century
CHIDŌ MUSEUM, Yamagata

This ingenious and convenient set from what is now Yamagata prefecture, north-eastern Japan, is made up of sixteen fan-shaped containers, each containing one portion. The owner's name, Tomigashi, is inscribed in varying styles of calligraphy on the boxes and his *mon* appears in the centre.

185 *Hexagonal tiered food box*

F/AR 紙撚六角重箱

Woven twisted paper decorated in ochre, black and red lacquer
17 × 15 cm
19th century
CHIDŌ MUSEUM, Yamagata

Boxes of this type were used for such occasions as cherry-blossom and maple-viewing outings; the deep bottom section is for rice and the shallower sections are for side-dishes. The plain

184

185

Wood, decorated in black lacquer and gold and silver
hiramaki-e and *takamaki-e* lacquer and gold and silver foil, with
gilt metal fittings;
the interior decorated with paintings of court scenes in Tosa
style
121 × 415 × 91 cm
1661–1663
TOKYO NATIONAL MUSEUM

lacquering, more for protection than for decoration, contrasts
strongly with the elaborate *maki-e* produced in the great cities,
but the technique of weaving twisted paper is no less
painstakingly executed than the more sophisticated methods at
the disposal of the urban craftsman.

186   *Ceremonial palanquin (norimono) with design of bamboo, peony and hollyhock and peony mon*

FS/G11   竹葵牡丹紋蒔絵女乗物

[also repr. in colour on p. 220]
Lacquermaster: KŌAMI CHŌHO (1628–1682)

The records of the Kōami family indicate that this *norimono* was
made by Chōho, the eleventh master, for the marriage in 1664 of
Tsunayoshi, the fifth Tokugawa shōgun (1646–1709, ruled
1680–1709) to Nobuko, daughter of Takatsukasa Nobufusa. It is
a magnificent example of the official style of lacquer decoration
which came into being during the second half of the seventeenth
century and was much used for the sets of furniture and other
equipment which were an indispensable feature of every daimyō
wedding. The hollyhock and peony *mon* with which the *norimono*
is liberally embellished are the emblems of, respectively, the
Tokugawa and Takatsukasa families.

186

187a

187b

187a *Koto called Hagiku*

F/G4 箏 銘葉菊

Paulownia wood; end fittings tortoiseshell, ivory and
sandalwood with a design of chrysanthemums inlaid in shell
and green-stained ivory; thirteen strings and thirteen bridges
13.5 × 190 × 26 cm
End-fittings second half of the 18th century; the body earlier
TOKYO NATIONAL MUSEUM

187b *Koto called Kimi ga chitose*

S/G4 箏 銘君が千歳

Paulownia wood; end fittings decorated with a design of
cranes, pines and bamboos in *maki-e* lacquer, with central
panels of tortoiseshell and ivory details; thirteen strings and
thirteen bridges
insc. in *maki-e* lacquer *Kimi ga chitose*
13 × 165 × 23 cm
Middle Edo period
TOKYO NATIONAL MUSEUM

The *koto* is derived from the *wagon* and the *gakusō*, themselves of
Chinese origin, used in *gagaku*, the imperial court music of the
Nara and later periods. Like the *gakusō*, it has thirteen strings
which are tuned by means of thirteen independent bridges (*ji*),
making it possible to produce any scale, although in practice only
a few were used. It is played on the floor, with the performer in
the normal Japanese kneeling position at a right or oblique angle
to the instrument with its lower end to his or her left. The strings
are plucked by three ivory picks (*tsume*) attached to three of the
fingers of the right hand.

Unlike the *shamisen* (see no. 188), the *koto* was not used to
accompany dramatic performances such as *Kabuki* and *Bunraku*;
instead it was the principal instrument for domestic music
making, either on its own or in combination with other
instruments or with voices. The popular tradition of Edo period
solo *koto* music is said to have been founded by a Kyushu
musician, Hōsui, who gave instruction to a *shamisen* player by
the name of Yatsuhashi Kengyō (1614–1685). This Yatsuhashi
then went to Kyoto and founded a school. Also in the
seventeenth century the *koto* was used for the first time in a
three-part ensemble (*sankyoku*) with the *shamisen* and the *kokyū*,
a bowed stringed instrument of European inspiration. The music
played by the *sankyoku* ensemble was *jiuta*, in which vocal and
instrumental passages alternate. *Jiuta* was played in homes as
well as in places of entertainment in the licensed quarters and
elsewhere and *sankyoku* ensembles are quite frequently depicted
in wood-block prints. The paulownia wood cut so as to give the
maximum prominence to the grain is a feature of most *koto*; the
back of the wood is hollowed out to form a sound-box.

These two *koto* were formerly the property of the Kii province
branch of the Tokugawa family. The *koto* known as *Kimi ga
chitose* ('The everlasting succession of emperors') takes its name
from a passage in the *Kokin wakashū* poetry anthology (*c.* 900 AD).

188 *Set of three Bunraku puppets representing Sambasō dancers*

F/LR 文樂人形

Wood, bamboo and paper frames; wood heads painted with
gofun; human hair; gold, black and red painted paper hats;
silk costumes in *suikan kariginu* (see no. 391) style
embroidered with pines and bamboos
Each *h* 138 cm
19th century
OSAKA MUNICIPAL MUSEUM

It was in the early seventeenth century that the *Jōruri* puppet
drama (*Bunraku* is a later term) made its first recognisable
appearance. The three elements which go to make up *Jōruri* are
the puppets, the stylised text recited by a single character and the
accompaniment on the *shamisen*, a three-stringed plucked
musical instrument introduced to Japan from the Ryukyu islands
in the sixteenth century. In the perfected form of the drama,
which gained overwhelming popularity in Kyoto and Osaka during
the eighteenth century, thanks to the brilliant talents of the
dramatist Chikamatsu Monzaemon (1653–1725) and the
chanter Takemoto Gidayū (1651–1714), each major puppet is
manipulated on the thirty-six foot stage by three operators
standing in a trench, two of them clad in black and hooded but
the principal, unhooded and more brightly dressed, maintaining
an illusion of invisibility through impassivity of facial expression.
By 1727 the puppets, which are operated not by external strings
but by sticks and internal springs and strings, were fully equipped
not only with arms (introduced in the 1690s) but also with
movable eyes, mouths and fingers.

These three figures are dressed in costumes decorated with the
auspicious pine and bamboo which were used for the *kotobuki shiki
Sambasō*, a dance of ancient origin performed before the first act
of a *Bunraku* drama. All of them wear the black and gold striped
cap associated with the dance and one carries a fan and a jingle.

189a *Bunraku puppet representing Sasaki Moritsuna in the play Ōmi Genji senjin yakata (1769) by Chikamatsu Hanji (d.? 1787)*

S/LR 文樂人形

Wood, bamboo and paper frame; wood head painted with
gofun; human hair; costume in *kamishimo* style, chiefly silk,
with the *mon* of the Sasaki family
h 121 cm
19th century
OSAKA MUNICIPAL MUSEUM

The play, which, although originally written for puppets by
Chikamatsu Monzaemon's pupil, later became a celebrated *Kabuki*
drama, concerns the rivalry between Moritsuna and his brother
Takatsuna, who does not actually appear on the stage. It is
supposedly set in the late twelfth century but in fact all the
characters stand for historical personalities concerned in the
siege of Osaka castle in 1614–5. Thus Sasaki Moritsuna is
Sanada Yukimura, who fought on the side of Hideyoshi's son
Toyotomi Hideyori, here called Minamoto Yoriie. Tokugawa
Ieyasu is called Hōjō Tokimasa and Osaka castle becomes
Sakamoto castle. This subterfuge, which resulted in a complex
combination of two historical stories, served to circumvent the
rigorous censorship imposed by the shōgunate.

189b *Bunraku puppet representing Danshichi Kurobei in the play Natsu matsuri Naniwa kagami (1746)*

S/LR   文樂人形

Wood, bamboo and paper frame; head wood painted with *gofun*; human hair; arms and legs painted to simulate tattooing; linen costume with chequer pattern
h 125 cm
19th century
OSAKA MUNICIPAL MUSEUM

The ruffianly Danshichi is a leading figure in the play, which was originally written for the *Kabuki* theatre but later adapted for puppets. Both the head, used for other parts, and the chequered costume are special characteristics of Danshichi. The left arm is longer than the right because the left arm operator has to stand further away from the puppet than the principal operator who works the body and the right hand. The third operator works the feet.

189a

189b

188

188

188

Ceramics

The ceramic tradition of Japan has been that of stoneware: no porcelain was made until the early Edo period. And yet Japan had always greatly admired Chinese porcelain and had imported it in large quantities, both ordinary trade wares and more luxurious wares, some of them made to order. Naturally enough such imports provoked imitation and by the fourteenth century Chinese ceramics were being imitated in stoneware in Japan, particularly at Seto, where the tradition of glazed and decorated stonewares that was later to flower in Mino began. Much of the better quality Chinese porcelain was used in Japan for the tea ceremony, which, in the beginning of the sixteenth century, was becoming more formal than the simple withdrawal from everyday affairs which it had previously been. The participants now made use of aesthetically pleasing objects during the making and drinking of tea.

The Momoyama period saw the major changes in the various styles of Japanese ceramics that were to affect the Edo period. With the rise, in the early sixteenth century, of a new bourgeoisie, more and more people became interested in the cult, as it was to become, of tea, and 'tea taste' became more widespread. This meant that there was a shortage of fine Chinese ceramics suitable for tea, so that taste had to widen to include rough Korean wares. Under the teaching of the tea-master Murata Shukō (c. 1421–1502) some Japanese wares (e.g. Shigaraki jars) had been admitted into the ranks of the permissible. This allowed people with no inherited Chinese heirlooms to participate in the tea ceremony for the first time. This in turn widened the circle of demand and soon the tea-masters were acting as middle-men, ordering tea wares to be specially made.

The first Japanese wares considered suitable for tea were the unglazed product of Bizen, Shigaraki and Iga. What was particularly admired was the irregular shape and the natural surface, with its variation of colour and texture caused by chance effects of firing in the kiln. Of course this was simple to exaggerate by warping of the unfired body and by the addition of materials that would oxidise to differing colours. Hence the Momoyama stonewares are often twisted, cut with a knife or otherwise misshapen.

These new styles associated with the new taste in tea began to alter the production of entire ceramic areas. Although wares not for the tea ceremony were made throughout the Edo period, few were unaffected by 'tea taste'. This irregularity of form and coarseness of surface seems to have been entirely to Momoyama and early Edo taste: it provides a great contrast to the perfection of Chinese porcelain and accords more with Korean taste.

By far the greatest production of glazed wares, both for tea and for ordinary use, was that of Mino, the inheritors of the Seto tradition. The first Mino wares specifically for the tea ceremony were the Black Seto tea bowls. These are hand-built, tall and slightly tapering towards the top. The origin of the low-fired Raku wares of Chōjirō is easily visible. A group called Black Oribe used the same dark iron glaze but, lower and wider, were warped into a so-called shoe shape which is meant to make them interesting to hold in the hand. Some are decorated with irregular patterning on areas of white slip reserves, and these are called Oribe-Black.

In great contrast are the carefully made Yellow Seto wares: the best of these are very finely potted, and of regular outline. They may have incised designs that are picked out in dark iron brown or copper green showing strongly against the yellow background. The painted decoration of Shino wares is bold and fluid, often of a striking simplicity, and is done in an iron oxide that sometimes breaks through the thick bubbly feldspathic glaze in a 'heaped and piled' effect. Another variety is Grey Shino (Nezumi-Shino), where an iron grey slip is scratched away to show the white body underneath.

The Oribe wares, also, are from Mino – often even from the same kilns as these former types. In Green Oribe, usually mukōzuke dishes and cups, the irregular but carefully made shape is partially covered in thick green glaze: this provides a great contrast with a painted area. The painting on Green Oribe is similar to that on the contemporary glazed wares of Karatsu, on Kyushu. Karatsu wares had been made by Korean potters who used the noborigama, the climbing chambered kiln. Decoration is in sparse strokes of underglaze iron under a very thin transparent glaze. Clearly there is some exchange of styles between Karatsu and Mino at this time, towards the end of the sixteenth century.

These Mino and Karatsu wares, the descendants of the 'found' wares of Shigaraki and Bizen and especially the Raku wares of Chōjirō, were all desired for the new simple style of tea taught by Sen Rikyū. Careful lack of ostentation became as important as elegance. Rikyū encouraged and even directed Chōjirō towards the Raku that would best suit his style of tea-making. The rôle of the tea-master was still all-important.

The beginning of the Edo period was preceded by an event that was of great importance to Japanese ceramics, the invasion of Korea by Toyotomi Hideyoshi. His returning armies brought with them Korean potters. Immediately affected was Karatsu, which, after a peak of production in the first decades of the seventeenth century, began to decline in favour of the Arita porcelains which had themselves been started by Korean potters in a southern group of Karatsu kilns. Almost the same happened in Mino – a peak of production in the first two decades was followed by steady decline, though here there was no porcelain until neighbouring Seto began to make it in the eighteenth century. Meanwhile Seto continued to make dark stonewares as it had in the Muromachi and Momoyama periods. In Shigaraki and Iga there was also a tendency towards decline, while Bizen flourished, though remaining fairly conservative. The kiln area of Tamba, hitherto a simple country pottery, began to make tea wares and Korean potters began a new kiln area on Honshu at Hagi. On Kyushu, three new kiln areas at Agano, Takatori and Satsuma were begun by Koreans under the direction of the local lords, to make everyday wares as well as those for the tea ceremony. Irregularity is less in evidence after the early Edo period and in general the tendency of Edo taste was to be once again toward a greater perfection of shape.

Agano wares tend to be covered in thick streaky – almost flambé – glazes that in some cases resemble Chōsen–Karatsu ('Korean' Karatsu). The early stages of Takatori and Satsuma used dark glazes – particularly for cha-ire – and only later tended towards decorative wares, such as the low-fired blue and white of later Edo Satsuma. Both Satsuma and Takatori declined after the middle Edo, while potters from Agano were taken by the Lord Hosokawa when he moved to Kumamoto, to found the Yatsushiro kilns. Hagi, in western Honshu, produced wares of Korean shapes with a thick coarse glaze that often allowed bubbles to break through, producing a rough, almost sharp texture. Perhaps because of this, the glaze actually changes with use, as does that of Raku, a property much admired for tea. Hagi wares were not greatly esteemed until the middle Edo period.

In the first years of the seventeenth century some Karatsu stoneware and new kilns began expressly to make porcelain: among these was Tengudani. The earliest porcelains (Shoki-Imari) were simply made out of a poor quality porcelain clay, high in iron content. The decoration was usually in cobalt oxide under glaze of a bluish tinge. The earliest style of painting is usually one of simply but powerfully drawn flowers or landscape, partly reflecting Korean styles as transmitted through Karatsu stoneware.

The Shoki-Imari styles soon diversify. A more sophisticated approach to the painting of landscape and other representational motifs goes hand in hand with an attractive geometric or abstract style of pattern – often the two can be found on the same piece. Some Arita kilns soon made porcelains specifically for the tea ceremony; these included *mizusashi*, *cha-ire*, serving dishes and small dishes for the *kaiseki* meal. *Temmoku* and celadon were made at many Arita kilns, while underglaze copper red was tried briefly, but was apparently never very successful.

The great change in the porcelain industry came at the mid-point of the seventeenth century, when the Arita potters first learned how to use overglaze enamel pigments. This occurred at about the same time as the first orders for porcelains were made by the Dutch East India Company. Overglaze enamelled wares had recently been made for the first time at Kyoto – but here in a low-fired body – and this technique was soon to appear on the wares of the new porcelain kiln at Kutani, on Honshu.

In the mid-seventeenth century the Dutch started to buy Japanese porcelain to export to South East Asia and Europe. Blue and white wares in Chinese Wanli style and in Chinese 'transitional' style were made in Arita after models shipped from Holland. As before, Japan absorbed these styles and added its own ingredients, utilising the best new technology (in this case overglaze enamelling) and producing a series of new products that rival or surpass their models.

These wares, after a gestation period of experimentation with shapes, colours of enamels and painting styles, settled down with the two styles that are called Ko-Imari (Old Imari, or Arita) and Kakiemon. Meanwhile, of course, some kilns continued to make developed Shoki-Imari wares for internal trade. Huge quantities of Imari wares were exported to Europe and South East Asia. Mostly these were in a gaudy ostentatious style that well suited the European search for exotic luxury. Some of the better quality pieces are however very fine. The best of the export wares are the Kakiemon porcelains, justly famed and often imitated for their superb quality translucent enamels, for the elegant style of their decoration and for their whiteness of glaze and body.

In Kyoto a tradition arose for gorgeously decorated tea wares that was to persist, side by side with the taste for Raku, until the end of the Edo period. The Kyoto enamelled wares are low-fired; this allowed the use of inglaze pigments by Kenzan and Dōhachi, as well as overglaze enamelling. The decorated wares by Ninsei are quite outstanding, not only for their skill and beauty, but also for the very fact of their use as tea wares: a marked change in

taste from *wabi* tea. Some of Kenzan's pieces were painted by his elder brother, Kōrin. This is one of the few cases known of a celebrated painter decorating ceramics and it is worth the comment that such decoration was done in iron pigment, in the style and technique of ink-painting.

In quite another taste is the third group of overglaze decorated wares, the Kutani porcelains of Kaga (and elsewhere). Much of the porcelain hitherto called Old Kutani can now be seen to be either not old, or not made in Kutani, but this does not alter the fact that some of the wares called Old Kutani are porcelains of the seventeenth century that were not made in Arita. These are basically of two types: one type is clearly differentiated as Green Kutani and the other might be called Painted Kutani. It is difficult to see the most delicate of all the so-called Ko-Kutani wares, the nine-sided dishes and their allies, as anything but a late Edo revival. Such revivals seem to have been characteristic of the Bunka-Bunsei periods (1804–1830), as also in Arita and Kyoto, and many Kutani types seem to date from about that time.

Perhaps these revivals were inevitable after a long period of inactivity in the ceramic tradition and market in the middle of the eighteenth century. At the end of the century there was a wave of production and new kilns began all over Japan; many of these made simple everyday blue and white porcelain. These can be seen illustrated in *Ukiyo-e* woodblock prints.

The rise of Seto as a porcelain centre to rival Arita and the new porcelains of Kyoto are the most important developments, though some of the finest porcelains were made in Kyushu at Mikawachi (Hirado) and Kameyama. Other kilns made pottery or stoneware for local use, often darkly glazed and in traditional shapes. Now porcelain caught the eye of the artist potters in Kyoto; Kenzan had never made porcelain, but in the early nineteenth century Eisen and his followers, Mokubei and Dōhachi, and Hozen made porcelain in Chinese revival styles which well suited the *Nanga* milieu in which they lived.

Edo period ceramics began with a flourish; the last twenty years of the Momoyama period and the first twenty years of the Edo were high points of tea ceremony wares. The mid century and the Genroku period were high points for decorated wares and porcelain. Later in the eighteenth century an inward-looking sophistication seems to have stultified design to some extent, and it may well have been the rise of new markets in the late eighteenth century that stimulated the new wave of ceramics of the late Edo period.

ORI

190

190 *Tea bowl called Omokage*

FS/G4 黒樂茶碗銘面影 長次郎作

CHŌJIRŌ (1516–c. 1592)
Chōjirō-Raku ware
8.1 × 9.9 cm
Late 16th century
RAKU ART MUSEUM, Kyoto

Chōjirō was the first to use soft, low-fired glazed pottery for tea wares. The technique may be derived from Chinese prototypes – possibly Kochi wares – but the shape and the style of glazing is something new to Japanese ceramics. Almost certainly this was due to the taste and even to the direction of the tea-master Sen Rikyū (1552–1591). Rikyū's innovatory 'informal' tea style, with its insistence on simplicity as well as harmony, required ceramics that were quiet, unobtrusive and unsophisticated.

Chōjirō's wares are the first Raku wares: they are hand built, usually straight sided and simply shaped with a firm foot. Clearly they partly derive their style from the slightly earlier Black Seto wares of Mino.

Raku has several characteristics that Rikyū admired: the low firing gives it a soft texture, neither warm nor cold to the touch, the heat of the tea within the bowl is pleasantly transmitted to the hands, and furthermore the glaze of the interior actually changes with usage, giving the bowl a genuinely used feeling.

191

191 *Water vessel for the tea ceremony, called Shiba no iori*

FS/G4 信楽一重口水指銘柴庵

Shigaraki stoneware
h 15 cm
Late 16th century
TOKYO NATIONAL MUSEUM

The coarse texture of Shigaraki wares was recognised as something special even before Shukō's admission of Shigaraki wares into the repertoire of vessels used in the tea ceremony. Shigaraki jars (*tsubo*) were favoured for the storage of leaf tea.

Sometimes even *cha-ire* could be made of this rough clay; its use was not confined to large pieces. Here the cylindrical shape of the *mizusashi* is perfectly suited to its use for tea.

192

192 *Flower vase called Rashōmon*

FS/G4 伊賀筒花生銘羅生門

Iga stoneware
h 27.3 cm
16th century
PRIVATE COLLECTION, Japan

The Iga wares for the tea ceremony were hand built, without the use of the potter's wheel, and little concern is shown for fineness of shaping – indeed great care is taken that the pieces will not be symmetrical. This flower vase does not show the excessive warping favoured by some tea masters in their search for the rustic. This type of vase was used in the *tokonoma* to hold a branch of some considerable size.

193 *Lidded water vessel for the tea ceremony*

FS/G4 備前矢筈口水指

Bizen stoneware
h 18 cm
Late 16th century
FUKUOKA MUNICIPAL MUSEUM

The unglazed Bizen wares of the early Momoyama period were among those recognised as suitable for tea by Shukō, and the area was soon producing wares to order for the tea-masters. The main attraction of Bizen ware, apart from its rugged shape, is the texture and variability of colour, partly due to the clay and partly due to variables of temperature and of oxidisation or reduction in the kiln. As the kilns at Bizen were of the single-chambered type, this was difficult to control. This very difficulty led to its effects being admired: when, in the seventeenth century, Bizen began using the *noborigama*, or chambered kiln, the 'chance' effects were carefully contrived by the use of straw rope to aid oxidisation, and similar devices.

193

194 *Incense box in the shape of a sacred jewel*
FS/G4 黄瀬戸宝珠形香合

> Iron and copper glaze
> Yellow Seto stoneware
> *h* 4.8 cm
> *dm* 5.9 cm
> Late 16th century
> NEZU ART MUSEUM, Tokyo

The yellow Seto are the most refined and carefully made of the Mino wares. Thinly potted, they are sometimes incised with a slight design that may be picked out in iron brown or green. The surface is sometimes finely pitted and rough and this much admired effect is called *abura-agede*, because it looks like deep fried *tōfu* or bean curd.

The incense box for the tea ceremony was always an object over which great care was taken: yellow Seto was highly favoured and several other examples are known.

194

195 *Tea bowl called Hashihime*
FS/G4 絵志野茶碗銘橋姫

> [repr. in colour on p. 202]
> Underglaze iron decoration of a bridge; reverse with a simple building
> E-Shino (painted Shino) stoneware
> *h* 11.8 cm., mouth *dm* 12.5 cm
> Late 16th century
> TOKYO NATIONAL MUSEUM

Some thirty-odd kilns produced Shino wares, which can be found in almost every conceivable shape, but only a few central Mino kilns made the highly sophisticated tea wares of which *Hashihime* ('Bridge Princess') is a famous example. The body is wheel thrown and then reshaped to form a compact and powerful tea-bowl.

In painted Shino, perhaps the most beautiful type of Shino, the fluid strokes of iron pigment make simple designs under a thick creamy feldspathic glaze. The crumbly-looking effect of the glaze is due to much sand mixed into the body to give it a higher absorbency. This effect is much admired, particularly in tea bowls where it offsets the vivid green of the tea.

196

196 *Squared bowl with slip design of wagtail by a stream*
FS/G4 鼠志野鶺鴒文角鉢

> Nezumi-Shino (Grey Shino) stoneware
> maximum *dm* 28.5 cm; *h* 11 cm
> Late 16th century
> TOKYO NATIONAL MUSEUM
> Important Cultural Property

The central Shino-producing kilns of Mino made, after 1580, a variety of wares including Grey Shino, where an iron-bearing slip is cut away to reveal the white body underneath. Here it is even more interesting, for the liquid slip has been swirled around the dish, leaving three white patches. The decorator has decided that one of these patches looks like a rock and has made his picture by scratching through the slip, showing the wagtail and the stream, and painting in extra slip details of bamboo on the white rock.

This dish is a serving plate for the *kaiseki* meal that precedes a formal tea ceremony.

197 Squared bowl with green glaze and iron slip geometric decoration

FS/G4   織部角鉢

Oribe stoneware
5.6 × 21.4 × 20.4 cm
End of the 16th century
TOKYO NATIONAL MUSEUM

The striking effect of the slip-decorated pattern in almost random association with the rich green glaze is enhanced by the darkening of the clay of the slipped part with iron. This, in effect, means that two colours of clay are luted together when wet. Only certain Oribe wares are made thus, and these pieces are called Nezumi Oribe (Grey Oribe).

197

198 Set of five mukōzuke fan-shaped cups with green glaze and iron slip decoration

FS/G4   織部扇面形向付一組

[repr. in colour on p. 202]
Oribe stoneware
11.2 × 7.7 cm
Late 16th or early 17th century
PRIVATE COLLECTION, Japan

These pieces were not made as cups for liquid, but would have contained some small portion of food for the *kaiseki* meal, beautifully arranged to whet the appetite.

Many Oribe wares were made in unusual shapes and the fan-shape cross-section of these cups is typical. These cups may be from Motoyashiki kiln in central Mino, a kiln that also made Yellow Seto, Black Seto and Shino wares. They were made by pressing the piece around a cloth-covered wooden mould.

199

199 Tea bowl

FS/G4   黒織部茶碗

Oribe Black stoneware
h 8.5 cm; dm 15 cm
Late 16th century
UMEZAWA MEMORIAL MUSEUM, Tokyo

Typical of the Mino type in its so-called shoe shape, this tea bowl has a more restrained decoration than some of its contemporaries. The exterior is covered with randomly associated contrasting glazes and the only drawn decoration is on the inside of the bowl, where there is a painting of millet in white glaze. Such interior decoration on a tea bowl is uncommon as it is usually not considered to look well under whipped tea. But at this date decoration of any sort on Japanese-made tea bowls was relatively new. The contrasts in colour foreshadow the later Oribe style.

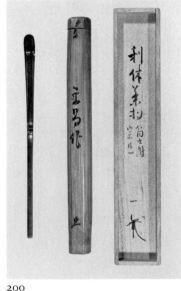
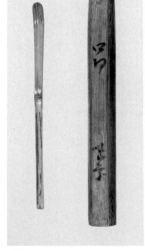

200   201

200 Tea scoop (chashaku)

FS/G4   茶杓　千利休作

SEN RIKYŪ (1521–91)
Bamboo, with wooden boxes
l 18.2 cm
Momoyama period
URASENKE FOUNDATION, Kyoto

The simple bamboo tea scoop is one of the most studied of tea utensils. In spite of their apparent simplicity, these scoops vary greatly in style and shape, as well as in the natural colour and configuration of the bamboo, all of which would have been carefully chosen.

Vital to the understanding of the importance of the scoop is the way in which it is handled during the ceremony, the noise it makes against lacquer or ceramic utensils and above all the fact that this was the one utensil that was usually made by the tea-master himself.

The inner box is inscribed by Sen Sōtan.

201 Tea scoop (chashaku) called Kuchikiri
FS/G4　茶杓銘口切　千宗旦作

SEN SŌTAN (1578–1658)
Bamboo, with wooden box
18.4 cm
Early Edo period
URASENKE FOUNDATION, Kyoto

Sōtan was the grandson of Sen Rikyū, whose tradition of *wabi* tea he perpetuated. His tea scoops, like those of Rikyū, are held in great esteem for their simple unassuming quality. They are thought to lack pretentious elegance and to typify *wabi* taste.

The box is signed *Totsutotsusai*, Sōtan's name as a tea-master.

202

202 Water jar with design of reeds and grasses in iron-brown underglaze painting
FS/G4　唐津芦文壺

Karatsu stoneware
16.1 × 22.9 cm
Late 16th century
IDEMITSU MUSEUM OF ARTS, Tokyo

The stoneware kilns of Karatsu were established in the mid-sixteenth century, possibly by Korean immigrants, as Karatsu is one of the parts of Japan nearest to Korea. Of the various different styles made at many kilns over a wide geographical area, the E-Garatsu or painted Karatsu ware, of which this is a fine example, is perhaps the best known.

Karatsu was probably the first ceramic ware in Japan to be fired in the Korean *noborigama* or stepped climbing chambered kiln. From Karatsu this technological advance spread to Mino, and there are some similarities between Karatsu and some of the Mino wares.

203

203 Mizusashi ewer
FS/G4　朝鮮唐津水指

Iron and ash glazed stoneware
Korean Karatsu ware
14 × 18.3 cm
Late 16th or early 17th century
PRIVATE COLLECTION, Japan

The so-called Korean Karatsu (Chōsen-Karatsu) style depends upon the dark glazed Karatsu body being partly obscured by a thick opaque bluish-white ash glaze or vice versa.

While these wares are often called sixteenth century, it is possible that they are later, for the style was much used at Agano, which did not commence production until the early seventeenth century. This suggests that the fashion for such wares may have been seventeenth-century.

204 Tea bowl called Azuma
FS/G3　黒楽茶碗銘東　光悦作

HON'AMI KŌETSU (1558–1637)
Raku ware pottery
8.8 × 12 cm
Early 17th century
KITAMURA BUNKA ZAIDAN, Kyoto

Kōetsu is in some ways the perfect all-round artist. He was never a professional potter, and though it must have been relatively simple for him to master the somewhat crude techniques of Raku production, his wares are so distinct that they are more appreciated by tea connoisseurs than the ceramics of any other artist. *Azuma* is of the almost straight-sided shape derived from Chōjirō, but the carefully contrived white ash glaze bubbling and dripping down the side invites no comparison. Other black Raku

204

bowls by Kōetsu have a rounded base and flare outwards slightly towards a lip that is more thinly modelled than that of most Raku wares.

205 *Tea caddy with small handles and iron glaze*

FS/G4 高取耳付茶入

Takatori stoneware
h 9.5 cm
Early 17th century
IDEMITSU MUSEUM OF ARTS, Tokyo

One tea caddy can scarcely stand as representative of the almost infinite variety of shapes and combinations of dark glazes that are found on the small tea-jars which are so vital a part of the equipment of the tea ceremony. Almost all the stoneware kiln areas of Japan must have made such pieces, particularly in the seventeenth century. Of these kilns, the best known for tea jars are Seto, on Honshu, and Takatori and Satsuma on Kyushu.

Many of the shapes and glazes are subtle and complex: this relatively simple shape is far from typical. Of course other styles of tea caddy were also used: in Kyoto, Ninsei made gorgeous tea caddies decorated in overglaze enamel. And it must be remembered that for most of the duration of the tea ceremony, the tea jar remains in its brocade bag: its unveiling for use at the appropriate moment should be a revelation.

205

206 *Jar for leaf tea with design of Mount Yoshino*

FS/G3 吉野山図茶壺　仁清作

[repr. in colour on p. 203]
NONOMURA NINSEI (*fl. c.* 1645–*c.* 1694)
Kyō-ware pottery with overglaze pigments and gold
h 28.6 cm, *dm* 27.1 cm
Mid-17th century
FUKUOKA MUNICIPAL MUSEUM
Important Cultural Property

Nonomura Seiemon, called after 1655 Ninsei, started his kiln in 1649 at Ninnaji, having trained at Tamba and at other kilns in Kyoto.

Ninsei can be regarded as the prototype of the Kyoto artist-potters: not only did he possibly create the demand in Kyoto for highly ornate and sophisticated tea ceramics, but as far as we can judge he made nothing else. The decoration on these wares is related to the ideas of the Rimpa school of painters with whom he clearly had some connection, as Kenzan was one of his followers.

The brilliant coloured enamels and the bold and beautiful style of painting contrast with the shape, which his public would instantly have recognised as that of the simple Shigaraki *tsubo* for holding leaf tea. This suggestion of a rustic origin would greatly have appealed to sophisticated Kyoto.

Many of Ninsei's pieces are marked with a seal-mark stamped into the wet clay: he was one of the earliest potters in Japan to sign his work, which may be some indication of his status as a potter.

207 *Tea bowl called Daimyō*

FS/G4 萩茶碗銘大名

White opaque glaze turned pink
Hagi stoneware
h 8.5 cm, *dm* 14.5 cm
Middle or late 17th century
NEZU ART MUSEUM, Tokyo

The clay from which Hagi ware is made has the property that small bubbles rise to the surface and burst through the glaze, giving it an effect akin to the unglazed Shigaraki. Not only that, but the warm thick glaze changes, as does that of Raku ware, with usage. Possibly the pink tinge of this famous bowl is partly due to this change of glaze.

Hagi wares often imitate in shape the Korean wares of the previous century, with their conical outline and strongly built foot.

207

208 *Large deep bowl with landscape design in underglaze blue*

FS/G7 初期伊万里染付山水文水甕

[repr. in colour on p. 207]
Shoki-Imari porcelain
20.6 × 33.9 cm
c. 1640–50
PRIVATE COLLECTION, Japan

One of the most striking of Shoki-Imari pieces, this deep bowl is too big for use in the tea ceremony and may therefore have had a more humble purpose.

It is not possible to be sure at which kiln this bowl was made, but only two or three of the Arita kilns were capable of making wares of such size at this time, and Sarugawa, Hiekoba and Hyakken are perhaps the only possible sources.

209 *Squared dish with celadon glaze and heron in underglaze blue*

FS/G7 初期伊万里青磁染付葦鷺文四方皿

[repr. in colour on p. 209]
Shoki-Imari porcelain
4.8 × 21.3 × 21.9 cm
c. 1640–50
PRIVATE COLLECTION, Japan

The use of celadon in conjunction with blue and white and also with *temmoku* occurs early in the history of Arita porcelain, being quite commonly found at Tengudani, one of the earliest kilns. Two kilns, however, specialised in such wares: Hyakken and Yamagoya. From the finding of potsherds it seems probable that this attractive dish comes from Hyakken kiln.

210 *Large bottle with landscape design in underglaze blue*

FS/G7 初期伊万里染付楼閣山水文大徳利

Shoki-Imari porcelain
h 37.2 cm *dm* 20.8 cm
c. 1650–1660
UMEZAWA MEMORIAL MUSEUM, Tokyo

Although bottles were the first porcelains mentioned in the Dutch East India Company's records as being exported to Batavia at about the time of the making of this bottle, this is not one of that type. Several kilns making Shoki-Imari wares ceased production at about this time, presumably so that their workmen could move to the few big kilns to whom the vast export order of 1659 was given. Some, however, continued to make porcelains for the internal market, and this bottle is from one of them.

211 *Large dish decorated with pomegranates and the VOC insignia in underglaze blue*

FS/G7 染付柘榴VOC文大皿

Arita porcelain
dm 34.3 cm
c. 1660
BRITISH MUSEUM

The first orders the Dutch East India Company (VOC) made for Arita porcelain to be shipped to Europe (1658 and 1659) were to be replacements for the Chinese porcelain they could no longer obtain, and were surely a reflection of Chinese Wanli styles.

210

211

212

213

212 *Jar with design of birds perching among flowers and rocks in overglaze enamels*

FS/G7 色絵花鳥図壺

Arita porcelain
h 25.7 cm
c. 1660
WEATHERHEAD COLLECTION, New York

With the advent of the use of enamels as overglaze colours to Japan, probably in the late 1640s or early 1650s, several groups of enamelling workshops arose. In Arita these groups can be distinguished by the range of enamels used, more than by the style of painting. Of these groups one can be differentiated by the dominant use of a fine green enamel with a thick, almost opaque blue.

The shapes on which this palette occurs vary – indeed, they are probably irrelevant in that such groups of enamellers probably used white wares from whichever kiln made the shape they wanted.

The painting of this early period is often characterized by bold designs such as are applied here: this was to settle down to a more stable style, just as the palettes were to differentiate into two major groups instead of many minor groups.

213 *Bottle decorated with overglaze enamel design of Chinese sages in reserved panels on a red scroll-work ground*

FS/G7 色絵唐人物図瓶

Arita porcelain
h 40.6 cm
c. 1670–80
ASHMOLEAN MUSEUM, Oxford (Reitlinger gift)

This type of Imari ware was formerly thought to be Kutani. The enamels are more harshly coloured than is normal for Imari, and the painting unusually bold. This, clearly, is of the early, somewhat experimental period.

214 *Large dish with decoration of peony and butterfly in underglaze blue and overglaze enamel*

FS/G7 古九谷色絵蝶牡丹亀甲繋文平鉢

[repr. in colour on p. 210]
Ko-Kutani porcelain
h 8.5 cm, *dm* 40.5 cm
Late 17th century
UMEZAWA MEMORIAL MUSEUM, Tokyo
Important Cultural Property

The characteristic dark pigments of Ko-Kutani are here used to give a strong contrast between the mass of the peonies, the delicacy of the exotic butterfly and the fine geometric border.

216

The back of this dish has the smeared glaze, underglaze blue lines and enamelled blue scrollwork characteristic of the type. This is not similar to sherds found at the Kutani kiln site, and it has been suggested that this type may come from Maruo kiln in Arita.

215 Large dish with overglaze decoration of a string of aubergines against a wave pattern on dark green ground in underglaze blue and overglaze enamel

FS/G7 古九谷青手茄子波文平鉢

[repr. in colour on p. 206]
Ko-Kutani porcelain
6.6 × 34 cm
Late 17th century
PRIVATE COLLECTION, Japan

Green Kutani (Aode Kutani) is usually enamelled on an opaque poor-quality body. Sherds of this type have not been found and its origin is even more obscure than that of most other types of Kutani.

The very striking pattern often found on these pieces suggests a market with a very definite taste. As such pieces have been found in South East Asia in recent years it has been suggested that they were made for export to those countries.

The style came into favour again in the early nineteenth century and was much imitated.

216 Decagonal bottle decorated with flowering trees in overglaze enamel

FS/G7 色絵花樹図十角瓶

Imari porcelain
h 23 cm
Late 17th century
ASHMOLEAN MUSEUM, Oxford (Reitlinger gift)

The quality of the various types of Arita export porcelains that are categorised as Imari (as opposed to Kakiemon) varies widely, probably according to the price bracket. One or two sub-groups of this ware have no underglaze blue decoration; as with the Kakiemon wares, this usually denotes a body of fine quality which is usually well painted. This bottle is of the finest quality; clearly the body is an attempt by some Arita kiln to imitate the *negoshide* body of the Kakiemon kiln wares, and the enamels are of exceptional quality and well painted, in the same spare taste as the fine quality Kakiemon wares. It is the palette of enamels that reveals its origin.

217 Chinese lion dog decorated in overglaze enamels

FS/G7 色絵獅子

[repr. in colour on p. 208]
Kakiemon-style porcelain, Arita
d. Genroku fifth year (1692)
h 49 cm
IDEMITSU MUSEUM OF ARTS, Tokyo

Pairs of *shishi* or Chinese lion dogs were favourite gifts to shrines and temples. Usually these were of stone or wood, but many examples of Seto, Tokoname and Mino pairs are known. Large porcelain sculptures such as this are very uncommon: this is even more interesing for the fact that it is dated.

The palette of enamels used here is not that of the Kakiemon, but of a similar group. We do not know at which kiln this was made nor are there many examples of porcelains decorated in this palette. Smaller figures of persons, animals and birds decorated in Kakiemon enamels are, however, not unusual.

218 Ewer decorated with flower patterns in underglaze blue

FS/G7 染付花文銀鍍金付水注

Arita porcelain, the silver-gilt mounts European
h 14 cm
Late 17th century
M. J. WEBB COLLECTION

The blue and white palette is particularly suitable for designs such as this, of flower-patterns in two different scales, that reflect textile patterning. Because the blue pigment is painted onto the unfired, unglazed body, a very precise definition of line is possible.

Not strictly a European shape, but perfectly adaptable to European usage, this kettle is a good example of the better and finer quality porcelain that was shipped to Europe in such quantities.

218

219

219 Ten-lobed bowl decorated with fruiting trees in overglaze enamels

FS/G7 色絵柘榴草石図十角鉢

Kakiemon porcelain
d 23.5 cm
End of the 17th century
VICTORIA AND ALBERT MUSEUM

The highest quality both of material and painting seems to have been reserved for bowls of this range of size, and for dishes. The Kakiemon kiln was one of the twelve or thirteen kilns in and around Arita that made wares specifically for export, and there is a great contrast between the quality of this bowl and the ordinary export wares.

This range of quality is reflected in the prices paid by the Dutch as recorded in the Company's records, where prices for individual items are often given. Details are insufficient to identify individual pieces, but the prices, taking size into account, give us some idea of the quality of the pieces supplied. The Chinese also bought Japanese porcelain, but shipping details do not survive.

220 Decagonal saucer dish decorated with quail and millet in overglaze enamels

FS/G7 色絵鶉粟文十角皿

Kakiemon porcelain
w 25.4 cm
End of the 17th century
ASHMOLEAN MUSEUM, Oxford (Reitlinger gift)

The excavation of the Kakiemon kiln sites revealed that the earliest of these kilns cannot have commenced before the 1680s. This confirms what one can deduce from earlier Kakiemon-style enamelled wares; the Kakiemon enamellers (whoever they were) were enamellers before they were potters. No doubt the invention of the famous *negoshide* (milky white) body, where the blue tinge of ordinary Arita wares is eliminated, caused the success of the kiln. The excavation showed, however, that enormous amounts of lesser quality wares were also produced, including much blue and white and some celadon.

The highest quality body was usually decorated in the spare

220

271

style seen here; the fine translucent enamels (except for the red, which was never very good) show off to best advantage the areas of white background.

221 Bowl with lid, decoration of quail and autumn grasses in underglaze blue

FS/G7 柿右衛門染付秋草鶉図蓋付鉢

Kakiemon porcelain
13.7 × 20.8 cm
Late 17th or early 18th century
PRIVATE COLLECTION, Japan

Kakiemon porcelain was famous for its fine white body and beautiful enamels, but the kiln also produced large quantities of blue and white. These are mostly in a delicately painted style that resembles the enamelling style. The body and glaze of the blue and white decorated pieces is not the *negoshide*, but a less fine and more blue-coloured ware.

221

222 Saucer dish with linked wheel pattern in underglaze blue and overglaze enamel

FS/G7 鍋島色絵染付輪繋文三脚皿

[repr. in colour on p. 210]
Nabeshima porcelain
h 8.3 cm, dm 26 cm
Early 18th century
PRIVATE COLLECTION, Japan

Striking designs of semi-abstract type were typical of the best of the Nabeshima wares. Often celadon glaze was used with great precision to cover part of the design as if it were painted.

Very often these dishes are of this standard shape. The foot is nearly always high and is usually decorated with a precise comb pattern in underglaze blue.

223 Large dish decorated in underglaze blue and overglaze enamels with design of brushwood fence

FS/G7 鍋島色絵染付柴垣図大皿

Nabeshima porcelain
h 8.2 cm; dm 30.8 cm

223

Early 18th century
TOKYO NATIONAL MUSEUM

The large kiln at Okawachi, some eight kilometres north of Arita, was made the 'official' kiln of the Nabeshima daimyō of Hizen in the early eighteenth century. Wares produced there for official gifts and other purposes were decorated in a very careful style based on the *doucai* technique of China, where an outline of underglaze blue is later filled in with enamels. This technique is not used in Arita except on the groups of wares in the so-called Matsugatani style which may be the forerunners of this Nabeshima ware.

Okawachi was presumably chosen because of its remote position, so that the secrets of its production could be preserved. Not until very late in the eighteenth century did the Nabeshima potters eliminate the excess iron content of the clay and glaze and so lose the blue tinge whose elimination had been the great success of the Kakiemon potters.

224 Water jar in the shape of a wooden bucket with inglaze decoration of waterplants and a stream

FS/G6 流水文手桶形水指　乾山作

[repr. in colour on p. 204]
OGATA KENZAN (1663–1743)
Kyō-ware pottery
h 29 cm
18th century
ITSUŌ MUSEUM, Osaka

Kenzan, as the follower of Ninsei, specialised in tea wares. Like Ninsei, he experimented with different types of clay on which he placed brightly coloured designs of striking originality. Whereas Ninsei had used overglaze enamels, Kenzan often used inglaze pigments to achieve his brightest effects; here he has made a simple stream in which, as it were, the bucket stands, with the use only of cobalt and iron in a white glaze.

The simple painting on the rustic shape has produced a jar of great presence; presumably it would be for summer tea ceremony use.

225 *Set of five dishes with landscape and plant designs in underglaze blue and slip with overglaze gold*

FS/G6 絵替り皿一組　乾山作

[repr. in colour on p. 205]
OGATA KENZAN (1663–1743)
Kyō-ware pottery
Each 2.4 × 16 cm
18th century
NEZU ART MUSEUM, Tokyo

Kenzan was a considerable painter in his own right, although he sometimes made dishes that were decorated by his more famous brother Kōrin. In the iron brown style both Kōrin and Kenzan were in effect imitating ink painting, but Kenzan, as a potter, was able to use more sophisticated techniques. Here he has preferred the colour contrasts afforded by the use of white slip on a dark body and cobalt inglaze pigment. On the dish with the ships, here, the waves are cut through the cobalt but painted on the white slip. The effect is heightened by the carefully considered use of overglaze gold, the one bright colour used.

226 *Bottle vase decorated in underglaze blue and overglaze enamels with design of 'the three friends' and mandarin orange*

FS/G7 鍋島色絵染付松竹梅橘文瓶子

Nabeshima porcelain
h 30.6 cm
18th century
PRIVATE COLLECTION, Japan
Important Cultural Property

Few pieces were made at Okawachi that were not dishes or small cups. A small number of jars and bottles is known, and there is considerable controversy over the date – and sometimes even the provenance – of these. This famous and elegant bottle, with its shape derived from *negoro* lacquer, shows every sign of being a revival piece.

226

227 *Lidded food container, or tiered box with decoration of flowers in underglaze blue*

FS/G10 染付百花十友図重蓋物　木米作

AOKI MOKUBEI (1767–1833)
Kyō-ware porcelain
h 21.5 cm, *dm* 16.6 cm
Early 19th century
KYOTO NATIONAL MUSEUM

Aoki Mokubei was a *Nanga* painter (see nos 86, 87) as well as a versatile potter. His teacher, Okuda Eisen (1753–1811), was responsible for the revival of Kyoto as a ceramic centre, and Mokubei is said to have perfected Eisen's porcelain technique. Both potters were experimental both in their material and in their choice of objects to make. Eisen specialised in copies of Swatow, while Mokubei was much more eclectic and copied both Chinese pottery and porcelain – especially Kochi wares (i.e. wares exported to the south seas) and blue and white – and made his own variations on Chinese themes. He also used his own Kyoto background as a source of inspiration.

On this ceramic *jūbako*, a familiar shape in lacquer, Mokubei has used his great skill as a painter to cover almost all the surface with flowers, which include peony, prunus and chrysanthemum. The characters on the top and bottom tier read 'beautiful friend' and 'elegant friend'.

227

228   *Set of implements for the green tea
      ceremony, pottery and porcelain*

FS/G10   煎茶道具　木米作

> [repr. in colour on p. 211]
> AOKI MOKUBEI (1767–1833)
> Kyō-ware, pottery and porcelain, and Chinese pottery
> Tea jars *h* 10.5 cm; hearth *h* 1.2 cm; cups *dm* 6.7 cm; kettle
> *h* 18.4 cm; napkin holder *h* 7.7 cm
> Early 19th century
> TOKYO NATIONAL MUSEUM

The implements needed for *sen-cha*, the green tea ceremony, are
quite different from those used in *chanoyu*. In this collection of
the works of Mokubei can be seen many of the techniques at
which he excelled – for instance, the tea jars reflect Ming blue
and white, the overhandled tea pot is in Kochi style, and the
napkin holder in Kangxi blue and white style.

The unglazed tea pot is in Chinese 'folk pottery' style, and a
Chinese original is included in the set.

229   *Tea bowl with design of a crane*

FS/G10   黑樂立鶴文茶碗　道八作

> NIN'AMI DŌHACHI (1783–1855)
> Black Raku ware
> *dm* 9.7 cm
> Mid-19th century
> TOKYO NATIONAL MUSEUM

Dōhachi was said to be the Kyoto potter who best reproduced the
spirit of the earlier works that he specialised in imitating. He was,
however, like Mokubei, an original also, and such pieces as this
chawan have no precedent. The simplified drawing and the strong
colour contrast do not look out of place on the basically
Momoyama shape.

229

Armour

The earliest examples of defensive armour to be excavated so far in Japan are a group of pieces of wood dating from around the first century BC which were probably part of a *tankō*, a type of armour made from horizontal strips held together by leather thongs. By the fourth century AD such armours were being made from iron and soon afterwards another type, the *keikō*, was introduced from the mainland. It was made up of small vertical plates tied together in rows which were themselves laced vertically.

The *keikō* continued in use, with some changes, until the tenth century when it gave way to the *ōyoroi*, a style of armour which is represented here by an eighteenth-century imitation (no. 230). The small plates of iron and leather which formed an important part of the *ōyoroi* and all later armours were tied together in rows before being heavily lacquered over; this heavy lacquering gave the armour an unprecedented strength and solidity. The *ōyoroi* was reasonably serviceable and when colourfully laced and embellished with gilt metal was a magnificent expression of a great samurai's power, but it was somewhat unwieldy and did not fit the body closely. Although it continued to be worn in the Kamakura period, the difficulty experienced by the mounted samurai in repelling the Mongol attacks of 1274 and 1281 made them realise the desirability of a more practical defence. They gradually began to adopt the *dōmaru* style, also represented here by an eighteenth-century revival (no. 231).

The *dōmaru* was at first worn by footsoldiers and consisted of a body protection in a single piece with a number of hanging tassets to protect the thighs, but when mounted warriors used it they retained the large helmet and shoulder-guards from the earlier style. In the late fourteenth and fifteenth centuries the still lighter and simpler *haramaki* came into use and in the sixteenth century, which saw the emergence of great schools of armourers among whom the Myōchin were pre-eminent, the intensification of warfare and the increasing use of lances and, later, muskets (no. 245) made further practical improvements necessary. The old knobbed helmet gave way to the stronger ridged helmet, sometimes made from as many as 122 plates fixed with over six hundred rivets, and the old style of close lacing, which offered too easy a purchase to polearms and often became infested, was frequently abandoned in favour of wider lacing with larger plates. Sometimes, under European influence, the lamellar system was dropped and solid plates of metal were used instead, especially for chest armour. The cuirass of the sixteenth-century armour style called *tōsei gusoku* ('modern equipment') was made of five (*gomaidō*, no. 232) or two (*nimaidō*, no. 233) hinged plates or sections of laced small plates. A full *tōsei gusoku* normally included an armour skirt in about seven or eight sections, sometimes with a lower skirt, as well as throat and shoulder guards, chain mail and plate sleeves, a whole or half mask and a helmet. The helmets became particularly ostentatious during the Momoyama period and were often fitted with eccentrically shaped forecrests and sidecrests. Sometimes the iron bowl of the helmet was completely obscured by an elaborately modelled, lacquered fitting in the form of a court cap or hood (nos 235, 236, 237). Such armours as were intended for use by great generals (nos 232, 233) were, although practical, also of

importance as emblems of rank and, since generals no longer played a combative role, the effort lavished on the decoration of their battle-dress was unlikely to be wasted as a result of damage.

During the peaceful years of the Edo period armour became a luxury item intended solely for display. Although some daimyō and their senior retainers continued to own a *tōsei gusoku*, they normally aspired to a suit of *ōyoroi* or *dōmaru* type. Many Edo period armours are made in a complex mixture of styles, often showing that their creators were unaware of the principles governing the construction of their medieval prototypes.

JVE

231

230 *Suit of armour in ōyoroi style*

F/G3 紺糸威大鎧

[repr. in colour on p. 213]
Black-lacquered iron and leather plates; dark blue and red silk
lacing; multicoloured and red silk tying cords; stencilled
leather and gilt metal decorations; iron helmet
h of helmet 23 cm, of body armour 82.2 cm
Early 18th century
TŌSHŌGŪ, Shizuoka

This suit is a comparatively restrained manifestation of the
tendency towards imitation of early armours which began in the
seventeenth century. The characteristics of the *ōyoroi*, originally
used by mounted warriors in the late Heian and Kamakura
periods, include the low, rounded helmet with prominent rivets,
the broad neck-guard with large turnbacks, the body armour
made up in two pieces, one protecting the right side and the other
the front, back and left side, the four thigh-guards and the
stencilled leather covering of the breastplate decorated with lions
and peonies. This armour, which is said to have been worn by
the shōgun Yoshimune (reigned 1716–1745), well known for
his love of military exercises, is further decorated with flaming
pearls and a modified version of the hollyhock badge of the
Tokugawa family.

231 *Suit of armour in dōmaru style*

S/G3 紅糸威胴丸具足

Black-lacquered iron and leather plates; red silk lacing and
tying cords;
stencilled leather and gilt metal decorations;
iron helmet; mail sleeves
h of helmet 16 cm, of body armour 68 cm
c. 1775
TŌSHŌGŪ, Shizuoka

This armour, said to have been used by Tokugawa Iemoto
(1763–1779), short-lived son of the tenth shōgun Ieharu, is
typical of many eighteenth-century revivals of the *dōmaru* style,
originally worn by footsoldiers and adopted by mounted samurai
during the fourteenth century. The chief points of difference from
the *ōyoroi* (see no. 230) are the close-fitting one-piece body
armour (*dō*) from which the style takes its name, the simple leaf-
shaped protections for the shoulder-straps, the smaller and more
numerous thigh-guards and the mail sleeves; but the large
square shoulder-guards are a survival from the earlier style.

232 *Suit of armour in gomaidō gusoku style*

F/G3 黒漆五枚胴具足

Black-lacquered iron plates; dark blue silk lacing;
iron helmet with gilded forecrest
Helmet s. Myōchin Munefuyu (fl. 1520s)
Helmet *h* 13 cm; body armour *h* 49 cm
Late 16th or early 17th century
SENDAI MUNICIPAL MUSEUM
Important Cultural Property

This armour was owned by Date Masamune (1567–1636), one
of the greatest of the Momoyama period daimyō, and the
construction of its cuirass, made up of five hinged plates, is
almost identical to that of one excavated from his mausoleum in
1975. Under European influence, large solid iron plates, as
opposed to small lamellae joined by silk lacing, became very
popular for body armour during the Momoyama period and
chain mail of the international type in which each ring passes
through four others appears to have been used for the first time.
The enormous crescent moon forecrest is as strongly associated
with Masamune as the antler fittings are with Honda Tadakatsu
(no. 239).

232

233 *Suit of armour in nimaidō gusoku style*

S/G3 色々威二枚胴具足

[repr. in colour on p. 212]
Black-lacquered iron and leather plates; red, white and blue
silk lacing; multicoloured tying cords; gilt metal and gold
lacquer decorations; silk brocade and mail sleeves; iron helmet
Late 16th century
YOKOTA COLLECTION, Hiroshima

This armour, which belonged to Toyotomi Hideyoshi, exemplifies
the combination of utility and display favoured by the great
generals of the Momoyama period. The construction is
lightweight and practical but every detail has been finished with
an eye to decorative effect: the ridges of the helmet are
embellished with gilt metal fittings, the sleeves under the mail are
of rich silk brocade, and dragons and paulownia *mon* are liberally

applied in gold lacquer. The extensive use of close lacing is a
survival from earlier styles, but the lower thigh defences of large
iron plates decorated with the sun motif favoured by Hideyoshi
are executed in the most up-to-date Momoyama technique.
About ten other armours of this design are known and it is likely
that they were used either by Hideyoshi's escort or by stand-ins
(*kagemusha*).

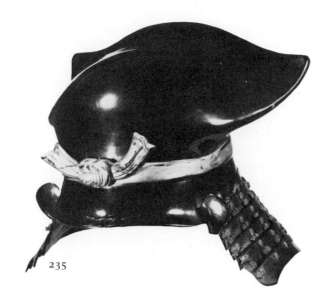

235

236 *Helmet fitting in the form of a court cap*
S/G3 透彫折烏帽子形兜

Leather covered in gold foil and cut with conventional foliage
decoration, with the character *mu* picked out in black lacquer
20 × 22 × 48 cm
Late Muromachi or early Momoyama period
UESUGI SHRINE, Yamagata

Court caps (*eboshi*) of various types were, like headcloths (*zukin*),
much imitated by Momoyama period armourers. This example,
said to have been used by the warrior Uesugi Kenshin (1530–
1578), was probably intended to be mounted on a helmet in
Hineno style which is also in the Uesugi shrine. Uesugi's strong
religious leanings are apparent in the highly unusual pierced
decoration which recalls the elaborate nimbuses surrounding
many Japanese Buddhist images and in the black-lacquered
character *mu* ('non-existence'), a key word in Zen Buddhism.

234

234 *Helmet in namban style*
FS/G3 金銀象嵌南蛮兜

Iron inlaid with gold and silver
h 25.5 cm
Momoyama or early Edo period
OSAKA CASTLE

The presence of Europeans in Japan during the Momoyama
period and the experience of the two unsuccessful expeditions
against Korea in 1592 and 1597 stimulated Japanese armourers
to imitate both European and Asian mainland models. In general
shape this helmet is based on the brimmed European hat of the
period, but the decorative finial and the gold and silver inlay are
both inspired by Korean or Chinese metalwork.

235 *Helmet in the form of a hood*
F/G3 投頭巾形兜

Iron base fitted with carved lacquered wood
32 × 35 cm
17th century
YOKOTA COLLECTION, Hiroshima

Among the eccentric helmets sported by the warriors of the late
sixteenth and early seventeenth century, those modelled on the
various forms of the headcloth (*zukin*) were perhaps the
commonest. The present example is made up of a simple helmet-
bowl of three pieces in Hineno style fitted with a covering which
realistically imitates a head cloth, tied by a cord simulated in gold
lacquer and lying back over the wearer's head.

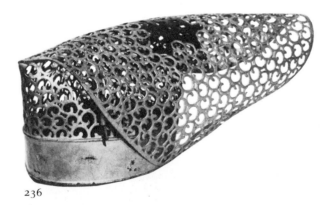

236

237 *Helmet in the form of a court cap*
F/G3 長烏帽子形兜

[repr. in colour on p. 215]
Iron base fitted with cloth and paper decorated in mottled
black and brown lacquer
67 × 33 cm
Momoyama period
YOKOTA COLLECTION, Hiroshima

A large number of unusually tall helmets, some in the form of elongated court caps, others more fancifully fashioned as hare's ears or catfish, were made during the Momoyama period; the elaborate lacquering on this example testifies to the decorative rather than practical function of such headgear. The helmet is fitted with a typical Momoyama neckguard in Hineno style, made up of four plates of black lacquered iron, tied with purple threads, the highest of which is continued forwards and folded back to form the *fukigaeshi* ('blow-back').

238 Helmet with wave-shaped fitting
S/G3 波頭形兜

Iron base with black-lacquered leather and horn-shaped decorations; gold-lacquered *mon* of the Sakai or Morikawa family
h 51 cm
Momoyama period
FUJIWARA COLLECTION, Osaka

The helmet with wave decoration is essentially an elaboration of the headcloth type (see no. 235) much favoured during the Momoyama period.

238

239 Helmet with fittings in the form of antlers
F/G3 鹿角脇立付筋兜

Bowl of flanged iron plates with gilt metal fittings; lacquered wood antlers; gilt metal helmet-horns (*kuwagata*) and central fitting in the form of a *ken* (Buddhist guardian's sword); gold-lacquered Honda family *mon*
50 × 46 cm
17th century
TOMODA COLLECTION, Kyoto

The antler decorations are especially associated with Honda Tadakatsu (1548–1610) and his descendants, one of whom, Masanaga (1628–1679), was the owner of the present helmet.

240

240 Helmet with fittings in the form of water buffalo horns
S/G3 大水牛角脇立付兜

Helmet black-lacquered iron; fittings lacquered paper and cloth covered with silver foil
80 × 75 cm
Momoyama or early Edo period
HAGA COLLECTION, Tokyo

The bowl is of Hineno type, made up of two side plates covered by a broad band running from front to back and a heavy reinforcing peak, and is fitted with a steeply-sloping Hineno neckguard of six solid iron bands. To this sturdy and austere helmet is fitted a pair of impractical but impressive buffalo horn fittings, which are embellished with conventional carved decoration.

241 Helmet in the form of a conch-shell
FS/G3 法螺貝形兜

[repr. in colour on p. 214]
Iron, repoussé, with a circular gilt crest attached by a cord
31.5 × 31 cm
Momoyama or early Edo period
YOKOTA COLLECTION, Hiroshima

The military conch-shell (see no. 243) shape was especially well suited to adaptation as a helmet, with the mouthpiece of the conch-shell corresponding to the traditional but functionless *tehen* hole in the top of the helmet. Marvellously realistic repoussé work of this type was produced throughout the Momoyama and Edo periods but, being of necessity manufactured from soft iron, it would have been useless as a defence against the highly tempered edge of a Japanese sword blade.

242 Saddle and stirrups with design of cranes and waves

F/G3 鶴波蒔絵鞍・鐙

Wood and iron, decorated in gold *nashiji* and thick *takamaki-e* lacquer
Saddle 33 × 39 × 34 cm, stirrups *h* 26 cm
18th century
KŌZU KOBUNKA KAIKAN, Kyoto

Matching sets of saddle and stirrups first became popular during the Momoyama period and there is one still in existence which is said to have been designed by no less an artist than Kanō Eitoku for the use of Toyotomi Hideyoshi. The Momoyama period also saw the Japanese saddle reach its final light-weight and elegant form; at the same time decoration in inlaid shell was largely abandoned in favour of the more luxurious but even less practical *takamaki-e* lacquer technique.

243 Saddle and stirrups with design of conch-shells and decorative cords

S/G3 法螺貝蒔絵鞍・鐙

Wood and iron decorated in gold *nashiji* and *takamaki-e*
Saddle 32.7 × 38.6 × 33.6 cm
17th century
KŌZU KOBUNKA KAIKAN, Kyoto

The conch-shell (*horagai*) was used from the Heian period onwards as a means of giving signals during battles and is thus a suitable motif for the decoration of saddles and stirrups. Designs including threads or tassels of some kind were much favoured for saddles, since they made it possible for the decoration to be extended over the whole of the rather awkward shape.

242

243

245

244 *Pair of stirrups with design of hares and waves*

FS/G3   波兎象嵌鐙

Iron with *sahari* (copper, tin and lead alloy) and brass inlay;
the interiors decorated with fragments of shell set in lacquer
s. 'Shigeyoshi of Kaga province'
23.5 × 29 cm
18th century
SWORD MUSEUM, Tokyo

It was probably after the attempted invasions of Korea by
Hideyoshi that stirrups first came to be decorated with inlay in
the Korean manner; the principal centre of production was Kaga
province, where brass, silver and the whitish pewter-like alloy
called *sahari* were used.

245 *Musket with design of Hosokawa family mon*

FS/G3   九曜紋散象嵌鉄砲銘重勝

Stock wood; barrel iron with gold overlay
l of barrel 101 cm
17th century
EISEI BUNKO, Tokyo

A seventeenth-century Japanese tradition relates that after the
accidental arrival of three Portuguese mariners at Tanegashima
in 1543 the swordsmith Kiyosada gave his daughter to their
captain in order to learn the secrets of musket manufacture.
Whatever the truth of this account, it is certain that copies of
European firearms were soon being made in large quantities and
played a decisive part in the history of the succeeding half
century. It seems, however, that after the establishment of the
Tokugawa régime they were produced in much smaller numbers.
This musket was probably intended more as a plaything for a
Hosokawa daimyō than as a practical weapon.

244

Sword blades

Although sword scholars of the Edo and subsequent periods have tended to see the late sixteenth century and in particular the year 1596, the first of Keichō, as a time of fundamental change in Japanese sword history and the turning point between the *kotō* ('old sword') and *shintō* ('new sword') eras, the developments which reached their climax at that time were the result of some two centuries of changing military and technological circumstances. The characteristically curved Japanese sword, whose shape was probably perfected in the eleventh century, was at first worn as the *tachi*, slung from the waist with the edge downwards and used from horseback, but as early as the twelfth century another type of sword, the *uchigatana* or *katana*, which was worn edge upwards, was being carried by foot-soldiers and in the fourteenth century mounted samurai began to adopt this more practical weapon for their own use. There was also a significant change in the shape of both *tachi* and *uchigatana*: the curve, previously located near the hilt, was moved towards the point end with the advantage that the actions of drawing and striking could be accomplished in a single movement.

During the fifteenth and sixteenth centuries sword production became increasingly concentrated in Bizen and Mino provinces and the Seki tradition of Mino in particular became overwhelmingly influential. The swords of Mino lacked the aesthetic qualities of the great *kotō* periods but they were strong, serviceable and cheap and the Mino smiths' ability to mass-produce assured the primacy of their unassuming style. The national 'sword hunt' ordered by Hideyoshi in 1588 and earlier local 'sword hunts', whose purpose was to disarm the peasantry and monks, are evidence of the extent to which ownership of swords had spread beyond the confines of the samurai class. In the Edo period the right to wear swords was restricted in the main to the samurai and although many merchants were allowed to wear one sword and a very few to wear two, regulations regarding sword ownership were more stringently enforced than at any other time.

Early in the Momoyama period the *daishō koshirae*, a long *katana* and a shorter companion sword (*wakizashi*) worn together and mounted *en suite*, established itself as the standard mounting style and was to remain so throughout the Edo period. Because of the lack of really good swords of the right shape and size for these mounts, fine old *tachi* blades were often pressed into service by being cut down at the hilt end to reduce their length and curve, but before long custom-made swords in the new shape were being produced. The resulting blades, whose makers attended as much to beauty of texture and temper line as to practical effectiveness, re-established the status of the sword as a work of art. The sword by Umetada Myōju (no. 246) sums up the style of the time: the texture of the metal is fine, there are many bright *nie* (small patches of very hard crystalline steel) in the tempered edge, whose outline has an air of restrained confidence, and the carvings in the blade are bold and vigorous.

The period following the full establishment of the Tokugawa shōgunate witnessed the rise to pre-eminence of Edo and Osaka as centres of sword production. The blades produced in the two cities from about 1655 onwards are characterised by meticulous skill in forging and perfection of finish (see nos 247 and 248) in contrast to the bravura of the late sixteenth and early seventeenth-century style, but they still passed with flying colours the demanding tests on corpses and the bodies of condemned criminals which were very commonly carried out at this time, especially in Edo (no. 247). From the end of the seventeenth century the decline in the economic position of the samurai and the preference of those merchants who were permitted to wear swords for decorative mountings rather than masterly blades caused a general decline to set in.

At the end of the following century a return to the style of the great *kotō* days and to higher technical standards in general ushered in the *shinshintō* ('new-new sword') period, which lasted until the abolition of sword-wearing in 1876.

JVE

246 *Blade for a slung sword (tachi) engraved with a dragon and the Buddhist deity Fudō*

FS/G3　太刀銘埋忠明寿

UMETADA MYŌJU (1558–1631)
Steel; gently undulating temper-line (*ōmidare hamon*); *itame* grain
s. 'Umetada Myōju of Nishijin in Yamashiro province on a day in the eighth month of the third year of Keichō (= 1598)'; insc. 'I cannot cross another river'
l 82.5 cm, curve 0.9 cm
1598
NATIONAL MUSEUM, KYOTO
Important Cultural Property

Although this blade can be seen to be a *tachi* from the fact that the smith's signature is engraved on the side of the tang which has the edge to the right, the shallow curve, the tight grain of the metal and the generously undulating temper-line make it more typical of the *katana*, the standard long sword of the later Momoyama and Edo periods which was normally worn in combination with the shorter *wakizashi* (see nos 247, 254 and 255). The blade thus stands at the very pivot of the *kotō* ('old sword') and *shintō* ('new sword') epochs. The meaning of the inscription, based on an old Chinese phrase, is that the warrior, once he has sworn to carry out a task, must see it through to the end before he can take on another.

247 *Blade for a short sword (wakizashi) engraved with a dragon, Buddhist sword (ken) and stylised Sanskrit characters (bonji) standing for the Buddhist deity Fudō*

FS/G3　脇差銘興里

NAGASONE KOTETSU OKISATO (c. 1614–1678)
Steel; undulating temper line (*notare gunome hamon*); *itame* grain
s. 'Made and engraved by Nagasone Okisato' with gold inlaid inscriptions: 'cut through two bodies, Yamano Kaemon Nagahisa; cut through three bodies, Yamano Kanjūrō Naganari; tested many times on one body; sword number thirty-three'
l 59.2 cm
c. 1659
SUZUKI COLLECTION, Tokyo

Lacking the opportunity to try out their blades in battle, seventeenth-century smiths often commissioned specialist sword tests. The Yamano were pre-eminent in this profession; Kotetsu lived near them in Edo and frequently engaged their services.

248 *Blade for a long sword (katana)*

FS/G3　刀銘津田助広

TSUTA SUKEHIRO (1637–1682)
Steel; sharply undulating temper-line (*tōranha*; *itame* grain)
s. 'Tsuta Echizen no kami Sukehiro on a day in the second month of the fourth year of Empō (= 1676)'
l 91.5 cm
1676
ENDŌ COLLECTION, Kanagawa

The most outstanding feature of the blades of Sukehiro, one of the great Osaka smiths, is the prominent and sharply undulating temper line called *tōran* ('billows'). The eccentric calligraphy of the signature is another distinctive characteristic which he shared with several of his contemporaries.

249 *Blade for a long sword (katana)*

FS/G3　刀銘国包

FUJIWARA KUNIKANE (1592–1664)
Steel; straight temper line (*suguha*); *masame* grain
s. *Yamashiro no daijō Fujiwara no Kunikane*
Length 89 cm
c. 1630
SUZUKI COLLECTION, Tokyo

Kunikane was a member of the Mishina school, typical of many which were founded by smiths from Mino province during the Momoyama period, and himself started a distinguished school of smiths which worked for the Date family in Sendai. The fine *masame* grain, resembling straight-grained wood, is a mark of his work.

246

247

248

249

Sword mounts

The tradition of elaborate soft metal and lacquer sword mountings dates back to the Nara period and one of the mounting styles of the Momoyama and Edo, the *kazaritachi* (see nos 250 and 251) for ceremonial use at the imperial court, is almost a direct descendant of the imported Chinese swords which were deposited in the Shōsōin repository in the mid-eighth century. Splendid as these *kazaritachi* are, they do not evoke the spirit of the Momoyama daimyō as fully as do the *itomaki no tachi* (see nos 252 and 253) decorated exclusively with *mon* and having the scabbard wrapped for a third of its length to prevent its being damaged when worn with armour, which combines function and ostentation as effectively as the armours worn by Hideyoshi and by Date Masamune. But the most important development in Momoyama was the introduction of the *daishō* style of long and short swords mounted *en suite* (see nos 254, 255 and 257). Flamboyant gold and red lacquered examples which belonged to Hideyoshi and to Maeda Toshiie (1538–1599) still exist today but in the early seventeenth century sober decoration with black lacquer became the norm.

The metal fittings associated with the Momoyama and later *daishō* are descended from those which embellished the *uchigatana* and the luxuriously mounted daggers of the Muromachi and earlier periods. The first maker of such fittings whose name we know is Gotō Yūjō (1440–1512), founder of the great Gotō line of craftsmen. His fittings, mostly made in the service of the Ashikaga shōgun Yoshimasa (1436–1490), consist of gold and silver decoration on a ground of *shakudō*, an alloy of copper with a small amount of gold patinated to a blue-black colour and almost invariably worked with minute and regular punched granulations, *nanako*.

The principal fitting of the Edo period sword was the *tsuba* or guard, roughly circular and pierced with a wedge-shaped hole to admit the sword blade and sometimes with one or two smaller holes to admit the ends of the *kozuka* and *kōgai*, a small dagger and a skewer-like implement which were carried in the scabbard of the main sword. The fittings of the hilt were the *fuchi* and *kashira*, pommel and collar, at either end and the *menuki*, two small pieces held in place by the hilt-wrapping, which improved the user's grip.

The Gotō school prospered throughout the sixteenth century, later enjoying the patronage of Hideyoshi, Ieyasu and their shōgunal successors, and continued to be responsible for the fittings on the most sober and formal *daishō* mountings until the end of the Edo period. In the later seventeenth century however the increasing importance of merchant rather than samurai patronage stimulated an explosion of creativity, led by the 'three great Nara masters' of whom Yasuchika (nos 256, 265) was one, the Yokoya school (nos 266, 267), Hamano Masayuki and others. These artists, many of whom had started their careers as assistants in the Gotō workshops, developed new techniques such as *katakiri* engraving (see no. 266), made extensive use of copper and *shibuichi*, a light or dark grey alloy of copper and silver, in addition to gold, silver and *shakudō*, introduced fresh subject-matter and generally freed themselves from the Gotō stylistic stranglehold; their work is referred to as *machibori* ('town carving') as opposed to the *iebori* ('(shōgunal) house carving') of the Gotō.

The other great tradition of pre-Momoyama sword-fitting manufacture, iron guards made at first by armourers and swordsmiths but later by specialist craftsmen, was continued in the Edo period by, among others, the schools of Higo province (nos 258, 259, 263 and 264), whose austere and practical guards became increasingly decorative during the peaceful years of the seventeenth century and eventually sometimes abandoned iron as the main metal, stimulated perhaps by the bold experimentation of Umetada Myōju (no. 262).

In the course of the eighteenth century a large number of schools sprang up at Edo, Kyoto and elsewhere whose fittings emphasised the decorative rather than the practical, and the combination of Gotō-derived virtuosity of craftsmanship with the boldness of the iron *tsuba* tradition made possible a vast range of styles and designs. In the nineteenth century Gotō Ichijō (no. 268) revived the flagging fortunes of the traditional Gotō style: his reinterpretation of the classical manner was one of the more creative products of the antiquarianism which also expressed itself in the blades of the *shinshintō* smiths and the medieval-style *ōyoroi* suits of the late Edo armourers.

JVE

250 *Mounting for a slung sword (kazaritachi) with design of paulownia and hollyhock mon*

F/G3 金装飾太刀拵

Scabbard wood decorated in gold *nashiji* and *hiramaki-e* lacquer; hilt wood covered in rayskin; metal fittings gilt copper, with enamel studs; slings and decorative hanging cord leather
l 102 cm
Early 17th century
WATANABE COLLECTION, Tokyo

This ceremonial court sword is said to have been given to Tokugawa Hidetada (1579–1632), son of Ieyasu, on the occasion of his formal installation as shōgun by the Emperor Goyōzei (r. 1586–1611) in 1605.

251 *Mounting for a slung sword (kazaritachi) with design of oak-leaf mon*

S/G3 金装飾太刀拵

Scabbard wood decorated in gold *nashiji* and *hiramaki-e* lacquer; hilt wood covered in rayskin; metal fittings gilt copper, with enamel studs; slings and decorative hanging cord leather
l 102 cm
Momoyama period
YOSHIDA COLLECTION, Tokyo

The Momoyama *kazaritachi*, with its elaborate openwork gilt metal fittings and unwrapped rayskin on the hilt, is essentially a descendant of the court sword of the later Heian period, itself derived from the extravagantly decorated mountings imported from Tang China during the Nara period.

250

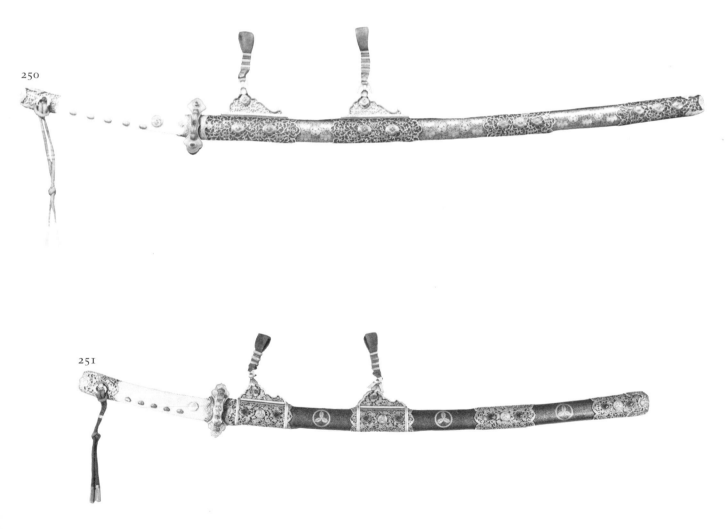

251

252   *Mounting for a slung sword (itomaki no tachi) with design of paulownia mon*

F/G3   梨子地桐紋蒔絵糸巻太刀拵

Scabbard wood decorated in gold *nashiji* and *hiramaki-e*
lacquer and partially wrapped with silk bands;
hilt wood covered in silk brocade wrapped with silk bands;
metal fittings *shakudō nanako* and gold;
slings leather and silk; decorative tying cords white, red and
black silk

l 110 cm
Momoyama period
SWORD MUSEUM, Tokyo
Important Cultural Property

The *itomaki no tachi* style of mounting, in which the upper part of
the scabbard is wrapped in the same way as the hilt, first
appeared in the fifteenth century, when it was used by the
Ashikaga shōguns, but it was not until the Momoyama that it
reached its final form, characterised by the gold *nashiji* scabbard
with decoration confined to *mon* in gold *hiramaki-e*, the *shakudō*
and gold fittings decorated with the same *mon* and the use of
richly coloured silk for the tying cords, slings and hilt wrapping.
The resulting combination of ostentation and formality appealed
strongly to the taste of Hideyoshi and his contemporaries.

253   *Mounting for a slung sword (itomaki no tachi) with design of the orange branch mon of the Ii family*

SG/3   梨子地橘紋蒔絵糸巻太刀拵

Scabbard wood decorated in gold *nashiji* and *hiramaki-e*
lacquer and partially wrapped with silk bands;
hilt wood covered in silk brocade wrapped with silk bands;
metal fittings *shakudō nanako* and gold;
slings silk brocade; decorative tying cords coloured silk

l 98.9 cm
Momoyama period
II COLLECTION, Shiga

The *itomaki no tachi* style was much favoured by the daimyō of
the Momoyama period; this example still belongs to the Ii family,
two of whose members, Naomasa (1561–1602), and his son
Naotaka (1590–1659), played a prominent part in the battles of
Sekigahara (1600) and Osaka (1614–1615).

252

253

254 *Mounting for a pair of swords (daishō) with design of the mon of the Nabeshima family*

F/G3 　黒漆大小拵

[repr. in colour on p. 216]
Scabbards wood decorated in plain black lacquer;
hilts wood covered in rayskin wrapped with silk bands;
pommels (*kashira*) horn; metal fittings *shakudō nanako*
decorated in gold and silver; tying cords silk
l 89 cm, 63 cm
Middle Edo period
SWORD MUSEUM, Tokyo

An example of the strictly formalised sword mountings worn by the daimyō during the Edo period. The special features of this particular style, prescribed for use with *kamishimo* costume, include the differently shaped butts (squared, with a metal fitting, on the long sword and rounded, with no fitting, on the short sword), the materials and decoration of the metal fittings, made by a member of the Gotō school, confined to family *mon* in gold on *shakudō nanako*, and the horn, rather than metal, pommels (*kashira*) which the hilt wrapping passes over rather than through.

255 *Mounting for a pair of swords (daishō) with dragon designs*

S/G3 　黒漆大小拵

Scabbards wood with ribbed carving decorated in plain black lacquer; hilts wood covered in rayskin wrapped with silk bands; metal fittings *shakudō nanako* decorated in gold and silver; tying cords silk
l 95.5 cm, 66.1 cm
Middle Edo period
TOKYO NATIONAL MUSEUM

This pair departs somewhat from the strict norms laid down for the *kamishimo* style (see no. 254). The metal fittings are decorated with formal dragons rather than family *mon* and silver is used in addition to gold. The austere black lacquer of the scabbard is relieved by ribbed carving whose pattern is discreetly varied one-third of the way along its length.

256 *Mounting for a long sword (katana) with striped design*

F/G3 　変塗打刀拵

Scabbard wood covered in rayskin decorated in spiralling black and red lacquer with silver foil; hilt wood covered in rayskin wrapped with rattan; guard brass decorated in gold, *shakudō* and copper with the *Sennin* Chōkarō, signed *Yasuchika* (1670–1744); pommel and collar (*fuchi-kashira*) decorated with paulownia *mon*; hilt ornaments (*menuki*) each modelled as a horse; tying-cord silk
l 96 cm
18th century
SWORD MUSEUM, Tokyo

This flamboyantly mounted sword was worn by the imperial loyalist Kuroda Kiyotaka (1840–1900) during his siege of adherents of the shōgunate at Hakodate in Hokkaido (1869).

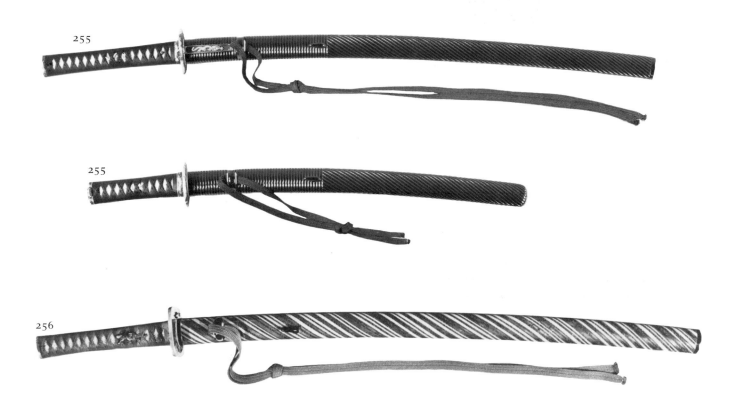

255

255

256

257 *Mounting for a pair of swords (daishō) with striped design*

S/G3 朱漆地青漆蛭巻塗大小拵

[repr. in colour on p. 216]
Scabbards wood decorated in red and dark green mottled lacquer; hilts wood covered in gold-lacquered rayskin wrapped with two-colour silk bands; pommels and collars (*fuchi-kashira*) shakudō, gold and copper layers carved with *guri* scrolls; guards plain *shakudō*; hilt ornaments (*menuki*) shakudō and silver modelled as flying cranes; tying cord brown and white silk
l 98.2 cm, 72.5 cm
Late 17th or early 18th century
II COLLECTION, Shiga

During the seventeenth century there was increasing freedom in the style of decoration of *daishō* pairs made for daily wear rather than formal occasions. The lacquering became more elaborate and some ingenious new metalworking techniques were devised. This example, another heirloom of the Ii family (see no. 253) of Hikone, is fitted with *fuchi-kashira* made from three different metals and then deeply carved to reveal their laminate construction.

258 *Sword guard with design of broken fans and falling cherry blossoms*

FS/G3 破扇図鐔　又七作

[repr. in colour on p. 218]
HAYASHI MATASHICHI (1605 or 1613 – 1691 or 1699)
Iron with gold overlay; the holes plugged with *shakudō*
dm 8.5 cm
17th century
EISEI BUNKO, Tokyo
Important Cultural Property

Matashichi, the founder of the Hayashi or Kasuga school and the father of sword-fitting manufacture in Higo province, worked like many of his co-provincials in the service of the Hosokawa family of daimyō. He is famous for the quality and colour of his iron and also for his skilful and sparingly applied gold overlay, in which the soft metal is hammered into shallow grooves cut in the iron as a key. Both broken fans and falling cherry blossoms are symbolic of the Buddhistic concept of impermanence.

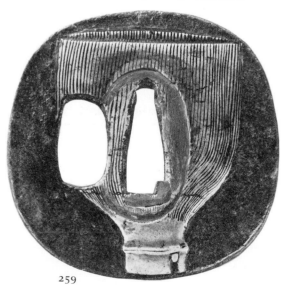

259

259 *Sword guard with tea whisk design*

FS/G3 茶筅図鐔　甚五作

SHIMIZU JINGO (d. 1675)
Iron and brass
dm 7.3 cm
mid-17th century
YONENO COLLECTION, Kumamoto

Jingo, the founder of the Shimizu, one of the four principal schools of Higo province, is best known for his boldly conceived guards with a single motif executed in high relief brass on iron.

260

260 *Sword guard with floral and cloud design*

FS/G3 花文七宝鐔　道仁作

Attributed to HIRATA DŌNIN (1591–1646)
Iron with translucent cloisonné enamels and gilt wire
dm 8.2 cm
Early 17th century
WATANABE COLLECTION, Tokyo

Although this guard is unsigned, it has been traditionally ascribed to Dōnin, the founder of the Hirata school, whose members appear to have been active in enamel decoration on sword fittings and other small metal items throughout the Edo period. According to nineteenth-century accounts, Dōnin learnt the technique of cloisonné enamelling from a Korean, but it is perhaps more likely that he took his inspiration from Chinese enamels of the Ming dynasty which were imported into Japan during the Muromachi period.

261 *Sword guard in the form of a fuki (butterbur) leaf*

FS/G3 蕗図鐔銘正阿弥伝兵衛

SHŌAMI DEMBEI (1651–1727)
Shibuichi and *shakudō* with gold inlay
s. 'Shōami Dembei of Akita in Dewa province'
8 × 7.6 cm
Late 17th or early 18th century
WAKAYAMA COLLECTION, Tokyo

261

Dembei was the leading member of an important branch of the Shōami school which is said to have moved early in the seventeenth century from Kyoto to Akita, whose *fuki* leaves are celebrated for their enormous size. The difference in colour between the two sides of the leaf is cleverly conveyed by the use of two different alloys of copper, *shakudō* and *shibuichi*. The faithful depiction of the insect-holes in the leaf is a premonition of the tendency towards hyper-realism which characterizes some of the miniature arts of the later Edo period.

262 Sword guard with grapevine and trellis design

FS/G3 葡萄棚図鐔銘埋忠明寿

[repr. in colour on p. 217]
UMETADA MYŌJU (1558–1631)
Copper with gold, silver and *shakudō*;
the holes plugged with silver *nanako*
s. *Umetada Myōju*; *d* 7.6 cm
Early 17th century
MORI COLLECTION, Kanagawa
Important Art Object

Umetada Myōju, who was famous also as a swordsmith (see no. 246), was one of the first craftsmen, apart from the members of the canonical Gotō school, to make guards in metals other than iron. This guard exemplifies the skill in conveying the impression of full polychromy with a limited range of materials which he shared with the makers of Kōdaiji lacquerware (p. 241).

263 Sword guard with design of the moon reflected in flooded rice fields

FS/G3 田毎川図鐔銘永久作

[repr. in colour on p. 217]
NISHIGAKI KANSHIRŌ (1639–1717)
Brass, with *shakudō*, *shibuichi*, patinated copper and gold
s. 'Made by Nishigaki Nagahisa at the age of seventy'
dm 7.8 cm
1709–1710
EISEI BUNKO, Tokyo
Important Art Object

Kanshirō, also called Nagahisa, was second master of the Nishigaki school. This guard is of special interest for its demonstration of the wide range of colours which can be obtained by the patination of copper and its alloys.

264 Sword guard with design of distant pine trees

FS/G3 遠見松透図鐔　勘四郎作

NISHIGAKI KANSHIRŌ (1639–1717)
Iron
dm 8 cm
Late 17th or early 18th century
YONENO COLLECTION, Kumamoto

Positive piercing and an irregular edge form one of the most characteristic of the Higo styles; it was widely copied by other schools.

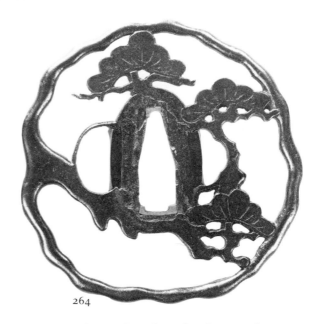

264

265 Sword guard with stylised crane design

FS/G3 鶴丸透図鐔銘東雨

[repr. in colour on p. 218]
TSUCHIYA YASUCHIKA (1670–1744)
Copper; the holes plugged with gilt metal
s. *Tōu*
dm 8.1 cm
1730–44
MIYAZAKI COLLECTION, Kanagawa
Important Art Object

Yasuchika is famous, like his contemporary Sōmin, for his contribution to the many changes in sword fitting design and technique which took place during the Genroku period. His styles are many, but his later work, signed with the name Tōu, which he took in 1730, is characterized by finely patinated copper pierced with stylised designs in positive silhouette.

266 Sword guard with design of tiger and bamboo

FS/G3 猛虎竹林図鐔銘宗与

YOKOYA SŌYO II (1700–1779)

Shibuichi with *katakiri* engraving; the hole plugged with *shakudō*
s. *Sōyo*, with a *kakihan*
dm 7.6 cm
18th century
SHIMANO COLLECTION, Chiba

The *katakiri* technique, in which variations in the width of the engraved line are achieved by altering the angle of the cutting tool, was well suited to the adaptation, as in this guard, of themes from ink painting.

266

267 Set of sword fittings with design of Guardian Kings (Niō)

FS/GII 二王図 二所物銘宗珉

YOKOYA SŌMIN (1670–1733)
Kozuka and pair of *menuki*
Shakudō nanako with copper, gold and *shibuichi*
Kozuka s. *Sōmin*
Kozuka l 9.8 cm
Early 18th century
KYOTO NATIONAL MUSEUM
Important Cultural Property

267

Sōmin started his career as an assistant in the Gotō workshops but broke away in the mid-1690s to develop the highly distinctive style which was to earn him the title 'father of *machibori*'. At first he worked chiefly in *katakiri* engraving (see no. 266); later he reverted to Gotō school techniques, but with a greater range of colours and higher relief. This set, with its design of the ferocious outsize Guardian Kings which stand at the entrance of many Buddhist temples, exemplifies his bold and lively manner.

268 Set of fittings for a pair of swords decorated with views of the Yoshino and Tatsuta rivers

FS/GII 吉野龍田川図大小揃物銘一乗

GOTŌ ICHIJŌ (1791–1876)
Two guards, two *kozuka*, two *kōgai* and two pairs of *menuki*
Shakudō nanako with gold, silver, *shakudō* and copper; holes and rims of guards lined with gilt metal
Variously s. *Gotō Hōgen Ichijō*, *Hōgen Ichijō* and *Ō Hōgen Ichijō* 'aged 74 and 75', the guards insc. 'made at the request of Mr Yonekawa Motomichi'
larger guard 8.4 × 7.8 cm;
smaller guard 7.8 × 7.1 cm
Variously dated to 1864 and the eleventh month of 1865
FURUKAWA COLLECTION, Tokyo
Important Cultural Property

Gotō Ichijō started his career as an adopted member of the Hachirobei branch of the Gotō school, which worked for the shōguns throughout the Edo period and produced pieces in a rigid classical style. He became *de facto* leader of the whole school during the first half of the nineteenth century, sometimes working, as here, in a version of the classical style, sometimes using materials and techniques, such as iron and *katakiri* engraving, which were forbidden by orthodox Gotō tradition. In the present set, the use of copper is a nineteenth-century innovation and the composition, which suggests genuine views rather than self-contained decorative schemes, is entirely untraditional. The Yoshino and Tatsuta rivers are associated respectively with spring and cherry blossoms and autumn and reddening maple leaves.

269 Set of fittings for a pair of swords with design of long-tailed birds and pine-trees

FS/GII 松樹尾長鳥図大小二所物銘政美

[repr. in colour on p. 218]
ISHIGURO MASAYOSHI (1764 – after 1850)
Two guards and two *fuchi-kashira*
Shakudō nanako with gold, *shakudō* and *shibuichi*
Both guards s. 'made by Jugakusai Ishiguro Masayoshi'
Guards *dm* 7.6 and 7.4 cm
Late 18th or first half of the 19th century
HON'AMI COLLECTION, Tokyo

The works of the Ishiguro, one of a number of important schools which sprang up at Edo during the eighteenth century, are especially celebrated for the outstanding quality of the granulation and patination of the *shakudō* alloy.

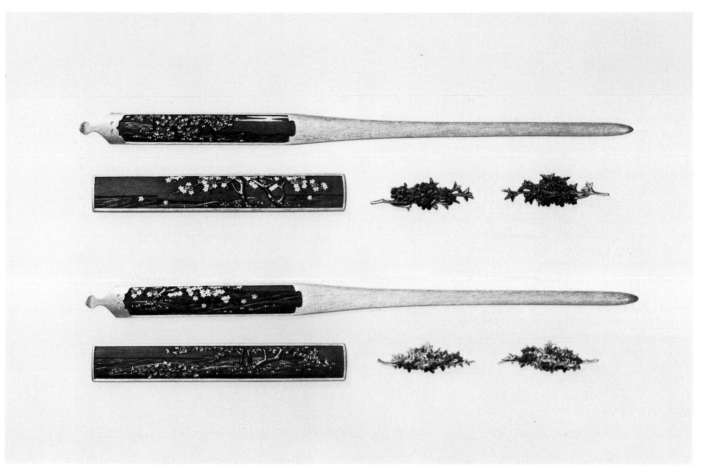

268

268

Clocks

Clocks and clockwork were introduced by the Portuguese in the late sixteenth century. The Japanese, skilled as they were in metalwork, did not have much trouble copying the mechanisms. The problem lay in adapting to the time system used in Edo period Japan. Each cycle of day and night was divided into twelve 'hours', named after the creatures of the zodiac (see under *netsuke*, p. 302). The periods of dark and daylight were each equally divided into six 'hours', so that in winter the daylight 'hours' were shorter than the night ones, and in summer the reverse. To complicate matters, the first six 'hours' were numbered from 4 to 9, and the second six from 9 to 4.

Earlier clocks (no. 271) worked on a single-foliot system and the dial was marked at regular intervals into twelve. Later a double-foliot mechanism was developed in which the intervals could be varied manually. Finally the clock was shaped as a pillar with a moving finger. On the pillar were several scales for periods of ten days throughout the year. On some clocks the scales are shown as a graph with co-ordinates for the time of year. After the Edo period the western time system was adopted.

270

270 Bronze armillary sphere supported on dragons

FS/G8 　渾天儀

109 × 68 cm
1669
TŌSHŌGU, Tochigi

The instrument was made by Kyoto craftsmen in 1669, on the order of Ishibara Nobutada (1619–1691), a vassal of the Sakai house of Wakasa (Fukui prefecture). The bronze bands representing the orbits of the planets are calibrated with inlay of gold, silver, ivory, cloisonné enamel and *maki-e* lacquer. Nobutada spent some twenty years working on the design. The sphere was offered to the shōgun in 1669 and placed in store at the Tōshōgu in the following year.

271 Lantern clock with single foliot

FS/G8 　鐵地銀象嵌燈籠形時計

Iron working in iron case inlaid with silver and gold
36 × 13.5 × 13.5 cm
d. 1678
BRITISH MUSEUM

The dial is simply marked off with the twelve hours of the day in equal divisions by the signs of the zodiac. The inlay has much in common with that found on guns of the same period.

272 Lantern clock with double foliot

FS/G8 　真鍮打出燈籠形時計

Iron working with *repoussé* brass case
30 × 11.2 × 11.2 cm
18th century
BRITISH MUSEUM

The outer dial is marked in equal division with the twelve 'hours' of the zodiac, giving a continuous numeration over the whole of the day and night. The inner dial is marked with six hours of day and six of night. Strangely, these are represented by the numerals four to nine, the numbers one to three being omitted because those strokes were used as signals on temple bells. The clock is manually adjustable to the varying hour lengths over winter and summer, but these cannot be shown on the dial. The style of brass decoration on the case is clearly influenced by European models.

273 Wall clock with changeable programme for the time of year

FS/G8 　木箱柱形時計

Brass working in wooden case with glass front and lacquered programme panel
53 × 80 × 70 cm
19th century
BRITISH MUSEUM

This type of clock replaces a dial with a pointer which runs vertically down the case and shows the unequal hours of day and night at different times of year against a panel specially marked off for each ten-day period in which the year was divided. The fixed plates at the right show the twelve 'hours' of the twenty-four-hour day with no adjustment for the time of year.

271

272

273

274 *Portable paper teahouse called Rokkaen*

FS/LR 組茶席

Paper, wood and bamboo
Dimensions when extended 156 × 232 × 183 cm
c. 1790–1800
KONISHI COLLECTION, Hyōgo

This remarkable structure in paper is thought to have been
produced by the same maker as the similar *Hotarukago* ('firefly
basket') in the Nishi Honganji Temple in Kyoto, which is known
to have been made in the 1790s. It folds into a box which can be
easily carried to a scenic spot where an informal tea ceremony
might be held. Unfolded, it turns into a complete three-*tatami*
teahouse with low entrance, windows, *tokonoma*, cupboards,
place for the kettle and all else needed. The dimensions when
folded are only 38 × 189 × 88 cm (cf. description on p. 31).

The teahouse is made like the *byōbu* screens, with paper
stretched over a lattice of wood. The illusion of solid surfaces,
such as the ceiling, is achieved with veneers; the unfolding of the
teahouse requires skill and experience in paper technique. The
teahouse is thought to be a by-product of the sophisticated
methods followed in the Osaka area on the construction and
repair of folding screens, for which there was always a keen
demand among the rich merchants.

275 *Viewer for perspective prints*

FS/LR 覗眼鏡

Dutch, mid 18th century
60 × 45 × 30 cm
YABUMOTO COLLECTION, Hyōgo

These instruments, called *nozokikarakuri* in Japanese, were
imported through Nagasaki and were sold in toy shops. There
were various types, but those for which perspective prints were
designed had a convex lens which produced an effect of depth.
They seem not to have been made in Japan, perhaps because the
lenses could not be made, and in any case their vogue was in
decline by the early nineteenth century.

274

275

Sculpture

The decline of Buddhism that occurred in the late Muromachi and Momoyama periods brought the virtual end of the tradition of monumental sculpture which image-making for Buddhist temples and, to a lesser extent, for Shintō temples had sustained for a thousand years. Edo work in this line is undistinguished in comparison with what was achieved earlier. Carving skills were not however moribund, but were applied to small-scale tasks and to some entirely new branches of the art, with new invention and a characteristic verve. Three classes of sculpture are represented in the exhibition, of which the masks for Nō drama are the only quite traditional product. The use of masks in drama was introduced into Japan in the seventh century from China, featuring in *Gigaku*, *Bugaku*, *Nō* and *Kyōgen*, of which the last two survived through the Middle Ages into modern times. Mask-carving was naturally a specialised craft, and the masks were preserved as jealously as any other craftwork of ancient date and historical association.

In the centuries before the Momoyama period the old ateliers of Buddhist sculpture had gradually closed, and in the Edo period there was little demand for the furnishing of new temples. Such wood-carving as was required, as in the ornament of the Tokugawa memorial shrines at Nikkō, dealt with floral and animal motifs on a small scale. Among the Buddhists emerged however a new type of executant: priests who demonstrated their piety by carving and dedicating figures in numerous temples. Their work was imitative or, at its best, amateurish and rustic. Tankai Risshi (1629–1716) and the Zen master Shōun Genkei (1648–1710) were among these. Mokujiki Myōman

276a

(1718–1810) was influenced by the style of the statues in the Mampukuji in Kyoto, which had been made under the direction of a Chinese master, Fan Daozheng, in about 1667. Attention is now given mainly to pieces attributed to the monk Enkū (1632–1695), who spent all his life in connexion with a pious institution called Shugendō on Mount Ibuki. He is said to have adopted the style of life of *kijishi*, itinerant woodcarvers whom he met in Minami near his native village. Twenty years ago his work was unknown to historians of art, but in recent years a wide-flung search for his carvings in remoter temples has been conducted, and at present pieces attributed to him are produced at the rate of about two a month. He is said to represent the re-emergence of the *natabori* (i.e. carving with a short-handled carpenter's axe) practised in eastern Japan in the Heian and Kamakura periods. Some life-size images are cut from a solid tree trunk (the tree is said sometimes to have been left standing). Images of Buddha and Bodhisattvas were distributed over most of Japan, according to the account now given by Japanese specialists, and many small figures were produced for dedication in temples. On an image discovered in Hokkaido is an inscription dating it to 1660 and ascribing it to 'an ascetic of Ibuki Mountain'. The axe-hewn style of the carving departs from the canons of any Japanese art whatever of earlier time, striking to the European eye an oddly post-1910 note.

The third class of Edo sculpture is represented by the *netsuke*, which stand apart from all traditional and monumental work, and are described separately below.

WW

276b

276 Buddhist images attributed to the monk Enkū

FS/G5 円空坊主の彫刻

a] average *h* 56 cm
b] *h* between 64 and 77 cm
17th century
YAKUSHIJI, SAITAMA (Triad)
SHŌKAKUJI, AICHI (Guardians)

a] Triad of a Buddha flanked by two Bodhisattvas. The Buddha is intended for Yakushi Nyorai (The Buddha Bhaishajyaguru), the recipient of an important cult dating back to the seventh century. His proper attendants are the Bodhisattvas Nikkō (Sūryaprabhā) and Gakkō (Candraprabhā) 'Splendour of Sun and Moon'. In principle Bhaishajyaguru presided over healing and medicine, and is therefore represented holding a small 'medicine jar'. This should be in the left hand, while the right hand is raised in the *abhaya* ('absence of fear') gesture. Here the jar has been enlarged to the size of a cottage loaf, and the Buddha is shown standing, whereas traditionally he is seated.

b] Yakushi Nyorai is often shown accompanied by twelve guardians in military attire who stand for his twelve vows made to relieve the suffering of mankind. In these wooden statues the soldier's armour is replaced by something more resembling court robes. Each figure is marked on the forehead with one of the twelve 'earth branches' which divide the celestial equator in ancient Chinese astronomy, and were used in Japan to denote the divisions of the day. One of the guardians holds the *gui* tablet which was held by persons in audience with the Chinese emperor, and another bears the pearl, or 'magic jewel', an ancient symbol of the Law. These twelve were possibly not conceived in connexion with Yakushi.

276b

298

277 *Wooden masks for Nō performance*

FS/CH　能樂の仮面

The maker's names are written in ink
on the back of each mask
Average *h* 25 cm
TOKYO NATIONAL MUSEUM

i] Jintai, a god in human disguise. The face is pinkish-white and brown-spotted; the moustache black, lips red, teeth gold and eyeballs red.
s. *Haruwaka*

ii] Ōtobide, a devil in human form. The face is dark gold and the teeth and eyeballs gilded, the lips red and the hair black.

iii] Asakura-jō, the face of a wood-cutter or fisherman. The face is suitably tanned to yellow-brown; the hair, moustaches and beard are ginger; gold teeth and red lips, some white on the eyebrows and in the wrinkles of the face.
s. *Sankō*

iv] Okina, an old man. The face is light brown with patchy white, and the underlying wood shows dark red through the broken gesso of the surface. The lips are red and the beard ginger.

v] Kurohige, a mask used in the rôle of the Dragon god. Red lips and mouth with gold teeth. Pinkish-yellow face with gold eyeballs and red eye-rims. The hair, eyebrows, moustaches and *royale* are black.
s. *Tokuwaka*

vi] [repr. in colour on p. 239]
Hannya, the female demon. The horns denote greater anger and the expression matches. Pinkish-brown face and brown horns, with black hair, red lips and gilded teeth.
s. *Fukurai*

vii] Mambi, a bewitching woman. Red lips and black teeth, the face uniformly white. The hair and the painted eyebrows are black (in ancient courtly fashion the eyebrows have been shaved off and replaced higher on the forehead by black smudges). The face is intended to be more mature than the following mask.

viii] [repr. in colour on p. 240]
Ko-omote, a young girl's mask. The colour and detail are similar to those of Mambi.
s. *Tsunezumi*

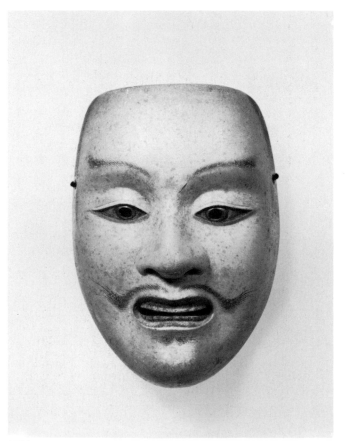

277 i

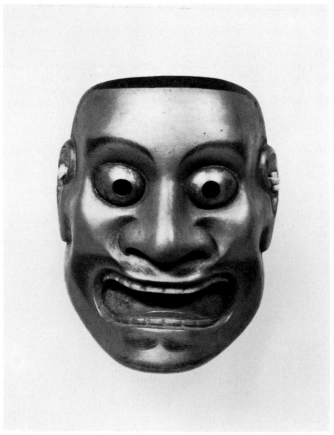

ii

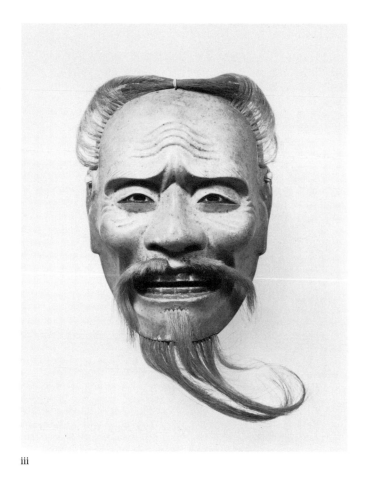

iii

iv

v

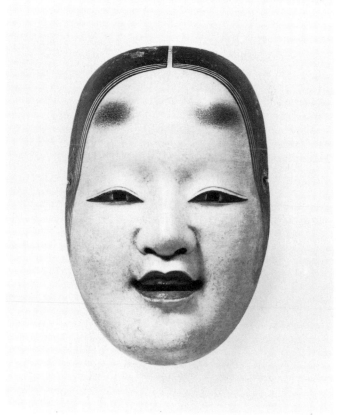

vii

Netsuke

Netsuke were toggles which stopped any object attached to a cord from slipping out of the sash through which it was slung. Since there were no pockets in Japanese dress, this was a convenient way of carrying a few personal belongings. Unimportant in themselves, the netsuke acquired distinction in the second half of the Edo period as almost the only kind of sculpture showing invention and vitality. They contributed incidentally to the mistaken western concept of Japanese miniaturism. Behind the artistic improvement of the carving lay a social reason. There had been a need for netsuke long before they became a craft in the seventeenth century, but thereafter an increasing number of customers with money to spend on personal luxury produced an enormous demand for objects of high craftsmanship in every area of life. The netsuke became a separate branch of art, whose first mention in this light is in a woodblock book Kimmō zui, published in the 1690s.

Netsuke were made of many materials. Since they had to be light as well as smooth they soon resolved themselves into three dominant materials: wood, lacquer and ivory. The first netsuke makers were those already working in these materials – the makers of lacquer inrō (nos 173–182), of ivory seals, of jiku (roller ends for paintings) and plectrums for musical instruments; and sculptors in wood, makers of Buddhist images and especially of miniature shrines and carvers of masks. Metal, pottery, porcelain and tortoiseshell were also used, but work in these materials belonged probably to craftsmen other than the netsuke specialists.

The first mention of netsuke carvers by name is in the woodblock book Sōken kishō, published in 1781. It describes a number of makers of carved netsuke, all of them well established and spread over the main populated areas of mainland Japan. By then a workshop tradition of master and pupil had clearly developed and netsuke makers had settled wherever they were needed. In the eighteenth century fairly large netsuke were favoured, up to 15 cm long. As skill increased, so netsuke got smaller and more minutely carved, but by the end of the Edo Period a restlessness with the limitations of these tiny sculptures can be detected. Kaigyokusai of Osaka, for example, expanded his craft into pipe cases, tea ceremony scoops, dagger hilts and other larger objects. At the end of the Edo Period and with the influx of Western taste these frustrations found an outlet in much larger models.

Novelty was the constant quest, and the carvers drew on every aspect of life and story. Here the netsuke are divided under the subjects they portray.

LRHS

Netsuke Group 1. The zodiac animals

These twelve creatures were used to number the hours of the day, the months of the year and the years themselves in a revolving cycle. From the middle Edo period onwards printed cards were exchanged at the New Year, often showing the animal of that year, and it is likely that netsuke were made for topical and fashionable wear or as New Year gifts in the same spirit. Every Japanese did, and still does, have a special affection for the animal of the year in which he was born, and it is not surprising that many good netsuke in that form have been treasured. When they represent hours of the day, the starting point is the hour around midnight (see entries on clocks, nos 271, 272, 273).

278 Tiger

FS/G11 虎・木製

TŌMIN of Tsu
Wood, eyes inlaid with mother-of-pearl with pupils of another material
s. Tōmin
h 35 mm
Late 18th century/early 19th century
VICTORIA AND ALBERT MUSEUM

Tōmin's master was Tanaka Minkō, who became famous for his tiger models which were apparently much in demand. This dynamic carving is of a quality the master would have approved. Tigers were not found in Japan, but there was a traditional and distorted concept of how they looked, based on Chinese paintings. As one of the four creatures of the principal compass-points, the tiger was a very ancient symbol in the Far East.

278

279 Boar with epidendrums and rock

FS/G11 石と猪・象牙製

KAIGYOKUSAI MASATSUGU of Osaka (1813–1892)
Ivory with coral dew-drops on the rock
insc. 'Masatsugu, one of the twelve zodiac signs'
l 52 mm
Mid 19th century
VICTORIA AND ALBERT MUSEUM

Kaigyokusai had the most advanced technique of ivory carving of all netsuke makers. The inscription suggests that this sleeping boar is one of a set of twelve made more for ornament than use, especially since there is no very obvious place to thread the cord. The creature is unusually shown with a rock and epidendrums.

279

which were favourite subjects for the *Nanga* artists inspired by Chinese painting, and this carving may have been made for such a man.

280 *Rat*

FS/GI I 鼠・木製

> GIFU TOMOKAZU
> Wood, with inlaid eyes and ivory teeth
> s. *Gifu Tomokazu*
> l 58 mm
> Late 18th century
> BRITISH MUSEUM

Rats were regarded with some affection, especially as the companions of the popular god Daikoku, and this superb carving is clearly the result of close observation.

280

281 *Snake*

FS/GI I 蛇・象牙製

> OKATOMO of Kyoto
> Ivory, the eyes inlaid
> s. *Okatomo*
> dm 43 mm
> Late 18th century
> BRITISH MUSEUM

Okatomo, best known for carvings of birds, has used a faceted off-cut of ivory and adapted it to a compact and comfortable design of a coiled snake. This creature was associated with the frog and the snail in a group of 'creeping things'.

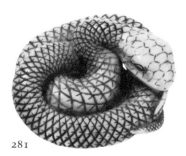

281

282 *Hare with loquat*

FS/GI I 枇杷と兎・象牙製

> TOMOKOTO
> Ivory, the eyes and fruit inlaid
> s. *Tomokoto*
> h 33 mm
> Late 18th century/early 19th century
> BRITISH MUSEUM

There is no strong connection between the loquat fruit and the hare, but this combination became a popular model nevertheless.

282

283 *Dog*

FS/GI I 犬・象牙製

> School of MASANAO of Kyoto
> Ivory
> s. *Masanao*
> h 48 mm
> Early 19th century
> BRITISH MUSEUM

Masanao was the most celebrated of the Kyoto animal carvers.

283

284 *Horse*

FS/GI I 馬・象牙製

> Anonymous, probably Osaka or Kyoto
> Ivory with inlaid eyes
> h 55 mm
> Mid/late 18th century
> VICTORIA AND ALBERT MUSEUM

The grazing horse was a very popular model for its smoothness and compactness, but the carvers were in fact making a virtue of the triangular off-cuts of ivory readily available to carvers.

284

285 Ox

FS/GII 牛・水牛角製

> HIDEMASA
> Buffalo horn
> s. *Hidemasa*
> l 35 mm
> Early 19th century
> BRITISH MUSEUM

The creature has been modelled in an appropriate material. The difficulties of carving it have led the maker, about whom nothing is known but his name, to integrate it into a seal-like base. The ox was often shown with a Chinese boy as a symbol of the search for enlightenment in Zen Buddhism.

285

286 Cockerel with millet

FS/GII 鶏と粟・象牙製

> OKATOMO of Kyoto
> Ivory with inlaid eyes
> s. *Okatomo*
> h 38 mm
> Mid/late 18th century
> BRITISH MUSEUM

The zodiac bird was normally shown in Japan as a cockerel. Okatomo has combined it with the heads of millet which his school more often associated with quails.

286

287 Dragon coiled round a driftwood tree-bough

FS/GII 流木と龍・象牙製

> Anonymous, probably Osaka
> Ivory
> h 101 mm
> Mid/late 18th century
> VICTORIA AND ALBERT MUSEUM

The dragon as a symbol came, like the tiger, originally from Western Asia via China to Japan, where it became associated at an early date with the imperial family. In this example, the dragon bears two of the imperial regalia – the jewel and the sword. The latter was found in the dragon's tail by the Shinto god Susano-o. The combination of dragon with driftwood is unusual, but the hollow wood allows for the cord to be threaded conveniently through the *netsuke*.

287

288 Goat

FS/GII 山羊・象牙製

> MITSUHARU of Kyoto
> Ivory, with inlaid eyes
> s. *Mitsuharu*
> h 38 mm
> Mid/late 18th century
> BRITISH MUSEUM

The carver has made very effective use of the triangular section of ivory he had to carve and has produced a design of crisp vitality.

288

289 Monkey 'playing' bamboo stick with a plectrum

FS/GII 猿・木製

TOMOCHIKA of Osaka
Wood, with inlaid eyes and ivory plectrum
s. *Tomochika* with a *kakihan*
h 35 mm
First half of 19th century
BRITISH MUSEUM

The monkey is clearly imitating a *shamisen* player, and the plectrum is picked out in ivory to emphasize it. Ivory carvers seem to have used the triangular off-cuts left from the making of plectrums, and sometimes the same men probably produced both types of article.

289

Netsuke Group 2. Other favourite creatures

The Japanese showed an interest in all living creatures and this is reflected in their *netsuke*, but they had an unusual and particular fondness for fish, reptiles, amphibians and insects. These are all treated with an affection which they rarely attract in other cultures.

290 Stag-beetles on a discarded straw sandal

FS/GII 草履と鍬形虫・木製

HŌJITSU of Edo (d. 1872)
Wood
s. *Hōjitsu*
l 51 mm
Mid 19th century
BRITISH MUSEUM

Netsuke of insects with protruding legs are rare because they are so easily broken, but this example is in remarkably fine condition.

290

291 Owl on an oak bough

FS/GII 梟・木製

SŌSHIN of Nagoya
Wood, with inlaid eyes
s. *Sōshin*
h 43 mm
First half of 19th century
BRITISH MUSEUM

291

292 Golden carp

FS/GII 金魚・木製

MASANAO of Yamada (1815–1890)
Wood, with eyes of amber and ebony
s. *Masanao*
l 55 mm
Mid 19th century
BRITISH MUSEUM

This is an ornamental variety of the golden carp which were prized inhabitants of ponds in the grounds of temples and large houses. The carver chose this fat variety to make a compact piece.

292

293 Mating toads

FS/GII 親子蛙・木製

MASANAO of Yamada (1815–1890)
Wood, with inlaid eyes
s. *Masanao*
l 38 mm
Mid 19th century
BRITISH MUSEUM

293

294 Group of turtles

FS/GII 亀・木製

MASANAO of Yamada (1815–1890)
Wood, with inlaid eyes
s. *Masanao*
h 50 mm
Mid 19th century
BRITISH MUSEUM

Like carp, turtles were prized inhabitants of ponds in Buddhist temples. Their habit of climbing on to a rock and then onto each other resulted in this favourite *netsuke* model, of which the base would lie flat against the wearer's hip.

294

295 Wasp on nest

FS/GII 雀蜂と巣・木製

TOYOMASA of Tamba (1773–1856)
Wood
s. *Toyomasa*
h 38 mm
First half of 19th century
BRITISH MUSEUM

This is a beautifully compact piece, in spite of its complexity. The cells of the nest have free-moving larvae in them which emerge to the openings when shaken but do not fall out.

295

296 Snail

FS/GII 蝸牛・木製

HIDARI ISSAN of Iwashiro
Wood
s. *Hidari Issan* with *kakihan* reading 'Uma'
l 38 mm
Early 19th century
BRITISH MUSEUM

As one of the 'creeping creatures' of land and water, the snail was much loved in Japan.

296

297 Lizard on an old straw hat

FS/GII 編笠と蜥蜴・象牙製

Anonymous, perhaps Osaka
Ivory
dm 42 mm
Early 19th century
BRITISH MUSEUM

The worm-eaten straw hat, twined with creeper and used as a hiding place by this delicately carved lizard, is a symbol of the transience of life.

297

298 Quails with heads of millet

FS/GII 鶉と粟・象牙製

OKATORI of Kyoto
Ivory with inlaid eyes
s. *Okatori*
h 29 mm
Late 18th century
VICTORIA AND ALBERT MUSEUM

This model was very popular, and uses a speciality of the school of Okatomo, whose brother Okatori was. The subject goes back to Chinese Song dynasty painting and became a favourite of the Tosa school, but the edibility of the quail and millet may have been a more immediate attraction to the Japanese of the Edo period, who took an increasing interest in food as the level of wealth increased.

298

299 *Octopus on seal base*

FS/GII 印章根付に蛸・象牙製

> Anonymous, probably Osaka
> Ivory
> *h* 38 mm
> Early 19th century
> VICTORIA AND ALBERT MUSEUM

Netsuke often took the form of a personal seal of which the upper part was a carved representation. Here the carver has made a very amusing shape of an octopus. This creature was a prized delicacy, especially in the *sushi* cooking which became popular in Edo and Osaka in the second half of the Edo period.

299

300 *Deer crying in autumn*

FS/GII 鳴き鹿・象牙製

> School of OKATOMO of Kyoto
> Ivory
> Unsigned
> *h* 93 mm
> Mid/late 18th century
> BRITISH MUSEUM

The deer crying in autumn was a feature of Japanese poetry from the seventh century onwards and always evoked melancholy. This is a very typical early piece made from a sharply angled triangular off-cut of ivory.

300

Netsuke Group 3. Mythical creatures

To their repertory of living creatures, the *netsuke* carvers added a number of imaginary ones. Most of them served to give extra humour and zest to the range of carvings available.

301 *Kirin*

FS/GII 麒麟・象牙製

> Anonymous, probably Kyoto
> Ivory
> *h* 83 mm
> Late 18th century
> BRITISH MUSEUM

The *Kirin* was in China one of the four creatures of the four principal points of the heavens. It varies in its make-up, but often had the head and shoulders of a dragon, (but with a horn or horns like a goat's); the body of a deer, and the tail of an ox or of a *shishi*. It was the most auspicious of all creatures and a symbol of good fortune.

301

302 *Tanuki wearing lotus leaf*

FS/GII 蓮の葉をかぶる狸・象牙製

> KŌGYOKUSAI of Edo
> Ivory
> s. *Kōgyokusai*
> *h* 51 mm
> First half of 19th century
> BRITISH MUSEUM

Tanuki is often translated 'badger' but the creature is in fact the racoon-faced dog. It is usually shown in one or other of the mythical activities associated with it, as here where it is distending its belly and wearing a lotus leaf as a diguise. The stalk of the leaf is probably a reference to another story where the *tanuki* turns into an iron kettle.

302

303 *Kappa caught in clam*

FS/GII 蛤と河童・木製

> SUKETADA of Tsu
> Wood, the eyes inlaid, one cord-hole ringed with ivory
> s. *Suketada*
> *h* 64 mm
> First half of 19th century
> BRITISH MUSEUM

The *kappa* was a river-creature, often shown with a turtle's carapace, long hair, and a depression in the top of his head which held his vital fluids. An object of terror to small children and travellers, here he is shown himself caught in a river-clam.

303

304 *Mermaid (ningyo)*

FS/GII 人魚・象牙製

> NATSUKI of Wakayama
> Ivory
> s. *Natsuki*
> *l* 38 mm
> First half of 19th century
> BRITISH MUSEUM

This mermaid is holding one of the jewels used by Ryūjin, the Dragon King of the Sea, and she may be intended to be one of his daughters.

304

305 *Kappa/shōjō*

FS/GII 河童・木製

> KITAMASA
> Wood, the eyes inlaid
> s. *Kitamasa* (or *Hokushō*)
> *h* 51 mm
> Late 18th/early 19th century
> BRITISH MUSEUM

The *kappa* (no. 303) is sometimes thought of more as a water-sprite than as an animal, and in this example he has apparently been combined with the *shōjō*, another water-sprite with long hair and webbed hands who is here given also a froglike skin. The *shōjō* is famous for liking saké, and here the *kappa*'s depression in the head has been converted into the shape of a saké-dish.

305

306 *Demon mask*

FS/GII 般若・木製漆塗り

> Anonymous
> Lacquered wood, the eyes inlaid in glass over black and gold pigment
> *h* 51 mm
> Late 18th/early 19th century
> BRITISH MUSEUM

Demons (*oni*) were considered mischievous rather than evil. They had two short horns and were small. Full-sized masks were used in dances and ceremonies for their exorcism.

306

307 *Fox as priest*

FS/GII 白蔵子・木製

Anonymous
Wood
h 108 mm
Late 18th century
BRITISH MUSEUM

The fox has more magical and mythical stories attached to it than any other Japanese creature. It is often associated with the rice-god Inari, and is thought to have great powers of transforming itself, for example into a beautiful woman or a Buddhist priest.

307

308 *Demon hiding under head-cloth*

FS/GII 頭巾をかぶる鬼・木製衣は色付

Anonymous
Wood, with eyes inlaid in mother-of-pearl and red and gold lacquer on cloth
h 89 mm
Early 19th century
BRITISH MUSEUM

The short, stocky demon is probably sheltering from the beans thrown to drive it away at the New Year.

308

Netsuke Group 4. Gods and mythical beings

The people of Edo Japan recognised large numbers of divinities and other figures drawn from Buddhism, Daoism, Confucianism, Shintō and popular myth. Of these, the best known were the Seven Gods of Good Fortune, treated separately under Group 5. The figures of Daoist *sennin* were particularly popular in the eighteenth century and seem to have been the earliest subjects for elaborately carved *netsuke*. The Dutch and Chinese traders at Nagasaki are included here, because their status was almost mythical to the Japanese of the period who never actually saw them.

309 *A Rakan (Disciple of the Buddha)*

FS/GII 饅頭根付羅漢・象牙製

DŌRAKU of Osaka
Ivory
s. *Dōraku*
l 45 mm
Early 19th century
BRITISH MUSEUM

The historical Buddha was credited with 500 disciples, of whom a group of 16 or 18 were his special associates. They are shown with the bald head of a priest and the long-lobed ears denoting wisdom. Being Indian in origin, they tend to be given a rather 'foreign' appearance. This *netsuke* is in the form of a small box, but it is carved in the solid and is not a true *hako netsuke* in which the box had a practical purpose.

309

310 *Daruma*
FS/GII 達磨・象牙製

TOMOTSUGU, probably of Osaka
Ivory
s. *Tomotsugu*
h 45 mm
Late 18th century
BRITISH MUSEUM

Daruma (Bodhidharma) was the semi-mystical founder of the Zen sect. He was said to have lost the use of his legs by spending nine years seated in meditation, and usually appears in *netsuke* in humorous form, wearing a hood and grimacing (see no. 21).

310

311 *The goddess Okame*
FS/GII おかめ・木製顔は象牙

HIDEMASA
Late 18th/early 19th century
Wood, with ivory mask
s. *Hidemasa*
h 133 mm
Late 18th/early 19th century
BRITISH MUSEUM

Okame is the popular name for the Shintō goddess Uzume. She lured the sulking sun-goddess Amaterasu from her cave by her antics and thus restored light to the world. In her popular form she represented mirth and bawdiness, and dancers often impersonated her wearing masks.

310

311

312 *Shōki subduing a demon*
FS/GII 鐘馗と鬼・木製

MINKOKU of Edo
Wood, the eyes inlaid
s. *Minkoku*
h 70 mm
Late 18th century
BRITISH MUSEUM

Shōki seems to be an entirely mythical Chinese Tang Dynasty figure who rid the empire of demons. He was much loved by the Japanese of the Edo period and is the commonest subject for carved *netsuke*. Often, as here, he has effectively quelled the demon, but there are many humorous carvings in which demons have got the better of him. He is always shown as a Chinese warrior with flowing beard, winged hat, and two-edged sword.

312

313 *Kiyohime turning to a dragon, coiled round the bell where Anchin is trapped*
FS/GII 道成寺・木と象牙製

MINKŌ of Tsu
Wood, the eyes inlaid and gilt, Anchin's face tinted white
s. *Konan Minkō*
l 51 mm
Late 18th century
BRITISH MUSEUM

This famous legend concerns the love of a young woman, Kiyohime, whose persistent love for the Buddhist monk Anchin forced him to hide her under the bell of the Dōjōji temple. Her passion turned her into a demonic dragon and she coiled round the bell and consumed both Anchin and herself with the heat engendered. In this *netsuke* the frightened face of Anchin can be seen through a crack in the bell.

313

314 Niō (Guardian King)

FS/GII 仁王・木製

SHŪZAN, probably of Ōsaka
Wood
insc. 'made by Ranrinsai'
h 126 mm
Late 18th century
BRITISH MUSEUM

This magnificent carving tells us much. In many Buddhist
temples pairs of Guardian Kings stood in semi-enclosure on each
side of the main gate. In the thirteenth century and after they
sometimes reached heights of over five metres and were among
the most vigorous and monumental of Japanese sculpture. It is
strange that in the Edo period this vigour could only be
recaptured in miniature. This Niō, however, is typically
humorous too and is shown with a pipe, a tobacco pouch and a
manjū netsuke, a rare example of a netsuke depicting a netsuke. It
also shows the close connection between netsuke and smoking
utensils.

315

314

315 The Bodhisattva Kannon

FS/GII 小犬に乳を飲ませる観音菩薩・木製

Anonymous
Wood
h 105 mm
Late 18th century
BRITISH MUSEUM

Kannon (Sanskrit Avalokitesvara) was the most popular of the
Bodhisattvas and assumed many forms as a goddess of mercy.
Here her form as a patroness of mothers has been extended so
that she is shown suckling a puppy; this is apparently a reference
to the Buddhist doctrine of mercy to all living beings.

316 Gama Sennin

FS/GII 蝦蟇仙人・木製

Anonymous
Wood, the eyes inlaid
h 102 mm
Late 18th century
BRITISH MUSEUM

The Sennin is carved here with his toad climbing on to his head.
He is typically ragged in dress.

316

311

317 Ikkaku Sennin carrying the beautiful princess

FS/GII 一角仙人・木製色付、象牙製

Anonymous, probably Ōsaka
Wood, painted in red, green and gold
h 115 mm
Late 18th century
BRITISH MUSEUM

The *Sennin* (Immortals) are mostly of Chinese Daoist origin, but Ikkaku ('One Horn') is Indian, and has some of the physical attributes of Buddhist wisdom, including long ear-lobes. He was an ascetic who was eventually reduced to mere mortality by falling in love with a princess sent to seduce him. He is shown carrying her home to her palace on his back. This powerful piece is painted in the style associated with Nagamachi Shūzan, who developed it from folk practices.

318

317

318 Ghost of a nun

FS/GII 墓と幽霊・木製

Anonymous
Wood
h 94 mm
Mid 19th century
BRITISH MUSEUM

The ghost of an emaciated woman rises above a grave-stone marked 'The Buddhist nun, Myōkō'.

319 Chōkarō and Gama Sennin

FS/GII 張果老と蝦蟇仙人・象牙製

Anonymous
Ivory
h 102 mm
Late 18th century
BRITISH MUSEUM

These two Chinese Immortals became the best known of the *Sennin* to the Japanese. Chōkarō's gourd held a white horse which he could magically conjure up, while Gama Sennin was named after the three-legged toad which always accompanied him. This very fine *netsuke* is most skilfully carved out of a piece of ivory of triangular section.

319

320 *Sculptor carving Niō's head*

FS/GII 仁王を彫る仏師・木製

Anonymous, probably Kyoto
Wood
h 51 mm
c. 1800
BRITISH MUSEUM

A sculptor, interestingly in the formal Shintō dress of a craftsman, is engaged in sculpting the enormous head of a *Niō*. The score marks of his chisel are left deliberately rough on the head. The implications of the size of the man and the head are that the finished figure would have been at least ten metres high. Monumental sculpture was still being produced in the Edo period in Kyoto and Nara, and it is tempting to wonder whether this unsigned *netsuke* was the work of a Buddhist sculptor frustrated by the lack of vitality in his everyday work.

320

321 *Dutchman*

FS/GII オランダ人・木製

Anonymous
Wood
h 128 mm
Mid/late 18th century
BRITISH MUSEUM

The Dutch traders confined to the man-made island of Deshima in Nagasaki Harbour were of the greatest interest to the Japanese as the only non-Asians permitted in the country. They were often shown carrying a cock, perhaps for cock-fighting or perhaps in recognition of their fondness for meat. The Japanese diet of the time included almost no red meat, and chicken was the nearest equivalent available. This Dutchman is also pulling down his eyelid in a traditional Japanese gesture of derision called *bekkakō*.

321

322 *Chinese merchant*

FS/GII 唐人・象牙製

Anonymous
Ivory
h 110 mm
Mid/late 18th century
BRITISH MUSEUM

Also confined to Nagasaki were the Chinese merchants, and in the atmosphere of curiosity aroused by the isolation they too became semi-mythical in status. Strangely, they were often shown as effeminate, although there is no evidence that they had those tendencies. To the Japanese, their main physical characteristics were cheerful grins, top-knots and pigtails, and pantaloons.

322

Netsuke Group 5. The Seven Gods of Good Fortune

These popular deities, known together as the *Shichifukujin*, are all debased forms of more serious deities from Japan, China or India, and are Shintō, Buddhist or Daoist in origin. They were brought together as a group in the seventeenth century, probably in imitation of the classic Chinese group of Seven Sages of the Bamboo Grove. They are sometimes shown together in the Treasure Ship bearing lucky objects on New Year's Eve. They are, in order of popularity, with their main attributes:

Hotei	god of happiness and children, with large stomach and bag
Daikoku	god of commerce, agriculture and craft, with mallet and rat
Ebisu	god of food and fishing, with angling rod and large *tai* fish
Fukurokuju	god of long life, always smiling, with a very elongated head
Jurōjin	god of long life and learning, with a scroll, a deer or a crane
Benten	goddess of music and love, with a musical instrument
Bishamon	god of wealth, but warlike appearance.

323 The Seven Gods of Good Fortune in the Treasure Ship

FS/GII 宝舟・象牙製

MASAHIRO, probably of Osaka
Ivory
s. *Masahiro* with a *kakihan*
h 57 mm
Mid 19th century
VICTORIA AND ALBERT MUSEUM

This intricately detailed carving of the gods in their dragon-headed ship, packed with and surrounded by lucky emblems, may not be a true *netsuke* because it is comparatively heavy. It illustrates the tendency of late Edo period carvers gradually to turn to larger and less practical objects in order to express their skill and enthusiasm.

323

324 Hotei in his sack pulled by two boys

FS/GII 布袋と唐子・木製

Anonymous
Wood
l 80 mm
Late 18th century
BRITISH MUSEUM

Hotei's sack is full of good things for the Chinese boys who often accompany him.

324

325 Daikoku and Hotei as sumō wrestlers

FS/GII 相撲を取る布袋と大黒・象牙製

Anonymous
Ivory
h 70 mm
Late 18th century
BRITISH MUSEUM

This was a favourite model making use of a spectacular wrestling hold. *Sumō* had developed in the eighteenth century into the principal national sport of Japan (see nos 115, 116).

325

Netsuke Group 6. Japanese legend and history

Legend always attaches itself to reality very quickly in Japan, and separating the two may be difficult. The three famous incidents in this section are, however, based on real people of widely different periods.

326   The poetess Ono no Komachi

FS/GII   小野の小町・木製

Anonymous
Wood
h 45 mm
Early 19th century
BRITISH MUSEUM

Ono no Komachi was one of the Six Great Poets of the ninth century and her life was filled with picturesque and probably legendary incidents. Here she is shown as an aged beggar, her beauty gone, forgotten by the courtly world in which she once shone. She represents the theme of the passing glories of the world which has always appealed so strongly to the Japanese temperament.

326

327   The head of Nitta no Yoshisada

FS/GII   新田義貞の首・木製血付赤塗

OE SHUNZŌ
Wood, with red lacquer representing blood
h 45 mm
First half of 19th century
BRITISH MUSEUM

Yoshisada, a fourteenth-century general, was a great supporter of the imperial house and was eventually defeated fighting for it against the Ashikaga family. At his last battle he cut off his own head, having been wounded between the eyes by an arrow. It is the blood of this wound which is picked out in red lacquer. Admiration for early loyal supporters of the emperors grew in the late Edo period and the Tokugawas, in theory loyalists themselves, were powerless to oppose it.

327

328   The night attack of the Forty-seven Rōnin

FS/GII   饅頭根付・四十七士討入・象牙製

KYŌMIN of Edo
Ivory, with brass cord-attachment
s. 'Kyōmin'
dm 70 mm
Mid 19th century
BRITISH MUSEUM

This large *manjū* netsuke, almost too big to be comfortably worn, is intricately carved with a scene from the most famous of all Edo period incidents, the revenge of the forty-seven loyal retainers. The story is recounted in an introductory chapter, on p. 27. As *Chūshingura* it became the most popular of all plays.

328

Netsuke Group 7. Entertainment

Dancers, actors, wrestlers and the like were favourite *netsuke* subjects. Amusement of every sort was much prized in Edo period society, and *netsuke* themselves often had an element of entertainment built into them.

329　Nō actor

FS/GII　能役者・木製色付

> SHIN'ICHI of Osaka
> Wood with pigments
> s. *Shin'ichi*
> *h* 51 mm
> Late 18th/early 19th century
> BRITISH MUSEUM

The *Nō* theatre had by the late Edo period lost official support and was patronized more by townsmen who appreciated its status as the most elevated form of drama.

329

330　Silhouette dancer as a crane

FS/GII　鶴の舞・木製

> SHŪGETSU of Edo
> Wood
> s. *Shūgetsu*
> *h* 64 mm
> Late 18th century
> BRITISH MUSEUM

This dancer has produced the silhouette of a crane with his cloak and a folded fan held upside-down. The shadows of people seen through the paper-covered *shōji* of houses encouraged this art.

330

331　Sambasō dancer

FS/GII　三番叟・象牙製

> JORYŪ of Edo
> Ivory, with fan and jingle in metal
> s. *Shōunsai Joryū*
> *h* 31 mm
> Late 18th century
> BRITISH MUSEUM

Sambasō was a popular dance of Shintō origin, connected with the New Year and often performed in the streets. The performer wears a hat with twelve stripes for the months of the year, a mask, and a robe decorated with New Year symbols. He carries the jingle and fan of a Shintō priest (see no. 188).

331

332　Manzai dancers

FS/GII　三河万歳・木製

> HŌJITSU of Edo (*d.* 1872)
> Wood
> s. *Hōjitsu*
> *h* 45 mm
> Mid 19th century
> BRITISH MUSEUM

Manzai was another New Year's dance, performed in various ways by two or three dancers. This elegant and compact *netsuke* is typical of the refined work of Hōjitsu.

332

333 Sumō wrestlers

FS/GⅡ 相撲・木製

MASANAO of Yamada (1815–1890)
Wood
s. *Masanao*
h 51 mm
Mid 19th century
BRITISH MUSEUM

This spirited carver has responded to the challenge of showing the *kawazu* throw, where the wrestler in the air is about to gain the victory in spite of appearances.

333

334 Mask for Kyōgen

FS/GⅡ ひょっとこ・木製

GARAKU of Osaka
Wood
s. *Garaku*
h 38 mm
Late 18th/early 19th century
BRITISH MUSEUM

The *Kyōgen* was the lighter side of *Nō*. *Kyōgen* actors performed roles of lower-class people in the *Nō* dramas, and also comic interludes between them. It is for these that masks were used like this one, which is of the type called *hyottoko*.

334

335 The Kabuki actor Danjūrō IX in Shibaraku

FS/GⅡ 鏡蓋根付市川団十郎・木金属製

MASAAKI of Musashino
Kagamibuta netsuke, the metal plate inlaid in copper, silver, gold and *shakudō*; the case in hardwood with ivory *himotōshi*
s. *Masaaki*, with a *kakihan* with the same name
dm 45 mm
Mid 19th century
BRITISH MUSEUM

Kabuki was, with *sumō* wrestling, the most popular of Edo entertainments, and actors like the Ichikawa family, who all called themselves Danjūrō, were popular heroes. They were most famous for playing the hero of the play *Shibaraku*, the great moment of which is shown on this splendid example of late Edo period metalwork. On the back of the plate the actor is identified as the ninth of the line.

335

336 Shōjō dancer from a Nō drama

FS/GⅡ 能役者・赤漆彫り

TOYOYOSHI
Carved lacquer
s. *Toyoyoshi*
h 42 mm
First half of 19th century
BRITISH MUSEUM

The water-sprite known as a *shōjō* here appears as a dancer in a well-known *Nō* play. Carved red lacquer had been imported from China since the fifteenth century. Its difficult technique was much admired and began to be copied in Japan in the Edo period. It became a favourite for *inrō*, *ojime* and *netsuke* because it was hard but light.

336

Textiles

The traditional dress of the Japanese is the kimono (literally 'the thing worn'), a loosely fitting garment overlapping in front of the body, with no buttons or fastenings, but bound around the waist or hips by a sash called an obi. For a people whose normal seated posture was either kneeling or sitting cross-legged on a straw-matted floor, such loose garments were essential. The looseness of fit, allied with the general lack of interest in the display of the human figure, led to the evolution of a garment which is minimally shaped; there is so little cut to it, in the western sense, that it consists mainly of a set of strips of material sewn together, which can even be unstitched to be cleaned and sewn together again. Only at collar and lapel is there any cut, for even the sleeves are barely shaped.

Lack of interest in the shape of the garment had led to much concentration upon its decoration. The great variety of techniques and the skill in their application and combination along with the resource of the Japanese designer in best exploiting, for decorative purposes, a difficult or elaborate motif, has allowed the kimono to become one of the most beautiful of Japanese art forms. Furthermore, the influence of dress-fabric design was felt in all the other arts of Japan, and the materials were important in such things as the mounting of scroll-paintings.

The kimono of today derives from the kosode of late Ashikaga times, when it was an informal undergarment of the lower classes of society: its adoption by the upper classes and perhaps more particularly by the chōnin class in the Momoyama period led to the great elaboration of decorative techniques mentioned above. As an outer garment, the kosode claimed strongly patterned ornament. The adoption of everyday dress into the Nō theatre, which occurred through the custom of the giving of a garment by a patron to an artist, led to further elaboration and to a complicated classification of robes according to shape, technique of decoration and the rôle to be played. Shape became important in the width, length and attachment of the sleeve, as well as the extent of its opening. These features of the sleeve were influential in the arm-movements used in Nō. The decoration of a robe, the material of which it is made (because this may give a stiff formal shape, or a loose relaxed shape) and whether or not it is lined are all matters governed by the rôle for which it is intended.

The fashion of Nō robes in turn had an effect on the dress of the well-to-do. The display of gorgeous dress characteristic in the Momoyama period for both men and women was proscribed during the Edo period by repeated sumptuary laws governing the proper dress for each class or occupation. These regulations seem continually to have been ignored or flouted, especially in the licensed quarters of the great cities, most notably the Yoshiwara of Edo. Differences in the dress of men and women are often scarcely to be detected. During the Edo period, increasing importance was attached to the obi for women, until both in material and in its elaborate tied shape it vied in splendour with the kimono. Ukiyo-e paintings often demonstrate the excessive size and elaboration of the obi of the great oiran.

The kosode ('small sleeve') was distinct from the large sleeve (ōsode) or wide sleeve (hirosode), and above all from the swinging sleeve (furisode, where the sleeves hang very far down

the length of the garment), all of which remain in current use. The distinction observed between costume types was fine, and in Nō and Kyōgen costume it was to be made still finer. Here the garments used for particular rôles come to be named after the technique that was at one time associated with the robe used for that rôle. Thus the nuihaku (no. 376) is a robe used for women's rôles, that is worn under a karaori (no. 380) and these terms describe both the robes and the techniques they represent. Karaori is a heavy brocade that partly imitates a Chinese weave: a stiff, heavy, formal material. By the late Edo period it was little used outside Nō except in the fabrics used for obi. The equivalent garment for men's roles is the atsuita (no. 387). Nuihaku is a material on which gold or silver foil is attached by glueing, usually with the use of a stencil, and which is also embroidered, a combination of at least two techniques. The other robe commonly used by women is the loose maiginu (no. 390), a robe for dancing.

Some of the garments used for male roles in both Nō and Kyōgen (the comic interludes in Nō) are short. The chōken (no. 389) is formal and has wide sleeves, while the Kyōgen kataginu (no. 384) is made of hemp and is sleeveless. Usually it is boldly patterned and worn over a striped kosode (noshime kosode). The former was usually of an embroidered fabric, the latter stencil dyed. To a great extent the technique used for a robe was chosen as appropriate to the rôle. Naturally Nō and Kyōgen costumes did not suffer the vigour of daily use. The dyed fabric of the Kyōgen kataginu reflects the origin of Kyōgen in the popular Muromachi period theatre. As proscriptive acts in the Edo period lowered the demand for richly woven, brocaded or embroidered fabrics, it was to this sort of dyeing that fashion returned. Tie-dyeing (shibori) and stencil dyeing (katazome) were both old techniques. In the Edo period two new techniques led dyed fabrics to become much more elaborate than simple stencilled patterns would allow. Chayazome used the improved, fine paper stencils and a dye-resistant paste, allowing both sides of the cloth to show the pattern (unlike the earlier tsujigahana), while the Yūzen technique was one of painting with dyestuffs, as in a picture, fixing the pigments and covering the painted area with a dye-resistant paste and then dyeing the background – the reverse of other processes. This allowed a brilliant decoration on a thin garment. Many of the more elaborate Edo period garments either for theatrical or private use use several techniques in combination.

There can be hardly any motif in the decorative repertoire which has not been used sometime in the woven, dyed or painted ornament of kimono. In the general design the main consideration was whether the ornament should be confined to the borders and shoulders of the garment, disposed more or less evenly over the whole surface; or arranged with dramatic asymmetry in the ōgara 'large build' manner. Subject to these principles the pattern might be small and compact, or large and sparse, and more or less stylised or realistic in its pictorial content. Dyeing technique invited experiment with overlapping design, and initiated a taste for the fantastic interruption of one scheme by another superimposed on it. Whether carrying ornament or left plain, a figured weave is a basic element.

The restraint seen in such a kosode as no. 366 with ornament confined to the borders and the self-colour given full effect is somewhat exceptional, and stands early in the Edo sequence. Sometimes the border is made deeper, and the ornament may be of close-set flowers, chequers, triangles or a small animal or other figure repeated without change. However, from the Momoyama period was inherited a fashion for overflowing design, which from the beginning of the Edo period was often interpreted in more consistent pictorial terms. A composition of bamboo, blossoming plum and flying cranes might fill the field of the design airily, with sparse line, its asymmetry unobtrusive in the natural scene (no. 365). These schemes, executed in embroidery, dyeing or *nuihaku*, sometimes imitate the general effect of figured brocade with the woven motifs much enlarged.

When overflowing ornament consists of close-set small elements the identity of the motifs may be lost to a brief sight of the garment, but the detail still received meticulous attention. Ornament of this kind led to a most promising innovation: the introduction of a large-spaced frame by which the abundance of detail was rendered legible and significant in the total combination. The frame could take many forms, geometric or organic, interpreted as plant stems or anonymous lines, and varied in scale to suit the motifs which are enclosed in its interstices or hung upon it. Regularity was reconciled with elaboration of detail, in terms which suited the cooperation of dyer and weaver very well. Bamboo rods, plum-tree trellis and lattice make their appearance and it mattered little if blooms grew from them or adhered fortuitously, provided that an attractive interplay of line and blossom was achieved. In the *nuihaku* no. 377 the weave-like motif in the middle zone contrasts nicely with the rest: upright and slanted rectangles, conventionalised rosettes and natural flowers. The use of the organizing frame was modified in schemes like that of no. 362, in which the bamboo lattice occupies the lower half of the garment while the flowers interspersed with written characters are confined to the upper.

The plant frame was only one of several methods used in making the detail of continuous ornament more telling to the eye. Stylised flowering tendrils may enclose oval spaces at regular intervals in which are placed realistic or conventional blooms, so that the surface presents three levels of interest: the figured ground, the elegant divisions and the enclosed flowers. But it was possible also to arrange compact elements on a ground of interlocking lines in a manner which maintained the individuality of the motifs while avoiding obvious parcelling by the plant frame. Instances are found of ornament presented in this way to create a busy effect which may strike one as somewhat alien to the normal clarity and inevitability of Edo design. Such arrangements recur through the period, the realism of the ordered motifs often betraying the taste of the late eighteenth and nineteenth centuries.

When the repeated motifs are disposed regularly, whether or not a defining frame is introduced, asymmetry may still be subtly contrived, as occurs especially in later examples of this composition. On the *kosode* with sedge hats and fans (no. 359) these objects are not similar nor do they resemble each other in the angles at which they are suspended on the strings (these differing also in the columns). Another method of variegating a complete field of overflowing ornament was to alternate square sections of it between columns, an arrangement no doubt first arrived at by using separate cuts of cloth; but latterly it is provided in the embroidered or dyed design.

In contrast to all these designs with repeating motifs are two devices which grow in favour through the Edo period. In one the field presented by the garment is broadly divided between groups of different motifs. These may be related in kind, like the books and paulownia leaves of the dark-ground *uchikake* of no. 364, or separated in groups of flowering shrubs and birds in a *chōken* (no. 391), or in an alternation of rectangles and leafy bunches which looks like a random scatter when the back and sleeves of the garment are seen together. From the late seventeenth century the broad waist sash, *obi*, became fashionable in women's dress and its presence invited the artist to divide his ornament clearly between the upper and lower parts of the garment. Often a plain zone was left at the waist, or this area was filled with a diaper unrelated to the remainder of the ornament. Since the tailoring of the garment did not of itself suggest this division of the design we must see the influence of the *obi* in instances of top-and-bottom separation even where there is not a clearly demarcated zone at the waist. The *kosode* on tea-coloured ground (no. 366) shows the broken line at skirt border and shoulders which is popular from the middle Edo period onwards, with a corresponding waist zone where the sash would lie.

The second device – indeed it amounts to a major departure in style – is a design in which the field contains a single subject. Although this subject is generally pictorial, it is not necessarily so, or only alludes formally to a natural scene. The latter case is well represented by the *kosode* with flowers between broad streams of water (no. 367), an ideal instance of *ōgara* where the decorative motif is not explicit. But the single-picture effect is more striking when the theme is treated realistically, or in one of the accepted painter's conventions. Such is the *kosode* (no. 350) on which Sakai Hōitsu has painted a blossoming plum such as he might have executed for a hanging scroll.

But whole-garment single subjects are less frequent than ornament which consists of large motifs entering the field from a side or a corner, covering it only in part and creating dramatic asymmetry. The motifs may be extremely stylised, in the manner of the wood grain, clematis and wistaria arranged over the shoulders and down one side of the white satin *kosode* (no. 354), the hats and maple leaves amusingly tumbling on the *kosode* (no. 353), the boats invading the scene on the more heavily decorated *kosode* (no. 351), or the magnified grass-blade tips darting over the *nuihaku* ground of the *kosode* (no. 344). Contrived asymmetry rules in schemes of layered ornament, in which, for example, flowering branches spread over falling streams revealed by illuminated windows above and behind.

Like all *ōgara* design, these asymmetrical schemes invited increasing pictorial narrative. In point of realism we may compare the old-style pines and wistaria of a *nuihaku* (no. 375), which echo a convention adopted a thousand years earlier, with the sea-creatures of a bathing robe which aims at the naturalism of the contemporary print. The taste for realistic pictorial ornament, like the taste for ever more richly and confusingly decorated *obi*, is an aspect of the late Edo style. A horse-race by warriors in ancient costume, represented in old Tosa style, might cover the whole back of a garment (no. 358); scattered glimpses recall the Eight Views of Lake Biwa and such landscape delights (no. 360); and what could be more entertaining than some of the Fifty-three Stations of the Tōkaidō (no. 407), all interpreted as travellers and local worthies? But this transfer of themes from painting, suitably challenging though it was to Yūzen dyers and other practitioners of minute method, marked the decline of the textile art.

ORI, WW

337 *Jimbaori of blue and red woollen cloth*

F/G2　紺、緋羅紗袖替陣羽織

[repr. in colour on p. 221]
The body blue and the sleeves in red outlined in gold with red
lines on the front; the lining of green and gold brocade
Worn by Uesugi Kenshin (1530–1578)
115 × 126 cm
Momoyama period
UESUGI SHRINE, Yamagata
Important Cultural Property

The *jimbaori* is a campaign jacket to be worn over armour. The
severe lines of this specimen contrast nicely with the rich lining.
Uesugi Kenshin served the Ashikaga shōguns as general, and
died while he was preparing to advance on Nobunaga's army.

338 *Jimbaori of black and red woollen cloth*

S/G2　黒羅紗地裾緋羅紗山形文陣羽織

The lower part red, edgings and lines from shoulders in gold
94 cm × 45 cm
Early Edo period
SENDAI MUNICIPAL MUSEUM
Important Cultural Property

The colours are divided along the so-called 'mountain line'. This
campaign jacket is said to have belonged to Date Masamune
(1567–1636), seventeenth chief of his clan and first lord of
Sendai. In their fastness of Mutsu and Dewa provinces the Date
leaders were a force Hideyoshi had to reckon with. In 1585, at
the age of nineteen, Masamune defeated a coalition of seven
other chieftains. In 1590, when Hideyoshi had reduced
Odawara, the stronghold of his confederate Hōjō Ujimasa, he
threw in his hand and swore fealty to the unifier of Japan.

338

339

339 *Two silk kosode mounted on a two-fold screen*

F/G4　紫地草花文様辻ヶ花染小袖

　　　白地石畳草花文様辻ヶ花染小袖

One kosode in *nuihaku* with *tsujigahana*, 'flowers of the cross-
roads', on the purple ground, the other with a pattern of stone
paving and floral bands on a pale brown ground
175 × 175 cm
Early Edo period
TOKYO NATIONAL MUSEUM. NOMURA COLLECTION

In *tsujigahana* technique the soft or blurred outlines of tie-dyed
flowers are improved by hand-painting, and some shading is
added. With the improvement of dyeing, painting could be
dispensed with, but sometimes the old method was revived for its
antique air.

340

341

340   *Two kosode mounted on a two-fold screen*

S/G4   黒地草花文様綾繡小袖

白地葡萄文様辻ヶ花染小袖

One *kosode* with white ground and grape pattern and with tie-dyed leaves and overlapping *hishi* pattern in yellow and purple; the other *kosode* with reserved white pattern of mountain and wave on a purple ground, tie-dyed circles, scattered fans and gold embroidered flowers

175 × 175 cm
Early Edo period

TOKYO NATIONAL MUSEUM. NOMURA COLLECTION

The *hishi* (water chestnut) has leaves suggesting the lozenges seen clearly on the light garment, and reserved in the mountain and wave of the other.

341   *Kosode with self-coloured figured satin ground tie-dyed and embroidered with plum tree and snow-wheel crest design*

F/G4   紫綸子地雪輪梅樹模様小袖

The snow-wheels tie-dyed, one on green and the other on blue reserved ground. The plum tree tie-dyed, the flowers embroidered in white and green on reserved white ground
Scarlet lining

149 × 125 cm
Early Edo period

TOKYO NATIONAL MUSEUM. NOMURA COLLECTION

A good example of layered design, with the flowers appearing to be in front of the snow-wheels and formal tree-trunks rather than lain on them. The *yukiwa*, a 'snow-wheel' or crystal, is one of the *mondokoro*, the stylised frames surrounding family crests.

343

344

342 *Uchikake of purple silk with tie-dyed crane and trellis pattern*

S/G4 　紫車鶴菱絞染田絞打掛

[repr. in colour on p. 223]
The ornament tie-dyed. The cranes stylised in the manner of *mon* crests. The segments of circles on one shoulder may represent an archery target
Scarlet lining
150 × 119 cm
Middle Edo period
KYOTO UNIVERSITY OF ARTEFACT AND FIBRE

Edo designers made informal use of formal motifs by presenting them incompletely and asymmetrically.

343 *Kosode of white satin with nuihaku design of bleached cotton spread on baskets*

F/G4 　白繻子地蛇籠に晒布文様縫箔小袖

123 × 103 cm
Early Edo period
TOKYO NATIONAL MUSEUM

The satin has mellowed to a light cream. The baskets are the *jakago* 'snake-baskets', the rolls of basket-work filled with stones and used to reinforce river banks. After dyeing, cloths were often washed in flowing streams (as still to-day in the Kamo river at Kyoto) and the *jakago* would readily suggest themselves as a decorative device. Here the motifs are freely interpreted, the lines bounding the swags of the material spread out to dry taking finally an independent course, the curve of the basket being inverted.

344 *Kosode of black silk in nuihaku with grass-blade pattern*

S/G4 　黒紅地草葉文様縫箔小袖

The black *nuihaku* ground in horizontal discontinued stripes, the grass-blade outlined in tie-dyed white and with a black stripe embroidered in black and white and gold scroll work
148 × 126 cm
Early Edo period
TOKYO NATIONAL MUSEUM. NOMURA COLLECTION

When the garment is worn only the back is seen. This *kosode* shows well the bold asymmetry of a leading Edo style. 'Grass leaves', *kusaba*, is the accepted name of the design, which may equally represent bamboo leaves.

345 *Obi of green velvet*

F/G4 　萌黄ビロード御殿帯

The velvet is trimmed with brocade at the ends
454 × 30 cm
Middle Edo period
KYOTO UNIVERSITY OF ARTEFACT AND FIBRE

The formality of the design, so different from the exuberance of most *obi* of the period, is unusual. It is of the type called *ontono obi*, 'palace sash'.

345

346

347

348

346 *Velvet obi*

S/G4 黄藍縞ビロード牡丹竹錫杖文様掛下帯

Bands of yellow and blue, with design of peonies,
bamboo and pilgrims' staffs
l 420 cm
Middle Edo period
SEISON-KAKU, Ishikawa

Only the head of the staff is shown. It is the *shakujō* carried by
Buddhist priests when journeying on foot. Below the decorative
plate are some rings which are said to be added so that their
rattle will warn little animals in the pilgrim's path and so save
them from being trampled. The sound also warned households of
the priests' approach. The name of the staff implies that the metal
parts are, or originally were, made of pewter (*shaku*).

347 *Obi of blue satin*

F/G4 水色繻子地波涛に碇芦水藻様繍掛下帯

Embroidery in gold and coloured silks of reeds, anchors and
seaweed among waves
378 × 25 cm
Late Edo period
TOKYO NATIONAL MUSEUM

The crowded pictorial ornament is characteristic of the late
period.

348 *Obi of purple satin*

S/G4 紫繻子地石畳菊文様繍掛下帯

Purple and silver embroidered lozenges alternating, overlaid
with chrysanthemums and peonies in gold and polychrome
silks
439 × 30 cm
Late Edo period
TOKYO NATIONAL MUSEUM

The creation of a regular embroidered ground, taking the place of
the figure pattern of the material, is an unusual and late device.

349 *Two silk kosode mounted on a two-fold screen*

F/G6 染分草花千鳥模様友禅染小袖

染分流水紅葉草花模様友禅染小袖

One *kosode* is dyed in *Yūzen* technique with flowers and maple
leaves around a stream in blue, white and green, on a scarlet
ground with cloud pattern. The other has overlapping
triangles showing white plovers against vermilion, and grass
and morning glories against white and cream
175 × 175 cm
Middle Edo period
TOKYO NATIONAL MUSEUM. NOMURA COLLECTION

By applying the rice-paste resist with the painter's brush the
finest detail of stems and petals could be represented. *Yūzen*
designs are normally contained in several well defined areas.

349

350 *Kosode in white silk painted with a plum tree by Sakai Hōitsu*

S/G6 梅樹描絵小袖　抱一筆

[repr. in colour on p. 222]
The plum tree in black ink, with red flowers and with small
plants in green and yellow at the base
Scarlet lining
149 × 114 cm
Late Edo period
TOKYO NATIONAL MUSEUM, NOMURA COLLECTION

Sakai Hōitsu published Kōrin's paintings and designs in wood-
cut books, and by his own work contributed to a revival of Rimpa
style. For his paintings see nos 37, 38.

351 *Kosode with boats and plum trees on white figured sayagata ground*

F/G7 白綸子地舟に梅枝観世水模様小袖

The boats, tie-dyed and embroidered, outline areas of black
water with *kanze mizu* pattern and plum blossom, separating
them from the white ground
Scarlet lining
152 × 132 cm
Middle Edo period
TOKYO NATIONAL MUSEUM, NOMURA COLLECTION

The point of view implied by the oblique positions of the boats,
their foreshortened and incomplete aspect, is characteristic of the
Rimpa school, whose tradition stems from Hon'ami Kōetsu and
the company of artists at Takagamine. *Sayagata* is a pattern of
interlocking lozenges or swastikas obtained in twill weave. The
kanze water pattern takes its name from the school of Nō drama
on whose costumes it appeared.

352 *Katabira of indigo hemp tie-dyed and embroidered*

S/G7   黒地蛇籠に波桜花散文様帷子

Embroidered and tie-dyed baskets stand in waves scattered with gold, red and white plum blossoms, and five characters in gold embroidery

140 × 122 cm
Late Edo period
TOKYO NATIONAL MUSEUM. NOMURA COLLECTION

The 'baskets', *jakago*, are those filled with stones that are used to reinforce river banks etc. Each is shown fixed between upright stakes. The characters read: fragrant, plain, river, waves, flowers.

353 *Kosode of white figured satin with hats and maple leaves*

F/G7   白綸子地紅葉に笠文様綾繡小袖

[repr. in colour on p. 224]
Tie-dyed straw hats in blue and red among hanging maple leaves, some in *shibori* and some embroidered in red, black and gold

Pink lining

149 × 135 cm
Middle Edo period
TOKYO NATIONAL MUSEUM

The hats are of a rustic kind affected by priests and holiday-makers in autumn, the season denoted by the varying red of the maple trees.

354 *Kosode of white figured satin with wood-grain, clematis and wistaria*

S/G7   白綸子地木目絞り流水に松藤文様小袖

[repr. in colour on p. 225]
The tie-dyed blue and white wood grain pattern partly overlaid by tie-dyed blue clematis flowers and embroidered in black and gold, and by wistaria embroidered red and gold with green leaves

Scarlet lining

h 160 cm
Middle Edo period
TOKYO NATIONAL MUSEUM

The wood-grain, sometimes mistakenly called a water pattern, here appearing like the prows of boats which sometimes project into the picture, exemplifies the Edo custom of magnifying a natural detail out of all proportion and in combination with unrelated objects.

355 *Katabira in white hemp dyed with the weaver's festival pattern*

F/G7   白麻地七夕文様友禅帷子

Yūzen-dyeing of poem-slips, books and lanterns in red, blue and yellow, hanging from bamboo and with bush-clover around the lower part

h 164 cm
Late Edo period
KYOTO NATIONAL MUSEUM

On the seventh night of the seventh lunar month the weaver girl and her cow-herd lover meet across the Milky Way. The understated decoration suits a hempen summer garment.

351

352

355

356

356 *Katabira in white hemp dyed with landscape*

S/G7 白麻地風景文様茶屋染帷子

Chayazome in indigo, pale brown, red and yellow with a landscape of buildings and lakes on a figured background
168 × 138 cm
Late Edo period
TABATA COLLECTION, Kyoto

The dyeing method used here, named after the Kyoto draper Chaya Shirōjirō, compares with *Yūzen* dyeing in its capacity for detail. Rice-paste was applied as resist to both sides of the cloth.

357 *Kosode of light yellow crêpe with dyed chequers and Yūzen-dyed hawks among maple leaves*

F/G7 薄黄縮緬地市松紅葉に鷹文様友禅染小袖

The chequers are brown, the streams and branches blue, the leaves scarlet, blue and yellow, the rocks mainly brownish red and the hawks a darker blue
143 cm × 125 cm
Middle Edo period
KANEBŌ COLLECTION, Osaka

Scarlet leaves indicate autumn. The fantastic treatment of falling streams is a frequent theme on the robes. Here they pass between the eccentrically irregular rocks chosen to ornament gardens, and the maples spring from their banks. Two hawks are on perches, one of which appears to be a sluice. Some spiralling tasselled cords add a distinctive note to the voluminous tracery. Characters are embroidered in green and gold along the top of the robe in pairs.

358 *Kosode in yellow crêpe with Kamo horse-race*

S/G7 薄黄縮緬地加茂競馬文様友禅染小袖

The upper part *Yūzen* dyed with brick-red chequer, the lower part with horsemen racing among multi-coloured maple trees
Scarlet lining
h 127 cm
Late Edo period
KYOTO NATIONAL MUSEUM

The horse-race in antique costume along the Kamo river in Kyoto is a long-standing and popular custom.

359 *Kosode of silk with hanging columns of straw hats and fans*

F/G7 染分縮緬地笠扇繋文様友禅染小袖

[repr. in colour on p. 226]
The pale straw-coloured crêpe divided by red borders encloses multi-coloured bands of hanging stripes of hats and fans in *Yūzen* technique, coloured red, yellow, blue, brown, lime. The flowers and leaves are embroidered in reddish brown and gold.
h 151 cm
Late Edo period
OKAJIMA COLLECTION, Kyoto

The ground imitates the fading of an old garment. The designer has performed a *tour de force*: almost every item in the scheme is unique in positioning and detail. The *katakana* characters included in the decoration read, from the right and from top to bottom, *sa ku mi ya yu no e na ra*, which can be reassembled as *sakura nayami no yue*: 'because of the anguish of the cherry blossom'.

357

360 *Kosode of light yellow silk with the Eight Views of Lake Biwa in Yūzen dyeing*

S/G7 薄黄地近江八景文様友禅染小袖

[repr. in colour on p. 227]
The sea is a rich blue and the buildings are in yellow and shades of red

h 147 cm
Late Edo period
KANEBŌ COLLECTION, Osaka

As places of retreat and holiday the shores and islands of Lake Biwa have been famous since the earliest times. The Eight Views have particular associations:

Autumn moon at Ishiyama
Lingering snow on Mount Hira
Evening glow at Seta
Evening bell at the Miidera temple
Returning sails at Yabase
Sunset sky at Awazu
Night rain at Karasaki
Wild geese alighting at Katata

At the temple Ishiyama-dera, depicted at the top of the robe, Murasaki Shikibu, authoress of the *Genji monogatari*, is said to have ended her life. The island shown beneath is named after her. To the right is a corner bastion of Azuchi castle which stood formerly on the hill called Azuchiyama, the site of Oda Nobunaga's tomb. The point of view is that of a topographical painting, horizontal bands of cloud surrounding the hilltops.

361 *Kosode in green crêpe with windows and flowering plum beside a waterfall*

F/G7 緑縮緬地梅樹掛泉窓文様小袖

[repr. in colour on p. 228]
Yūzen dyed elaborate windows in white reserve overlaid with plum trees with white, blue and red flowers overlook a waterfall in blue and white stripes. There are additional flowers embroidered in red and gold
Scarlet lining

165 × 125 cm
Late Edo period
KYOTO MARUBENI COLLECTION

The tea-house windows are shaped as fan, snow crystal and multiple lozenges. The illogic of the falling streams clashes with the considerable realism of blooms and branches.

358

362 Kosode in green crêpe with scattered plum blossom and characters above a bamboo trellis

S/G7 緑縮緬地竹垣に梅文様文字入小袖

[repr. in colour on p. 229]
Six characters in embroidery, tie-dyeing and self-colour are among tie-dyed and embroidered blossom in blue, red, white and gold and are above a white bamboo trellis overlaid with bamboo leaves in the same technique
Pink lining
155 × 126 cm
Late Edo period
TOKYO NATIONAL MUSEUM

The placing of flowers and written characters is studiedly random, the whole giving a version of the frequent fence-and-blooms design. The characters read, from right to left: 'Plum-*obi*-snow-flying-*koto*', the second word denoting the customary sash of the *kimono*, and the last the musical instrument.

363 Uchikake of indigo silk embroidered with poems

F/G7 紺繻子地色紙短冊散模様打掛

Plain weave satin with clear warps embroidered in gold and silver with *shikishi* and *tanzaku*
Scarlet lining
146 × 116 cm
Middle Edo period
TOKYO NATIONAL MUSEUM. NOMURA COLLECTION

Shikishi and *tanzaku* are slips of coloured paper for the writing of poems: here their size is exaggerated and they are placed so as to avoid repeating any juxtaposition. One poem reads: 'In your bamboo garden you laze away the livelong day. Drunk among the flowers I bid farewell to the lingering end of spring.' Another reads: 'In the Palace of Immortality, within the Portals of Eternal Youth, an autumn tomb. Slow the march of sun and moon.' The latter is quoted, with some characters omitted, from the anthology called *Wakan rōei shū*, and refers to the tragic Yang Guifei, concubine of the Tang emperor Xuan Zong.

364 Uchikake in purple figured silk tie-dyed and embroidered with paulownia and books

S/G7 黒地桐草紙模様綾繍打掛

The *kiri* leaves tie-dyed in white or gold embroidered, the books reserved on a white ground and embroidered in red, blue and gold
Scarlet lining
161 × 120 cm
Late Edo period?
TOKYO NATIONAL MUSEUM. NOMURA COLLECTION

An example of *ōgara* style using familiar objects, the books standing out against the double ground of self-colour and leaves, each in its individual disarray.

365 Furisode tie-dyed in purple on a white ground

F/G7 松竹梅鶴絞振袖

Design of pine, bamboo and plum and with flying cranes
h 157 cm
Late Edo period
TOKYO NATIONAL MUSEUM. NOMURA COLLECTION

The tie-dyeing provides the entire design unassisted, imitating the linear style of ink painting. The decoration is an excellent example of broad balance without symmetry of the parts. The *furisode*, 'swinging sleeve', with much of the inner edge of the sleeves unattached, is worn in certain *Nō* dancing.

366 Kosode of light tea-coloured silk with borders of bats

S/G7 白茶地八ッ橋織綾蝙蝠模様江戸褄小袖

Yatsuhashi twill with self-coloured alternating zones of columns and chequer. The bats in black, blue and gold forming an 'Edo border' (*Edo okumi*)
171 × 127 cm
Middle Edo period
TOKYO NATIONAL MUSEUM. NOMURA COLLECTION

The bats are stylised in the manner of the *mon* badges. Restraint of this order is comparatively rare in Edo textiles, and in this case must be adopted to allow the ground figuring its full effect.

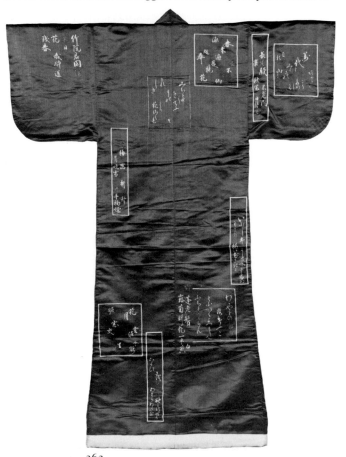

363

364

365

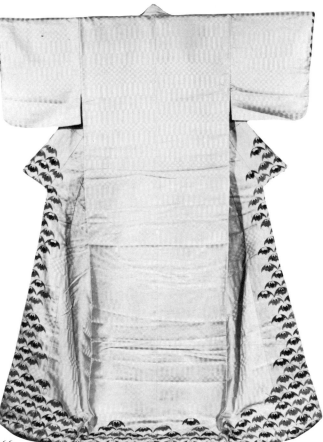

366

367 Uchikake of white ground figured silk tie-dyed and embroidered with bush-clover by a stream

F/G7　萩模様絞繍打掛

The stream tie-dyed blue and white and the flowers
embroidered and tie-dyed in red and blue

170 × 126 cm
Middle Edo period

TOKYO NATIONAL MUSEUM. NOMURA COLLECTION

The *uchikake* is a loose outer garment. Design of the Kōrin
tradition has inspired the meanders of the stream, where curves
are echoed, but without repetition or symmetry.

368 Katabira of white hemp with tie-dyed and embroidered plum-blossom trellis and gold characters

S/G7　白麻地梅垣模様帷子

The asymmetrical trellis tie-dyed in red and embroidered in
black with tie-dyed flowers, some embroidered in gold, black
flowers embroidered in red or gold, and embroidered small
branches

160 × 119 cm
Middle Edo period

TOKYO NATIONAL MUSEUM

A wide pattern on a summery light garment. The characters are
in the grass hand and read, *banzai raku*, 'long live pleasure'.

367

368

369 *Lined kariginu for Nō performance in gold brocade on indigo silk*

F/CH 紺地桐に角紋散文様金襴袷狩衣

[repr. in colour on p. 230]
The design of gold paulownia and squares containing peonies is scattered over the dark blue ground
172 × 202 cm
Middle Edo period
TOKYO NATIONAL MUSEUM

Originally a courtier's garment, the *kariginu* (literally a 'hunting silk') might be lined or unlined, usually in a light but closely woven cloth. In *Nō* use the *kariginu* is worn over another robe. This example is accompanied by short trousers in white silk.

370 *Lined kariginu of red silk for Nō performance with leaf roundels in gold*

S/CH 紅地松竹文様金襴袷狩衣

161 × 171 cm
Middle Edo period
FUJITA ART MUSEUM, Osaka

The lining of the *kariginu* in this instance is probably necessitated by the character of the weave. The gold of the ornament is inserted in the form of *kinranshi* used in the wefts. *Kinranshi* was made by glueing gold foil on to strong *torinoko* paper and cutting into narrow strips. The lining covers the comparatively large area of weft surface which does not appear on the front. The roundels are filled with leaves of bamboo and of vine or morning glory.

371 *Kariginu of white silk for Nō performance with wistaria in linking chains*

F/CH 白地藤分銅繋文縠織単狩衣

150 × 177 cm
Middle Edo period
FUJITA ART MUSEUM, Osaka

The pattern is termed 'wistaria in bronze-weight links', with reference to the dumb-bell-like areas defined in the spaces of the linking.

372 *Banded atsuita for Nō performance in damasked silk with dyed red and blue horizontal stripes*

S/CH 縞地桐唐草文段厚板

The ground is woven with paulownia and *karakusa*
Middle Edo period
OKAYAMA ART MUSEUM

The paulownia is the usual three-leaved device. *Karakusa* ('China grass') is a spiralling meander whose form hardly changes from its first adoption in the eighth century. The *atsuita* (literally 'thick board'), usually plain but for a striped band at the waist, is a gentleman's formal dress woven with raw silk in the wefts and treated silk in the warps. In Nō it is adopted for generals and demons. A similar garment, used in the Edo period by persons of military or higher status, was the *noshime*, in which the raw silk

370

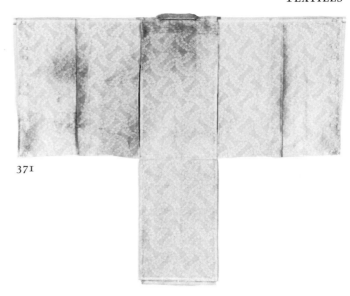

371

372

373

is in the warps and the treated silk in the wefts. It was to be worn beneath the *asagamishimo* 'hemp above and below', a strong outer robe. In Nō the banded robe is more often termed *noshime*, being worn by commoners, samurai of low degree, or occasionally by older low-born women. The banded *atsuita* was no doubt intended also for humbler characters in the play.

373   *Atsuita of silk for Nō performance with dangawari panels of tartan and floral design*

F/CH   格子唐草文段厚板

The chequers are in blue, white and brown; the floral panels are divided in halves horizontally, with 'Chinese grass' (*karakusa*) in light tone on tea-coloured ground and ground of vertical green and brown stripes
140 × 135 cm
NODA SHRINE, Yamaguchi

Dangawari, 'stepped change', refers to the alternation of panels which imitates the former alternation of contrasting cuts of weave.

331

374　*Atsuita for Nō performance in dangawari dyed with scatter of arrow-feathers, chrysanthemums and tartan*

S/CH　矢羽根捻菊格子段厚板

The flowers are in white, red, green, lime, blue and purple, the feathers on a brown ground, the tartan with broad blue and narrow red and yellow stripes
Middle Edo period
OKAYAMA ART MUSEUM

For *dangawari* see no. 373.

375　*Nuihaku of silk for Nō performance on tea-coloured ground with butterflies, pine trees and wistaria*

F/CH　茶地松藤蝶文様縫箔

[repr. in colour on p. 231]
The upper part with gold and silver foil butterflies over a trellis which is overlaid with embroidered yellow and blue pine trees and white and yellow wistaria
Early Edo period
KONGŌ COLLECTION, Kyoto

The form of the pines recalls the convention of *Yamato-e* painting of the Nara period. A dividing line at the waist based on the *hishi* lozenge is partly worn away. The knotting of the pine trunks is in antique style.

376　*Nuihaku of white silk with ground imitating basketwork and zigzag bands with embroidered dianthus sprays*

S/CH　白地網代に女郎花文様縫箔

The flowers are red, orange, pale blue and purple
Middle Edo period
OKAYAMA ART MUSEUM

In Japanese the blooms are *jorō-hana* ('the courtesan's flowers'). The ground pattern is variously described as wickerwork and netting.

377　*Nuihaku for Nō performance with plum-blossom trellis on a white ground*

F/CH　胴箔地梅格子文様縫箔

The upper and lower parts with red and pink plum blossoms on a black trellis are divided by a gold-leaf pattern of interlocking lozenges enclosing flower heads
Early to middle Edo period
MAEDA COLLECTION, Hyōgo

The regularity of the plum-branch frame recalls the effect of switching cuts of material to create squares alternating vertically and horizontally.

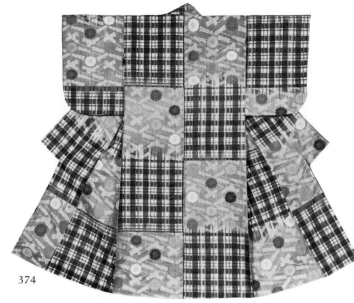

374

376

378　*Karaori of brocaded silk for Nō performance with streams, water-wheels, rushes and chrysanthemums on a red ground*

S/CH　芦に水車菊水文唐織

The detail is in white, black, yellow, lime, red, light blue
157 × 158 cm
Middle Edo period
FUJITA ART MUSEUM, Osaka

Karaori, literally 'Chinese weave', is a common name for Hakata weaves. In *Nō* it denotes a richly brocaded outer garment for female rôles. In Japanese brocades, *nishiki*, a stout cloth is woven using glossed silk in the warps and either glossed or raw silk in the wefts. The colours introduced in the wefts may include gold and silver thread. Floating coloured wefts may be secured by fine twists of plain silk. Such garments were worn on special occasions by Shintō and Buddhist priests as well as in the *Nō* play. The effect of brocade could be obtained, as here, partly by dyeing and embroidery.

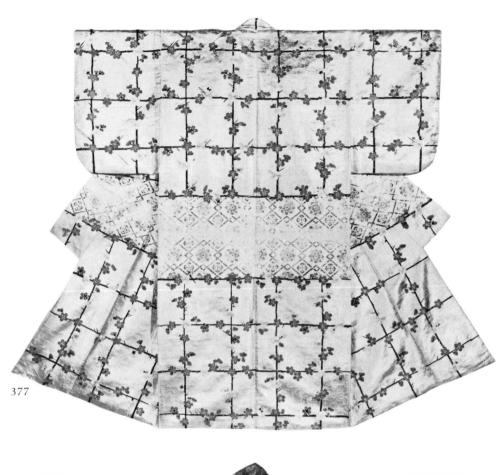

377

378

379 *Karaori of white brocaded silk for Nō performance with chrysanthemum leaves and flowers on reticulated gold ground*

F/CH 聯角乱菊文唐織

The reticulation in applied gold leaf, the flowers in red, blue, brown, pink, lime, the leaves in brown and green
154 × 141 cm
Middle Edo period
KYOTO MARUBENI CO.

The scatter of leaves and blooms is not intended to cohere into sprays. Colour apart, two types of chrysanthemum are represented.

379

380 *Karaori of silk for Nō performance, dangawari with autumn grasses*

S/CH 浅葱茶段秋草文様色無唐織

[repr. in colour on p. 232]
Three alternating squares with backgrounds of purple, cream and red are brocaded with flowers and autumn grasses in red, blue, green and yellow
h 153 cm
Middle Edo period
TOKYO NATIONAL MUSEUM

The material presents three ground designs and two layers of further decoration. No square exactly repeats another, although the effect is that of the assemblage of cut pieces in the old *dangawari* or *katamigawari* manner which legitimated a similar treatment of dyed ornament.

381 *Kataginu for Kyōgen performance in pale blue hemp with gourds and half-wheels*

F/CH 浅葱地瓢簞片輪車文様狂言肩衣

[repr. in colour on p. 233]
The bold stencil-dyed pattern of black half-wheels and orange and yellow gourds with green leaves is outlined in white against the pale blue ground
h 89 cm
Late Edo period
SHIGEYAMA COLLECTION, Kyoto

The half-wheels, *katawaguruma*, are a motif found in lacquer and in other media in the eleventh–twelfth century. No specific symbolism attaches to it, beyond the suggestion in a Buddhist sense of the transient illusion of life.

382 *Suō of dark purple silk for Kyōgen performance with waves and reeds in resist dyeing*

S/CH 黒地波に芦文様狂言素袍

[repr. in colour on p. 233]
The blooms at the neck and on the upper part of the sleeves are white with touches of red, the waves white and the reeds golden yellow
Middle Edo period
SHIGEYAMA COLLECTION, Kyoto

Suō properly designated the whole costume adopted in the fifteenth century as formal attire for soldiers of middle rank downwards. It consisted of a jacket like the one exhibited, combined with *hakama*, the wide trousers whose legs extended well beyond the feet and were dragged behind as the wearer shuffled forward. The jacket alone was termed *hitatare*, an officer's and courtier's unadorned garment. Worn by samurai the jacket carried the *mon* of the lord under whom the wearer served, at five places: behind at the neck, and at the middle of the sleeves back and front. Hence the jacket was called also *daimon* ('great *mon*'); it was properly made of cloth other than silk. But in *Nō* the term formerly denoting a whole costume was retained for the jacket alone. In this instance flowers are substituted for *mon*, as befits *Kyōgen*.

383 *Kataginu of silk for Kyōgen performance with windows, bamboo and flowering plum in resist dyeing*

F/CH 梅に竹窓文様狂言肩衣

[repr. in colour on p. 234]
The ground is dark blue, the detail in yellow, light blue, white, red, brown, the flowers embroidered with gold
Early Edo period
OKAYAMA ART MUSEUM

The *kataginu* waistcoat was of humble origin, and is reserved for the *Kyōgen* interludes of *Nō* drama. In the Edo period it was widely worn by samurai as semi-formal dress, though then not so extravagantly decorated as it appears in *Kyōgen*.

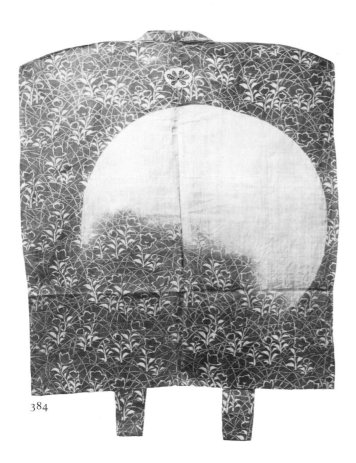

384

385

386

384 *Kataginu for Kyōgen performance in green hemp with moon and Chinese bellflower*

S/CH 桔梗に月文様狂言肩衣

A large three-quarter moon and Chinese bellflowers are stencilled on the pale green ground

h 78 cm

Late Edo period

SHIGEYAMA COLLECTION, Kyoto

Originally a servant's sleeveless jacket in coarse cloth, the *kataginu* was adopted in the Momoyama period as half-formal court dress for military officers.

385 *Kataginu of silk for Kyōgen performance with stencil-dyed sword-guards*

F/CH 鐔尽し文様狂言肩衣

The sword-guards are reserved in white against the dark blue ground

Middle Edo period

SHIGEYAMA COLLECTION, Kyoto

The sword-guard in the middle is wrongly drawn: the trees are shown the right way up but the perforation for the blade has the edge on the lower side. As the sword was worn with the edge uppermost the design of the *tsuba* would in this case appear inverted. The *tsuba* are of the fanciful kind favoured in Edo times.

386 *Kataginu of silk for Kyōgen performance dyed with gourd and bamboo fence*

S/CH 瓢箪文様狂言肩衣

The ground is dark blue, the rest slightly purplish white

Late Edo period

SHIGEYAMA COLLECTION, Kyoto

389

387   *Banded atsuita of black silk*
for Nō performance with coloured triangles
and waterwheels, cloud-roundels and
floral squares in gold

F/CH   鱗地紋散し段厚板

[repr. in colour on p. 235]
The triangles are red, light blue and brown
Middle Edo period
OKAYAMA ART MUSEUM

The roundels show clouds in the ancient convention of Yamato painting, as stylised horizontal bars. For the banded *atsuita* see no. 372.

388   *Atsuita of silk for Nō performance*
with dyed paulownia and gongs
on tortoise-shell ground

S/CH   亀甲地桐大紋雲版文様厚板

[repr. in colour on p. 238]
The hexagons of the ground are dyed in red, pink, brown, yellow, lime, white and black; the gongs in red and white, and the sprays of paulownia in white, brown and yellow
Middle Edo period
ŌTSUKI COLLECTION, Osaka

The paulownia is stylised in the manner of a *mon* emblem, displaying its flowers over a spray of three leaves. The gongs are *unpan*, 'cloud plates' of bronze with edges lobed in a conventional cloud figure. The tortoise-shell pattern is first found woven in twill in the seventh century and is particularly favoured for *Nō* robes from the Momoyama period. Hideyoshi is said to have worn

a *nuihaku uchikake* decorated with this design. Tortoise-shell, *bekkō*, the material for combs, hairpins, spectacle frames etc., fell under sumptuary proscription in the Edo period. The prohibition was circumvented by pronouncing the same characters as *suppon no kō*, i.e. shell of the snapping turtle, and proceeding as before.

389   *Chōken of purple silk for Nō performance*
with morning glory and spiderwort

F/CH   紫地籬に夕顔露草文絽金長絹

123 × 214 cm
Middle Edo period
FUJITA ART MUSEUM, Osaka

The morning glory is placed over two-fold screens plaited of bamboo, the only variation in the design being a change made between the left and right versions made to preserve symmetry. The gold appears to be introduced as *kinranshi* (see no 370). For an account of the *chōken* see no. 391.

390   *Maiginu in red ground brocade silk*
with formal flower-heads and
vertical scrolls

S/CH   赤地丁字立桙牡丹文舞衣

Formal vertical undulating scrolls enclose formal peony flower-heads in white, blue and purple with gold brocading
134 × 222 cm
Late Edo period
TOKYO NATIONAL MUSEUM

In this loose garment intended for *Nō* dancing the sleeves are twice the normal length, being composed of two widths of the weave. The design alludes to ancient classical style, in which medallions and confronted animals are enclosed in a similar undulating frame, such as is seen in early Iranian cloths and survived in Luccan brocades.

390

391 *Chōken of blue silk for Nō performance woven with multi-coloured birds and grasses*

F/CH 緑地秋草尾長鳥文様長絹

> Long-tailed birds fly above gold and coloured autumn grasses
> *h* 109 cm
> Late Edo period
> TOKYO NATIONAL MUSEUM

The *chōken*, literally 'long robe', was originally a court robe with skirts extending well beyond the feet. In this case the title stands for *chōken no suikan*, i.e. an unstarched short version of the garment, and in fact one developed from the *kariginu* which became the domestic wear of nobles in the eleventh century and was later adopted by the military caste. It is naturally unlined, and may be compared in design with the *kariginu* (no. 369) which it resembles by its two-piece long sleeves.

391

392 *Chōken of bluish silk with dyed ornament of boats in reeds*

S/CH 浅黄芦舟文様長絹

> The ornament appears light yellow
> 110 × 184 cm
> Middle Edo period
> NODA SHRINE, Yamaguchi

The motif of the skiff among reeds or flowering trees is frequent in various branches of decorative art, see no. 158. For an explanation of *chōken* see no. 391.

393 *Kosode of blue figured silk with drum roundels embroidered in red and gold*

F/CH 紫地火焔太鼓文金襴半切

> The ground figuring represents large peony leaves and blooms. The drum-tops are worked in embroidery with applied gold foil. Accompanied by *hangiri* trousers decorated with gold
>
> Early Edo period
> FUJITA ART MUSEUM, Osaka

392

The drums, appurtenance of the Thunder God (*Raiden*), have the latter's three-comma emblem at the centre. The dentated fringes denote the whirling of the drum. The placing of the ornament shows well the taste for controlled asymmetry characteristic of the early Edo period.

393

394

394 *Fans for the Nō drama (chūkei)*

FS/CH 中啓

Sticks plain and lacquered bamboo; papers painted in colours, ink and gold
l 30 cm, 34 cm
Middle Edo period
TOKYO NATIONAL MUSEUM

The fan is the most important of the *Nō* or *Kyōgen* actor's accessories. It plays a vital part in virtually all the stylised gestures of the drama and can also represent other objects.

395 *Two katsura-obi of embroidered silk for Nō performance*

FS/CH 鬘帯

One with balloon-flower sprays in white, red, purple and green on a dark-blue ground; the other with chrysanthemums and *susuki* grass in blue, red, green, brown and white on a gold *nurihaku* ground
240 × 4 cm and 230 × 4 cm
Middle Edo period
KONGŌ COLLECTION, Kyoto

The bands secure the wigs, *katsura*, used in *Nō*, passing across the forehead to a knot behind the head, the long ends falling down the back. The ornament is confined to the two ends on both sides.

395

396 Koshi-obi of dyed and embroidered silk for Nō performance

FS/CH 腰 帯

> With camellia, narcissus, peonies and balloon flowers in red, green and yellow
> *l* overall 271 cm, the decorated ends 27.3 cm;
> *w* 7.7 cm
> Middle Edo period
> KONGŌ COLLECTION, Kyoto

The *koshi-obi* 'waist sash' for use with various types of *Nō* costume differs from the *shita-obi* 'lower sash' (nos 346, 347) and the *ontono-obi* 'palace sash' (no. 345) by custom rather than by design or decoration. The narcissus and balloon-flowers decorate the outer side and the peonies and camellia the reverse.

397 Uchikake of white woollen cloth with peonies in undulating bands and phoenixes embroidered in gold

F/LR 白羅紗地牡丹立涌鳳凰金糸繍打掛

> 155 × 121 cm
> Late 18th century
> NAKAGAWA COLLECTION, Kyoto

The general effect of the design recalls a style of ornament traditional since the ninth century. Here it is applied however to a kind of cloth known in Japan only from the time of the first contacts with the Portuguese. The Japanese term for it, *rasha*, is regularly defined as woollen stuff, whereas the Portuguese word *raxa* from which it derives is generally described as cotton, and with stripes in several colours.

397

396

398 *Uchikake of dark grey satin with design of persimmon tree and monkey*

S/LR 納戸繻子地柿木猿文繍打掛

The persimmons golden, the trunk and branches yellow and brown, the leaves mostly bluish-grey edged with yellow
144 × 123 cm
Late 18th century
NAKAGAWA COLLECTION, Kyoto

The association of persimmon tree and monkey may refer to the folk-tale of the battle of monkeys and crabs, though it is not usual for such a theme to be altered as it is here. This garment, like the preceding one (no. 397), was used by a woman of the Shimabara licenced quarter of Kyoto.

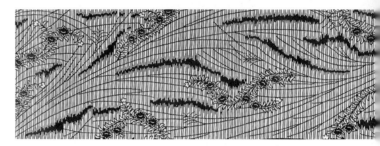

398

399 *Fifteen paper stencils for dyeing textile*

FS/AR 小紋・中型形紙

w of the stencils *ca* 40 cm
1796–1850
KYOTO NATIONAL MUSEUM

The designs are for the over-all diaper called *komon* 'small pattern', and for medium-sized repeated motifs. The *komon* stencil bottom left on p. 342 is dated to 1796. Its style compares with that of the *kosode* no. 401, where a similar stencil has been used to place the resist wax or paste which produced the ornament in reserve against the dark ground. Other stencils are dated in the period between 1804 and 1840. Suggestions of basketwork, bamboo stems and leaves and various forms of matting are among the designs, as well as vegetable motifs imitating embroidery. Such stencils were employed in the naturalistic ornament of the late-Edo dyers, particularly those working in the Yūzen tradition (*cf.* no. 360).

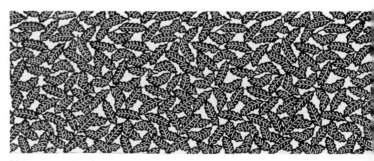

399

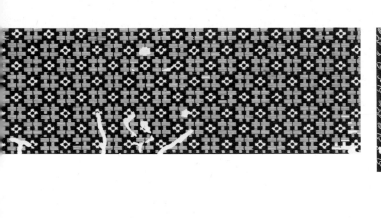

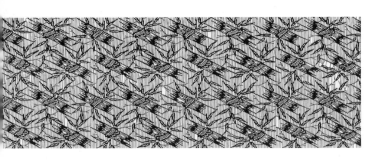

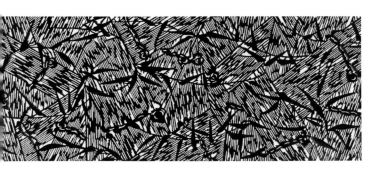

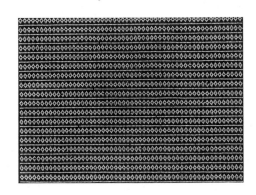

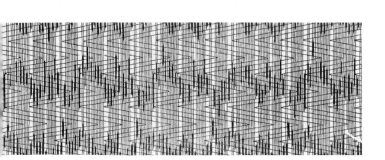

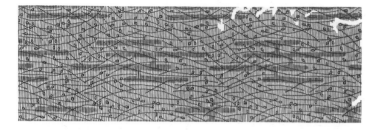

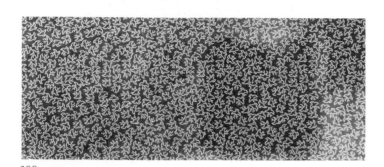

399

400

400 *Kosode of black crêpe with spear pines in komon*

F/G11   黒縮緬槍松小紋小袖

152 × 116 cm
Middle Edo period
KYOTO PREFECTURAL MUSEUM OF SYNTHETIC MATERIALS

Komon, 'small pattern', dyeing characteristically uses uniform small dots in its designs, which are generally floral.

401 *Kosode of plain black weave with komon of wistaria*

S/G11   黒平絹地藤小紋小袖

With *mon* embroidered on back and sleeves
158 cm × 114 cm
Middle Edo period
KYOTO PREFECTURAL MUSEUM OF SYNTHETIC MATERIALS

Komon ('small pattern') was a term applied both to the woven ground design of fabrics, as in this case, and to the small-scale floral ornament which was made possible by the *Yūzen* method and other methods of dye painting.

402 *Koshimaki of dark red silk embroidered with 'All Treasures'*

F/GII 黒紅地宝尽文様繍腰巻

Embroidered in red, pink, yellow and orange
Middle Edo period
KANEBŌ COLLECTION, Osaka

The list of treasures originated with the Buddhists, numbering eight 'precious things' of uncertain symbolism, but containing a few clear allusions: a pair of books for scholarship, a coin for riches, a jewel for the Law. Other items – lozenges open and closed, the artemisia leaf, a pair of horns – are more obscure. The list varies, and the Japanese have included items of their own, such as the money purse, the straw raincoat and bamboo hat which render their wearers invisible, and a mallet. This last, and the books, lozenges, horns, hat and raincoat, are to be found in the ornament of this robe.

403 *Koshimaki of dark red silk embroidered with 'All Treasures'*

S/GII 黒紅地宝尽文様繍腰巻

Embroidered in gold, green, red, white with flowers, bamboo, birds, drums, umbrellas, scrolls, hats and a recurrent design of tortoise-shell
171 × 126 cm
Late Edo period
TOKYO NATIONAL MUSEUM, NOMURA COLLECTION

In the Middle Ages the 'waist wrap', *koshimaki*, was a skirt worn by women servants in the palace. In the Edo period it has become a full-length garment worn ceremonially by ladies of the samurai caste.

404 *Katsugi with design of blinds and peonies in blue ground on linen*

F/AR 麻地簾牡丹文型染被着

[repr. in colour on p. 236]
Purple cloud patterns at top and bottom are divided by a stencilled pattern of blue and white rolled blinds decorated with peonies in purple and red
144 × 117 cm
Late Edo period
TABATA COLLECTION, Kyoto

A familiar object is made strange by its presentation in typical Edo style, the variously fringed blinds curiously dividing repeats of motifs differing in colour. *Katsugi*, or *kazuki*, meant in general a cloth worn on the head. The name came to be used for an outer garment worn by the women of noble families when they left their houses, designed to cover the head and hide the face. It might also denote an over-robe which may not extend to the head.

401

402

405 *Katsugi of linen with stencil-dyed butterflies on espaliered branches*

S/AR 麻地蝶文型染被着

[repr. in colour on p. 237]
The rhomboid border at neck and skirt dyed purple, the butterflies blue and red; linear chequered ground of blue and white

139 cm × 134 cm
Late Edo period
TABATA COLLECTION, Kyoto

For *katsugi* see no. 404.

406 *Yukata with the design of a good catch on cotton*

F/AR 大漁模様浴衣

Blue stencilled pattern of crawfish, octopus and fishes against a regular net

h 142 cm
Late Edo period
MATSUZAKAYA COLLECTION, Kyoto

Yukata, bath-robe, is the garment in which one takes an evening stroll at a holiday place on the sea or near hot-water springs.

407 *Yukata with the Fifty-three Stations of the Tōkaidō road on cotton*

S/AR 五十三次模様浴衣

The blue stencilled pattern of groups of figures illustrating the fifty-three stations
Late Edo period
NAKAMURA MINORU COLLECTION, Tokyo

The figures are in *Ukiyo-e* style, some of them resembling Hokusai's *Manga* drawings. Note the fishmonger, dyed cloths drying, traveller asking for a ride, giant bed-bugs, saké-drinking priests, noodle-eater, *shamisen*-player. On the shop there are notices of celebrated items, *meibutsu*; one reads *tororojiru*, 'clear yam broth', *kyōbaku-gire* 'buckwheat strips'. There is also a topographical joke: the place-name board reads 'Tiger Rock', and a traveller nearby is lifting a large boulder.

408 *Fireman's haori of silk painted inside with the figure of the demon Jiraiya*

FS/AR 刺子自雷也描絵火事羽織

The figure inside painted in blue, grey, orange, pink, black and white
Late Edo period
TOKYO NATIONAL MUSEUM

This half coat is quilted, the inner and outer cloths sewn together at close-set points so as to make it extremely strong and suitable for wearing in fire-fighting, judo and sword exercise. The figure fully painted, and not dyed, on the inner surface proclaims work of the late period.

403

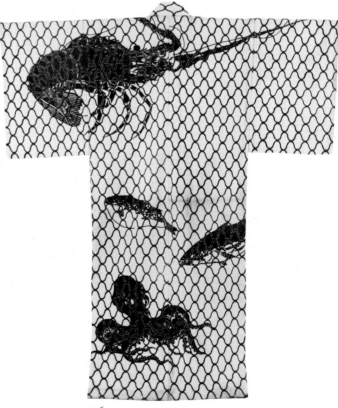

406

407

409a

409b

408

409 Two carrying-pads (bandori)

FS/AR   ばんどり

Woven straw and textile
l 91 cm and 86 cm
19th century
CHIDŌ MUSEUM, Yamagata

The *bandori* is used to cushion the weight of heavy loads carried
on the back. The word *bandori* also means 'sparrow' and was
probably applied to these carrying-pads, which were made and
used in what is now Yamagata prefecture, north-eastern Japan,
because they give their wearers a birdlike appearance.

410

411

410 *Fisherman's sashiko jacket of dark blue and lighter blue cotton sewn in white with nanamegōshi*

FS/AR　刺子（漁村用）

100 × 124 cm
19th century
CHIDŌ MUSEUM, Yamagata

The *sashiko* consists of two layers of cotton cloth held together by the ornamental sewing of *nanamegōshi*, 'oblique trellis'. It is designed specially to resist wear and weather.

411 *Fisherman's sashiko jacket of dark blue and lighter blue cotton sewn in white with yamagatamon*

FS/AR　刺子（漁村用）

110 × 116 cm
19th century
CHIDŌ MUSEUM, Yamagata

The continuous mountain peaks, *yamagatamon*, are one of the common geometric designs used in the decoration of these jackets. Like the previous example (no. 410), the work is characteristic of the craft of the fishing villages in Yamagata prefecture.

412 *Kasuri cloths*

FS/AR　絣裂地

The ornament appears in white or in light purplish blue, on a ground of dark purplish blue
w 33 cm
Late Edo period
YAMANOBE COLLECTION, Saitama

Kasuri moyō, 'lightly touched' or 'splashed pattern', is produced by pre-dyeing segments of warp and weft yarn, in the manner of *ikat*. It consists characteristically of repeated small and medium-sized geometric figures and is suited best to cloths hung as curtains or used for wrappings or covers. The pre-dyeing technique facilitates symmetrical design. The dye is normally indigo, as here, applied in varied density.

412a

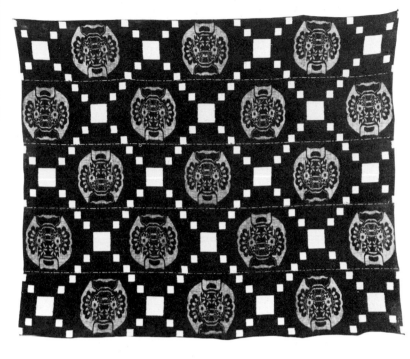

412b

412c

Japanese Historical Periods

Jōmon	to *c* 200 BC
Yayoi	*c* 200 BC–*c* 250 AD
Kofun (Tumulus)	*c* 250–552
Asuka	552–646
Nara	646–794
Heian	794–1185
Kamakura	1185–1392
Muromachi	1392–1568
Momoyama	1568–1600
Edo	1600–1868
Meiji	1868–1912
Taishō	1912–1926
Shōwa	1926–

Era names (nengō) of the Momoyama and Edo Periods

Much used in dating works of art
The dates cited give the first year of the era.

Eiroku	1558	Hōreki	1751
Genki	1570	Meiwa	1764
Tenshō	1573	An'ei	1772
Bunroku	1592	Temmei	1781
Keichō	1596	Kansei	1789
Genna	1615	Kyōwa	1801
Kan'ei	1624	Bunka	1804
Shōhō	1644	Bunsei	1818
Keian	1648	Tempō	1830
Jōō	1652	Kōka	1844
Meireki	1655	Kaei	1848
Manji	1658	Ansei	1854
Kambun	1661	Man'en	1860
Empō	1673	Bunkyū	1861
Tenna	1681	Genji	1864
Jōkyō	1684	Keiō	1865
Genroku	1688		
Hōei	1704		
Shōtoku	1711		
Kyōhō	1716		
Gembun	1736		
Kampō	1741		
Enkyō	1744		
Kan'en	1748		

Bibliography

Terukazu Akiyama *Japanese Painting*. Geneva, EDITIONS SKIRA, 1961

R. Alcock *The Capital of the Tycoon. A Narrative of a Three Years' Residence in Japan*. 2 vols. London, 1863

L. J. Anderson *Japanese Armour*. London, ARMS AND ARMOUR PRESS, 1968

W. G. Beasley *The Modern History of Japan*. 3rd ed. London, WEIDENFELD AND NICOLSON, 1981

R. Bellah *Tokugawa Religion*. Glencoe, 1957

Raymond Bushell *The Inro Handbook*. New York and Tokyo, WEATHERHILL, 1979

David Chibbett *The History of Japanese Printing and Book Illustration*. Tokyo, KODANSHA INTERNATIONAL 1977

Louise Cort *Shigaraki, Potters' Valley*, Tokyo. KODANSHA INTERNATIONAL 1979

Tsuguyoshi Doi *Momoyama Decorative Painting*. New York/Tokyo. WEATHERHILL/HEIBONSHA, Tokyo, 1977

C. J. Dunn *The Early Japanese Puppet Drama*. London, LUZAC, 1966

C. J. Dunn *Everyday Life in Traditional Japan*. London, BATSFORD 1969

E. Ernst *The Kabuki Theatre*. London, 1956

J. Earle *An Introduction to Japanese Prints*. London, V & A/ COMPTON/PITMAN, 1980

J. Earle *An Introduction to Netsuke*. London, V & A/COMPTON/PITMAN, 1980

D. et V. Elisseeff *L'art de l'ancien Japon*. Paris, MAZENOD, 1980

D. et V. Elisseeff *La civilisation japonaise*. Paris, ARTHAUD, 1974

R. F. J. Faulkner and O. R. Impey *Shino and Oribe Kiln Sites*. Oxford, SAWERS/ASHMOLEAN MUSEUM, 1981

Martin Feddersen *Japanese Decorative Art*. London, FABER AND FABER, 1962

C. French *The Poet-painters. 'Buson and His Followers'*. Exhibition, Ann Arbor, Michigan, 1974

C. French *Shiba Kōkan*. Tokyo & New York, WEATHERHILL, 1974

Basil Gray *Japanese Screen Painting*. London, FABER AND FABER, 1955

E. Grilli *The Art of the Japanese Screen*. Tokyo and New York, 1970

J. Hillier *The Uninhibited Brush*. London, H. M. MOSS, 1974

J. Hillier and L. Smith *Japanese Prints: 300 years of Albums and Books*. London, BRITISH MUSEUM, 1980

Soame Jenyns *Japanese Porcelain*. London, FABER AND FABER, 1965

Soame Jenyns *Japanese Pottery*. London, FABER AND FABER, 1971

D. Keene *The Japanese Discovery of Europe. Honda Toshiaki and Other Discoverers 1720–1798*. London, ROUTLEDGE & KEGAN PAUL, 1952

R. Lane *Masters of the Japanese Print*. London, THAMES AND HUDSON, 1962

Bernard Leach *A Potter in Japan*. London, FABER AND FABER, 1960

Tsugio Mikami *The Art of Japanese Ceramics*. New York/Tokyo, WEATHERHILL/HEIBONSHA, 1972

C. H. Mitchell *The Illustrated Books of the Nanga, Maruyama, Shijō and Other Related Schools of Japan. (A Biobibliography)*. Los Angeles, 1972

Hiroshi Mizuo *Edo Painting: Sōtatsu and Kōrin*. Heibonsha Survey of Japanese Art, vol. 18, Tokyo, 1972

Yūjirō Nakata *The Art of Japanese Calligraphy*. Heibonsha Survey of Japanese Art, vol. 27. Tokyo, 1973

Seiroku Noma *Japanese Costume and Textile Arts*. New York/Tokyo, WEATHERHILL/HEIBONSHA, 1979

Yoshitomo Okamoto *The Namban Art of Japan*. Heibonsha Survey of Japanese Art, vol. 19. Tokyo, 1972

P. G. O'Neill *A Guide to Nō*. Tokyo, 1955

P. G. O'Neill *Early Nō Drama*. London, 1958

R. T. Paine and A. Soper, *The Art and Architecture of Japan*. London, PENGUIN BOOKS, 1955

Beatrix von Ragué *A History of Japanese Lacquerwork*. Toronto and Buffalo, TORONTO UNIVERSITY PRESS, 1976

L. P. Roberts *A Dictionary of Japanese Artists*. Tokyo and New York, WEATHERHILL, 1976

Daniel Rhodes *Tamba Pottery*. Tokyo, KODANSHA INTERNATIONAL, 1970

B. W. Robinson *Arms and Armour of Old Japan*. London, H.M.S.O., 1951

B. W. Robinson *The Arts of the Japanese Sword*. London, FABER AND FABER, 1961, 1970

J. M. Rosenfield and S. Shimada *Traditions of Japanese Art* (Powers collection). FOGG ART MUSEUM, Harvard, 1970

H. Russell Robinson *A Short History of Japanese Armour*. London, H.M.S.O., 1965

G. B. Sansom *Japan. A Short Cultural History*. 2nd ed. London, BARRIE & JENKINS, 1950

G. B. Sansom *The Western World and Japan*. London, BARRIE & JENKINS, 1950

Jōhei Sasaki *Ōkyo and the Maruyama – Shijō School of Japanese Painting*. Exhibition, St Louis, 1980

Masahiko Satō *Kyoto Ceramics*. Tokyo, WEATHERHILL/SHIBUNDŌ, 1973

N. Saunders *The World of Japanese Ceramics*. Tokyo, KŌDANSHA INTERNATIONAL, 1967

A. C. Scott *The Kabuki Theatre of Japan*. London, GEORGE ALLEN & UNWIN, 1955

Tōru Shimbō *Exquisite Visions: Rimpa Paintings from Japan*. Exhibition, Honolulu, 1980

L. Smith and R. Barker, *Netsuke, the Miniature Sculpture of Japan*. London, 1976.

L. Smith and P. Hulton, *Flowers in Art from East and West*. London, BRITISH MUSEUM, 1979

Tsuneo Takeda *Kanō Eitoku*. Tokyo, KODANSHA INTERNATIONAL, 1977

Victoria and Albert Museum *Art Treasures from Japan. An Exhibition of Paintings and Sculpture*. London, THE ARTS COUNCIL, 1958

D. Waterhouse *Harunobu and His Age*. London, BRITISH MUSEUM, 1964

William Watson *Sculpture of Japan*. London, STUDIO, 1959

William Watson *Sōtatsu*. London, FABER AND FABER, 1959

William Watson *Buson*. London, FABER AND FABER, 1960

Ed. William Watson *Artistic Personality and Decorative Style in Japanese Art*, Percival David Foundation Colloquies on Art and Archaeology in Asia No 6. London, SCHOOL OF ORIENTAL AND AFRICAN STUDIES, 1976

Yūzō Yamane *Momoyama Genre Painting*. Heibonsha Survey of Japanese Art, vol. 16. Tokyo, 1973

Takeo Yazaki *Social Change and the City of Japan*. Tokyo, 1968

Toshiho Yonezawa, Chū Yoshizawa *Japanese Painting in the Literati Style*. Heibonsha Survey of Japanese art, Vol. 23. Tokyo, 1974

Glossary

abura-agede — The surface on *ki-Seto* wares supposed to resemble fried bean curd.

aode-Kutani — Ko-Kutani almost completely covered with dark enamel, often green, as background to the design.

asagamishimo — An outer hemp robe.

atsuita — A woven fabric, often used for *kimono* worn by *Nō* actors playing men's roles.

bekkō — Turtle-shell, and the design derived from it. Also *kikkō*.

bijin — A beautiful woman, the favourite subject of the *Ukiyo-e* school.

biwa — The Chinese lute; an aristocratic instrument.

bunjin — A scholar, particularly in reference to a painting tradition.

Bunraku — Puppet theatre centred on Osaka.

byōbu — A folding screen: they are usually in pairs, of two to six hinged panels.

celadon — A green glazed porcelain or stoneware.

cha-ire — A small, usually ceramic, tea-caddy.

cha-no-yu — The tea ceremony, and hence the spirit of the tea ceremony.

chashaku — A bamboo tea-scoop used in the tea ceremony.

chawan — A tea-bowl.

chaya-zome — A technique of dyeing named after Chaya Shirōjirō whereby resist techniques allowed great detail to be obtained without later painting.

chōnin — Townsman, merchant.

Chōsen-Karatsu — Korean-style Karatsu ware.

daimon — Jacket of a retainer, named after the daimyō's mon with which it is decorated.

daimyō — A feudal lord.

dangawari — Sections of different textiles sewn together to make a garment.

doucai — A technique of decoration in five colours of overglaze enamels on an area which has been outlined in underglaze blue (a Chinese term).

Edo okumi — 'Edo border', a decoration around the bottom and up the front of a garment.

e-garatsu — Painted Karatsu ware.

ema — 'Horse pictures'. Paintings executed usually on wood boards and presented to Shintō shrines.

e-nashiji — *Nashiji* (*qv.*) used to heighten details of the design rather than as an overall background treatment.

e-Shino — Painted Shino ware.

fuchi-kashira — The principal fittings of the hilt of a *katana* or *wakizashi* (*qqv.*). The *kashira* covers the end of the hilt and is held on by the hilt-wrapping; the *fuchi* fits over the other end, next to the *tsuba*.

fundame — A dull gold lacquer ground, made up of very fine particles of gold mixed with lacquer.

furisode — 'Swinging sleeve', i.e. a deep sleeve not attached to the side of the garment along its lower inner edge.

fusuma — Paper-covered sliding doors with paintings on them.

Genji monogatari — A novel of court life written by Murasaki Shikibu about AD 1000.

geta — High wooden clogs worn by both sexes.

go — Board-game, originally from China, played with black and white counters on a grid of 19 lines by 19.

gofun — Powdered sea-shells used as white pigment or as a base to raise paint proud of a surface.

gyōsho — Semi-cursive script, often used in Japan, a 'going hand'.

haiga — Sketches done to accompany *haiku* verses.

haiku — Seventeen-syllable verses linked to the season of the year. The typical verse-form of the Edo period.

hakama — Formal over-trousers.

harigaki — A time-saving technique in which designs are drawn with a sharp instrument in lacquer which is not yet fully dried.

hiramaki-e — *Maki-e* (*qv.*) decoration which is raised above the ground only by the thickness of its coats of lacquer.

hishi — Water chestnut (i.e. a lozenge shape).

hitatare — The jacket alone of *suō* (*qv.*).

hōgen — 'Eye of the law'. Buddhist title awarded to artists and craftsmen.

hōin — 'Seal of the law'. The highest Buddhist title awarded to artists and craftsmen.

hōjō — Abbot's quarters in a temple.

iebori — *See machibori*

inrō — A miniature set of interlocking compartments, hung from the *obi* (*qv.*) by a silk cord with a *netsuke* (*qv.*) at its other end and used to carry a supply of medicines.

Ise monogatari — Classic collection of poems by and stories about the ninth-century poet Narihira, much illustrated.

itomaki no tachi — *See tachi.*

Jidai matsuri — An historical pageant and festival held annually in Kyoto.

jimbaori — A campaign jacket worn over armour.

jorō-hana — 'Courtesans' flowers' - wild pinks.

jūbako — A box with tiers of compartments.

Kabuki — The popular drama of the Edo period, on historical and domestic themes.

kagamibuta netsuke — A circular netsuke made from ivory, fitted with a round metal centre.

kaiseki — The meal served in a full tea ceremony.

kaisho — 'Square' script in calligraphy.

kakemono — A hanging scroll, for painting or calligraphy.

kake shitaobi — Outer *obi*.

kakihan — A cursive monogram.

kami — A Shintō god.

kamuro — Child attendant of a courtesan.

kana — The Japanese written syllabary, a series of simple symbols used alone or together with Chinese characters.

Kanō school — Major school of painters from the 15th to the 19th century. Official artists to the Tokugawa Government. In the 18th century almost monopolized the teaching of painting.

Kanze mizu — Formal water-pattern first adopted in *Kanze Nō*.

karakusa — 'Chinese grasses' – tendril scroll, a common decoration on textiles and ceramics.

karaori — Robe and fabric often used for the *kimono* worn by *Nō* actors playing women's roles.

kariginu — 'Hunting silk', a light over-robe for *Nō* performance.

kashira — *See fuchi-kashira*

katabokashi — Technique of loading a brush with ink of uneven strength to produce varied line.

kataginu — A sleeveless, short garment made of hemp, often boldly patterned, used in *Kyōgen*.

katamigawari — Sections of different textiles sewn together irregularly to make the pattern of a garment.

353

katana or *uchigatana*	The standard long sword of the Momoyama and Edo periods worn with the *wakizashi* (*qv.*) and thrust edge upwards through the *obi* (*qv.*); length approximately 90 cm.
kata-zome	Stencil dyeing.
katsugi	Outer robe that covers the head.
kazaritachi	See *tachi*.
kazugi	See *katsugi*.
kikkō	Turtle-shell pattern, used on textiles, lacquer and ceramics. Also *bekkō*.
kiri	The leaves and flowers of the paulownia tree, used as a *mon* emblem or in decoration.
Kōdaiji maki-e	A style of lacquer decoration associated with the Kōdaiji temple, Kyoto, and much in vogue during the Momoyama and early Edo periods.
kōgai	A short skewer-like implement carried in the scabbard of the *katana* or *wakizashi* (*qqv.*); also a type of hairpin.
ko-Kutani	Old Kutani, a term covering a number of wares of different date and provenance. It should apply to porcelains made in Kaga in the 17th and 18th centuries.
komon	'Small pattern', a close diaper dyed using a stencil.
kon	A deep blue pigment.
koshimaki	Formerly a skirt, which became a long robe in the Edo period.
kosode	'Small sleeves', the standard-sized *kimono* of today, formerly an undergarment.
koto	Plucked musical instrument with 13 strings.
kozuka	The handle of a small knife carried in the scabbard of the *katana* or *wakizashi*; also used to refer to the knife itself.
kusaba	'Grass leaves' design.
Kyōgen	The comic interludes in a *Nō* performance.
Kyō-yaki	Kyoto enamelled pottery.
machibori	The freer style of sword-fitting decoration which appeared towards the end of the 17th century; contrasted with *iebori*, the stiff classical style of the Gotō school.
maki-e	A design sprinkled in metal dust onto a coat of still-wet lacquer.
makimono	A horizontal hand-scroll for painting and calligraphy.
mandara	A schematic painting, usually of circular design, showing the Buddhist view of creation.
manjū netsuke	A *netsuke* of flat circular form.
megane-e	Perspective pictures for a *nozoki karakuri* (*q.v.*).
menuki	Small metal fittings underneath the hilt wrapping of *katana* and *wakizashi* (*qqv.*); they are said to improve the grip.
mizusashi	Cold-water jar for the tea ceremony.
mon	Heraldic badges used at first by daimyō and other senior samurai; later adopted by commercial enterprises as trade marks.
mondokoro	The frame around a *mon*.
moriage	Shell-white pigment built up above the surface of a screen-painting, e.g. in chrysanthemum blossoms.
mukōzuke	A small cup or dish used for food in the *kaiseki* (*q.v.*).
namban	'Southern Barbarians', i.e. Portuguese and Spanish visitors to Japan in the 16th century. It denotes an art either favoured by these foreigners or imitating their fashions.
nanako	A surface treatment often applied to *shakudō* (*qv.*), consisting of minute regular granulations formed by a cup-headed punch.
nanga	'Southern painting', i.e. that imitating the Chinese scholars' style.
nashiji	Flakes of gold of irregular shape and varying size, set at differing angles in a bed of wet lacquer and then lacquered over.

negoro	Monochrome red lacquer, much in fashion in late Muromachi and Momoyama times, where the red lacquer is in places polished off to reveal a black lower layer.
negoshide	The milky white porcelain body that was the speciality of the Kakiemon kiln.
nenjū gyōji	Pictorial accounts of the events of the year at the imperial court.
netsuke	A toggle made of various materials and tied to the upper end of the silk cord which holds the *inrō* or other hanging container.
nezumi-Oribe	Oribe ware made of clay of two colours fused together.
nezumi-Shino	Grey Shino stoneware.
Nō	The ancient heroic drama using masks and splendid costume.
noshime	*Nō* robe in stripes or checks.
nozoki karakuri	A three-dimensional peep-show device.
nuihaku	A robe used for women's roles in *Nō* – also a material onto which gold or silver foil is glued.
obi	The sash worn with any robe, specially ornate in *Nō*.
ōgara	Pattern covering much of the garment on a large scale.
oiran	A courtesan of the first rank in Edo.
ojime	A small bead of metal, coral, horn, ivory or stone which tightens the silk cord joining the *inrō* and *netsuke* (*qqv.*).
ōkubi-e	Bust portrait prints of the late 18th century and after.
ontono obi	'Palace sash'.
Raku	A low-fired hand-made ware, usually for tea-ceremony, named after the Raku line of potters.
Rangaku-sha	Students of Dutch books who found in them information on scientific subjects, and examples of a European style of drawing.
Rimpa	A school of painting deriving from the Sōtatsu-Kōrin decorative tradition.
samurai	A soldier, but in the Edo period one with a defined civil status, and empowered to carry two swords.
sansui	'Mountains and water', i.e. landscape painting.
sayagata	A pattern made up of interlocking lozenges or swastikas.
semmen	A fan shape.
sencha	'Boiled tea' – the tea ceremony as practised by Chinese scholars.
sennin	A mythical semi-divine sage of Chinese origin.
shaku	Pewter; or a different written character 'scoop'.
shakudō	An alloy of copper with a small percentage of gold, patinated to a blue-black colour, much used for sword-fittings.
shakujō	A Buddhist pilgrim's staff.
shamisen	Three-stringed musical instrument used by entertainers.
shibori-zome	Tie-dyeing.
shibuichi	An alloy of approximately three parts copper to one part silver, patinated to a light or dark grey, much used for sword-fittings.
shikishi	A square of paper for the writing of poems.
Shino-Oribe	A Shino ware painted in Oribe style.
shishi	Chinese 'lion-dog', deriving from the lions of Buddhist altars.
shitōga	'Finger painting'. Practised especially by Ikeno Taiga.
shōgi	Japanese chess.
shōgun	The military dictator, only nominally subservient to the emperor.
shoin	'Writing room'. A day apartment in a temple or palace.
shoki Imari	Porcelain made in Arita before the period of export, i.e. before about 1650.

sōsho	'Grass character', the most cursive of the scripts.
suiboku	'Water and ink'. Painting in ink.
sumi-e	Painting in ink only.
sumō	Japanese wrestling.
suō	Formal, middle rank dress, often includes both jacket and *hakama* trousers.
surimono	'Printed thing'. A high-quality print on thick paper, made for stationery or to be sent as a greeting-card.
suzuribako	A writing box, normally containing a brush, inkstone, inkstick and waterdropper, sometimes with additional space for paper.
tachi	The traditional long sword, slung edge downwards from the waist; styles of mounting include the *kazaritachi*, worn at court ceremonies, and the *itomaki no tachi*, worn with armour and at formal shōgunal occasions.
takamaki-e	*Maki-e* (*qv*.) technique in which the design is built up and modelled in a mixture of lacquer and charcoal or clay dust.
Takeo-Karatsu	A coarse, boldly decorated stoneware made from the 17th century in the Takeo area of Kyushu, south-east of Karatsu.
tan	A red pigment applied to prints by hand.
tanzaku	Poem-slips, strips of paper for the writing of poems.
tatami	Mats woven of rice-straw. They are the modular flooring unit of a Japanese house.
temmoku	A black-glazed Chinese stoneware used for tea-bowls.
tōchin	The dumb-bell shaped stand that was the normal kiln support in Arita from 1600 to about 1635.
tōfu	Bean curd.
togidashi-e	*Maki-e* (*qv*.) technique in which the completed *hiramaki-e* (*qv*.) design and its ground are covered in further layers of lacquer which are then polished down until the design reappears, flush with the new ground.
tokonoma	Art-display alcove in palace, house or tea-room.
torii	The gateway to a Shintō shrine.
Tosa school	An ancient school of painters working in the Yamato-e tradition, revived from the 16th century.
tsuba	Sword guard, fitted at the blade end of the hilt next to the *fuchi* (*qv*.), pierced with a wedge-shaped central hole to take the blade and often with one or two smaller holes to admit the ends of the *kozuka* and *kōgai* (*qqv*.).
tsubo	A large storage jar.
tsujigahana	'Flowers of the cross-roads', a technique for the dyeing and hand painting of textiles.
uchigatana	*See katana.*
uchikake	An outer robe.
uchiwa	A round fan on a straight handle; does not fold.
Ukiyo-e	'Pictures of the floating world' – designation of the art to which the Edo woodblock prints and many books belong; *Ukiyo-e* painters and print designers were centred first in Kyoto, later in Osaka and Edo.
unpan	Gong.
wabi	The sense of detachment and simplicity sought by tea-masters.
waka	Poem in 31 syllables and five lines. The classic courtly form from the 7th century onwards.
wakashū	A fashionable young man who was not yet fully adult.
wakizashi	The standard short sword of the Momoyama and Edo periods worn with the *katana* (*qv*.) and thrust edge upwards through the *obi* (*qv*.); length approximately 60 cm.
warabi	Young bracken shoots, a favourite subject for painting.
Yamato-e	'Japanese pictures'. Style based on outline and flat colour, contrasted from the 10th century onwards with Chinese styles. Revived by the Tosa school.
yokozuna	A wrestler of the highest rank.
yukiwa	'Snow wheels', a motif representing snow crystals used in decoration of ceramics and textiles.
Yūzen-zome	Ornament applied by stencil and resist following the method perfected by Miyazaki Yūzen at the beginning of the 18th century.
Zhe school	A painting school of Ming China, in a tradition opposed to 'scholar's painting'.

Index of artists

SHŌJŌ SHŌKADŌ (1584–1639)
Calligrapher, one of The Three Brushes of the early 17th century, and the most eccentric of them; also an ink painter. No. 93

SUMIYOSHI GUKEI (1631–1705)
Sumiyoshi school; son of its founder Jokei. Worked mainly in Edo. No. 69

SUZUKI HARUNOBU (1724–1770)
Ukiyo-e school; worked in Edo. Pioneer of multi-colour woodblock prints. Nos 102, 103, 137

SUZUKI HIROSHIGE II (1826–1869)
Also called Shigenobu, print designer. Ukiyo-e school. No. 134

TAKE HIRATSUGI (fl. c. 1690)
Ukiyo-e school; designed books. No. 135

TANI BUNCHŌ (1763–1840)
Nanga school, but very many styles. A master of ink-paintings. Nos 82, 83

TANOMURA CHIKUDEN (1777–1835)
Nanga school; the most 'Chinese' of the Nanga artists. No. 80

TAN'YŪ (1602–1674)
Kanō school; most influential artist of his day, dominated painting for two centuries after his death. Nos 14, 18, 25

TAWARAYA SŌTATSU (? d. 1643)
Invented the style which came to be called Rimpa; worked with Kōetsu, but little known of his life. Nos 19, 24, 94

TAWARAYA SŌSETSU (fl. c. 1640–1650)
Rimpa school; pupil of Sōtatsu. No. 23

TORII KIYOMASU (fl. 1696–mid 1720s)
Ukiyo-e school; designed actor prints. No. 109

TORII KIYONAGA (1752–1815)
Ukiyo-e school. No. 104, 105

TORII KIYOTADA (fl. c. 1720–1750)
Ukiyo-e school. No. 100

TŌSHŪSAI SHARAKU (fl. 1794–1795)
Ukiyo-e school; designed prints of actors. Nos 112, 113

UKITA IKKEI (1795–1859)
Revival Yamato-e artist; a political figure in trouble with Tokugawa government. No. 88

URAGAMI GYOKUDŌ (1745–1820)
Nanga school, but very individual; painter, musician, poet, scholar. Nos 78, 79

UTAGAWA TOYOHARU (1735–1814)
Ukiyo-e school; designed prints in semi-western style. Nos 107, 114

UTAGAWA TOYOKUNI (1769–1825)
Ukiyo-e school; founder of the Utagawa subschool of print-designers. No. 141

UTAGAWA TOYOSHIGE (TOYOKUNI II, 1777–1835)
Ukiyo-e school. No. 120

UTAGAWA YOSHITORA (act. 1850–1880)
Ukiyo-e school. Nos 130, 132

UTAMARO, see KITAGAWA UTAMARO

WATANABE KAZAN (1793–1841)
Nanga school; interested in naval defences, committed suicide in confinement for his political views. Nos 89, 90, 91

WATANABE SHIKŌ (1683–1755)
Rimpa school; combined naturalism and decorative style. Nos 33, 34, 39

YASHIMA GAKUTEI (c. 1786–1868)
Ukiyo-e school. No. 119

YOSA BUSON (1716–1783)
Nanga school; also a haiku poet of distinction. Nos 58, 59

Lacquerers, Metalworkers, Potters, Tea Masters

AOKI MOKUBEI (1767–1833)
Painter and potter. Nos 227, 228

FUJIWARA KUNIKANE (1592–1664)
Swordsmith. No. 249

FURUTA ORIBE (1544–1615)
Tea-master. Nos 149, 197, 198, 199

GOTŌ ICHIJŌ (1791–1876)
Sword fitting maker. No 268.

HARA YŌYŪSAI (1772–1845)
Lacquerer. Nos 179, 183

HASEGAWA SHIGEYOSHI (act. late 18th century)
Lacquerer. No. 178

HAYASHI MATASHICHI (1605 or 1613–1691 or 1699)
Sword fitting maker. No. 258

HIRATA DŌNIN (1591–1646)
Sword fitting maker. No. 260

HON'AMI KŌETSU (1558–1637)
Potter, calligrapher and designer. Nos 150, 158, 159, 162, 204

IIZUKA TŌYŌ (fl. second half of the 18th century)
Lacquerer. No. 180

ISHIGURO MASAYOSHI (1764–after 1850)
Sword fitting maker. No. 269

KŌAMI CHŌGEN (1572–1607)
Lacquerer. No. 149

KŌAMI CHŌHO (1628–1682)
Lacquerer. No. 186

KOMA KANSAI II (1766–1835)
Lacquerer. No. 177

KOMA KORYŪ (act. 1764–1789)
Lacquerer. No. 176

MYŌCHIN MUNEFUYU (fl. 1520s)
Armourer. No. 232

NAGASONE KOTETSU (Okisato, c. 1614–1678)
Swordsmith. No. 247

NIN'AMI DŌHACHI (1783–1855)
Potter. No. 229

NISHIGAKI KANSHIRŌ (Nagahisa, 1639–1717)
Sword fitting maker. Nos 263, 264

NONOMURA NINSEI (fl. c. 1645–c. 1694)
Potter. No. 206

OGATA KENZAN (1663–1743)
Potter and painter. Nos 224, 225

OGATA KŌRIN (1658–1716)
Nos 162, 163, 164, 165

SEN RIKYŪ (1521–1591)
Tea master. No. 200

SEN SŌTAN (1578–1658)
Tea master. No. 201

SHIMIZU JINGO (d. 1675)
Sword fitting maker. No. 259

SHIOMI SEISEI (1647–1722)
Lacquerer. No. 174

SHŌAMI DEMBEI (1651–1727)
Sword fitting maker. No. 261

TANAKA CHŌJIRŌ (1516–c. 1592)
Potter. No. 190

TSUCHIYA YASUCHIKA (1670–1744)
Sword fitting maker. Nos 256, 265

TSUTA SUKEHIRO (1637–1682)
Swordsmith. No. 248

UMETADA MYŌJU (1558–1631)
Swordsmith and sword fitting maker. Nos 246, 262

YAMADA JŌKASAI (act. c. 1681–c. 1704)
Lacquerer. No. 175

YOKOYA SŌMIN (1670–1733)
Sword fitting maker. No. 267

YOKOYA SŌYO II (1700–1779)
Sword fitting maker. No. 266

Carvers

DŌRAKU No. 309
ENKŪ No. 276
GARAKU No. 334
HIDARI ISSAN No. 296
HIDEMASA Nos 285, 311
HŌJITSU Nos 290, 332
JORYŪ No. 331
KITAMASA No. 305
KŌGYOKUSAI No. 302
KYŌMIN No. 328
MASAAKI No. 335
MASAHIRO No. 323
MASANAO Nos 283, 292, 293, 294, 333
MASATSUGU No. 279
MINKŌ No. 313
MINKOKU No. 312
MITSUHARU No. 288

NATSUKI No. 304
OE SHUNZŌ No. 327
OKATOMO Nos 281, 286, 300
OKATORI No. 298
SHIN'ICHI No. 329
SHŪGETSU No. 330
SHŪZAN No. 314
SŌSHIN No. 291
SUKETADA No. 303
TŌMIN No. 278
TOMOCHIKA No. 289
TOMOKAZU No. 280
TOMOKOTO No. 282
TOMOTSUGU No. 310
TOYOMASA No. 295
TOYOYOSHI No. 336

Index of Lenders

Royal Academy Trust

The Friends of the Royal Academy

Patron H.R.H. The Duke of Edinburgh, KG, KT

FRIENDS

£15·50 annually, or £12·50 annually for museum staff and teachers, or £10·00 annually for pensioners and young friends (16–25 years).

Gain free and immediate admission to all Royal Academy Exhibitions with a guest or husband/wife and children under 16.

Obtain catalogues at a reduced price.

Enjoy the privacy of the Friends' Room in Burlington House.

Receive Private View invitations to various exhibitions including the Summer Exhibition.

Have access to the Library and Archives.

Benefit from other special arrangements including lectures, concerts and tours.

ARTIST SUBSCRIBERS

£25·00 annually.

Receive all the privileges shown above.

Receive free submission forms for the Summer Exhibition.

Obtain art materials at a reduced price.

SPONSORS

£500 (corporate) £150 (individual) annually.

Receive all the privileges offered to Friends.

Enjoy the particular privilege of reserving the Royal Academy's Private Rooms when appropriate and similarly of arranging evening viewings of certain exhibitions.

Receive acknowledgement through the inclusion of the Sponsor's name on official documents

BENEFACTORS

£5000 or more.

An involvement with the Royal Academy which will be honoured in every way.

Further information is available from The Secretary, The Friends of the Royal Academy.

BENEFACTORS

Mrs Hilda Benham
Lady Brinton
Mr & Mrs Nigel Broackes
Keith Bromley, Esq.
The John S. Cohen Foundation
The Colby Trust
The Lady Gibson
Jack Goldhill, Esq.
Mrs Mary Graves
D.J. Hoare, Esq.
Sir Antony Hornby
George Howard, Esq.
Irene and Hyman Kreitman
The Landmark Trust
Roland Lay, Esq.
The Trustees of the Leach Fourteenth Trust
Hugh Leggatt, Esq.
Sir Jack Lyons, CBE
The Manor Charitable Trustees
Lieutenant-Colonel L.S. Michael, OBE
Jan Mitchell, Esq.
The Lord Moyne
Mrs Sylvia Mulcahy
G.R. Nicholas, Esq.
Lieutenant-Colonel Vincent Paravicini
Mrs Vincent Paravicini
Richard Park, Esq.
Phillips Fine Art Auctioneers
Mrs Denese Rapp
Mrs Adrianne Reed
Mrs Basil Samuel
Eric Sharp, Esq., CBE
The Revd Prebendary E.F. Shotter
Sir Keith Showering
Dr Francis Singer
Lady Daphne Straight
Mrs Pamela Synge
Harry Teacher, Esq.
Henry Vyner Charitable Trust
Charles Wollaston, Esq.

CORPORATE SPONSORS

Barclays Bank International Limited
Bourne Leisure Group Limited
The British Petroleum Company Limited
Christie Manson and Woods Limited
Christie's South Kensington Limited
Citibank
Consolidated Safeguards Limited
Courage Limited
Debenhams Limited
Delta Group p.l.c.
Ford of Europe Incorporated
The Worshipful Company of Goldsmiths
The Granada Group
Arthur Guinness Son and Company Limited
Guinness Peat Group
House of Fraser Limited
Alexander Howden Underwriting Limited
IBM United Kingdom Limited
Imperial Chemical Industries Limited
Lex Service Group Limited
Marks and Spencer Limited
Mars Limited
The Worshipful Company of Mercers
Merrett Syndicates Limited
Midland Bank Limited
The Nestlé Charitable Trust
Ocean Transport and Trading Limited (P.H. Holt Trust)
Ove Arup Partnership
Philips Electronic and Associated Industries Limited
Playboy Club International
The Rio Tinto-Zinc Corporation Limited
Rowe and Pitman
The Royal Bank of Scotland Limited
J. Henry Schroder Wagg and Company Limited
The Seascope Group
Shell UK Limited
The Swan Trust
Thames Television Limited
J. Walter Thompson Company Limited
Ultramar Company Limited
United Biscuits (U.K.) Limited
Waddington Galleries Limited

INDIVIDUAL SPONSORS

The A.B. Charitable Trust
Mrs John W. Anderson II
Mrs Ann Appelbe
Dwight W. Arundale, Esq.
Edgar Astaire, Esq.
The Rt Hon. Lord Astor of Hever
The Rt Hon. Lady Astor of Hever
Miss Margaret Louise Band
A. Chester Beatty, Esq.
Godfrey Bonsack, Esq.
Peter Bowring, Esq.
Mrs Susan Bradman
Cornelis Broere, Esq.
Jeremy Brown, Esq.
Derek Carver, Esq.
Simon Cawkwell, Esq.
W.J. Chapman, Esq.
Major A.J. Chrystal
Alec Clifton-Taylor, Esq.
Henry M. Cohen, Esq.
Mrs Elizabeth Corob
Mrs Yvonne Datnow
Raphael Djanogly, Esq., JP
Mrs Gilbert Edgar
Brian E. Eldridge, Esq.
Mrs Erica C. Eske
Friedrich W. Eske, Esq.
Eric Ford, Esq.
Mrs Myrtle Franklin
Victor Gauntlett, Esq.
Lady Gibberd
Peter George Goulandris, Esq.
J.A. Hadjipateras, Esq.
Mrs Penelope Heseltine
Geoffrey J.E. Howard, Esq.
Mrs Patricia D. Howard
Roger Hughes, Esq.
Mrs Manya Igel
J.P. Jacobs, Esq.
Mrs Christopher James
Alan Jeavons, Esq.
Irwin Joffe, Esq.
S.D.M. Kahan, Esq.
David J. Kingston, Esq.
Peter W. Kininmouth, Esq.
Beverly Le Blanc
H.V. Litchfield, Esq.

Owen Luder, Esq.
A. Lyall Lush, Esq.
Mrs Graham Lyons
Jeremy Maas, Esq.
Ciarán MacGonigal, Esq.
José Martin, Esq.
Peter Ian McMean, Esq.
Princess Helena Moutafian, MBE
David A. Newton, Esq.
P.D. Northall-Laurie, Esq.
Mrs M.C.S. Philip
S.H. Picker, Esq.
Dr L. Polonsky
Dr Malcolm Quantrill
Cyril Ray, Esq.
Mrs Margaret Reeves
The Rt Hon. Lord Rootes
The Hon. Sir Steven Runciman
Sir Robert Sainsbury
Mrs Pamela Sheridan
R.J. Simia, Esq.
Steven H. Smith, Esq.
Thomas Stainton, Esq.
Cyril Stein, Esq.
Mrs A. Susman
Mrs G.M. Susman
K.A.C. Thorogood, Esq.
The Hon. Mrs Quentin Wallop
Sidney S. Wayne, Esq.
Frank S. Wenstrom, Esq.
Humphrey Whitbread, Esq.
David Whitehead, Esq.
Lawrence Wood, Esq.

There are also anonymous Benefactors and Sponsors

Photographic acknowledgements

The Royal Academy is most grateful to The Japan Foundation for supplying the photographs and relevant information for this catalogue.

The following persons and institutions have also supplied photographs:

Agency for Cultural Affairs
Benridō
Bijutsu Shuppansha
Chūō Kōronsha
Colory Co.
Eisei Bunko
Emman-in
Fuji Art Shuppan
Fujimori Takeshi
Hatakeyama Memorial Museum
Ibaragi Museum of History
Idemitsu Museum of Arts
Imperial Household Agency
Itsuō Museum
Japan Air Line Publisher
Kawaguchi Masao
Kodaira Tadao
Kōdansha
Kojima Hirokazu
Kōrinsha
Kōzu Kobunka Kaikan
Kyoto Film Agency
Kyoto National Museum
Kyoto Prefectural Museum
Kyoto University of Artefact and Fiber

Mainichi Shimbunsha
Maria Shobō
Mikami Shiro
Nagoya City
Nihon Keizai Shimbunsha
Ohashi Tetsuro
Okayama Museum of Arts
Oki Shigemi
Osaka Castle
Osaka Municipal Museum
Ōtsuka Kōgeisha
Seikadō Bunko
Seki Photos
Sendai Municipal Museum
Shikata Kunihiro
Shimizu Kōgeisha
Shiono Naoshige
Shōgakukan
Suntory Museum of Art
Ian Thomas
Tokyo National Museum
Tokyo National University of Fine Arts
Urasenke Foundation
Wakayama Prefectural Museum
Yoneda Tasaburo
Zauhō Kankōkai

ERRATUM: Picture No 45 on p. 172 MARUYAMA ŌKYO, *Waterfall* has been printed upside down.